TOPOLOGY

Gustave Choquet
FACULTÉ DES SCIENCES
UNIVERSITÉ DE PARIS À LA SORBONNE
PARIS, FRANCE

Translated by Amiel Feinstein

1966

ACADEMIC PRESS   New York and London

ACADEMIC PRESS INC.
111 Fifth Avenue, New York, New York 10003

United Kingdom Edition published by
ACADEMIC PRESS INC. (LONDON) LTD.
Berkeley Square House, London W.1

LIBRARY OF CONGRESS CATALOG CARD NUMBER: 65-26391

PRINTED IN THE UNITED STATES OF AMERICA

TOPOLOGY was originally published under the title
COURS D'ANALYSE; TOME II, TOPOLOGIE and
copyright in 1964 by Masson et Cie, Editeurs, Paris

Preface

This book contains the second part of a Course of Analysis consisting of three parts: Algebra, Topology, Integration and Differential Calculus.

It is the outgrowth of a course taught at Paris for several years, of which hectographed sections have been released by the University Document Center.

The exposition in the present volume assumes little previous knowledge beyond elementary calculus and the simplest facts about vector spaces.

Our aim is to present, in as simple a setting as possible, some of the powerful tools of modern analysis, and their applications.

The fundamental notions are nearly always presented in general form after a preliminary study of one or two examples intended to justify the choice of definitions. Thus, we introduce arbitrary topological spaces after a brief study of the real line; metric spaces are brought in only later when questions of uniformity arise. Similarly, normed vector spaces and Hilbert spaces appear only after a study of locally convex spaces, whose importance in modern analysis and its applications never ceases to increase.

We have been careful to make precise the domain of validity of theorems by examples and counterexamples. Numerous problems of varying difficulty will allow students to test their understanding of the course and to exercise their creative faculties.

GUSTAVE CHOQUET

Notation

The symbol **Z**, marking certain passages, is intended to caution the reader against serious errors which he could fall into.

The symbol $\div$ is used to denote the ordinary set-theoretic difference; that is, $X \div Y$ denotes the set of elements of X which do not belong to Y. It has been chosen to avoid confusion, when dealing with sets in a vector space, with the algebraic difference $X - Y$ of X and Y.

Contents

PREFACE v

NOTATION vi

CHAPTER I

Topological Spaces and Metric Spaces

Introduction 1

I. Topology of the Line R 2

1. Open Sets, Closed Sets, Neighborhoods, Bounds of a Set 2
2. Limit of a Sequence. The Cauchy Criterion for Convergence 6
3. Compactness of Closed Bounded Intervals 8
4. Topology of the Space $\mathbf{R}^n$ 9

II. Topological Spaces 11

5. Open Sets, Closed Sets, Neighborhoods 11
6. Closure, Interior, Boundary 14
7. Continuous Functions. Homeomorphisms 18
8. Notion of a Limit 23
9. Subspaces of a Topological Space 27
10. Finite Products of Spaces 30
11. Compact Spaces 34
12. Locally Compact Spaces; Compactification 41
13. Connectivity 45
14. Topological Groups, Rings, and Fields 51

III. Metric Spaces 60

15. Metrics and Ecarts 60
16. Topology of a Metric Space 67
17. Uniform Continuity 71
18. Compact Metric Spaces 75
19. Connected Metric Spaces 78
20. Cauchy Sequences and Complete Spaces 80
21. Idea of the Method of Successive Approximations 86
22. Pointwise Convergence and Uniform Convergence 89
23. Equicontinuous Spaces of Functions 98
24. Total Variation and Length 102

Problems 110

    The Line **R** and the Space **R**^{n} 110
    Topological Spaces 111
    Metric Spaces 116
DEFINITIONS AND AXIOMS 125

REVIEW OF SOME CLASSICAL NOTATION 126

BIBLIOGRAPHY 126

CHAPTER II

Numerical Functions

I. Numerical Functions Defined on an Arbitrary Set 127

1. Order Relation on $\mathcal{F}(E, \mathbf{R})$ and on $\mathcal{F}(E, \overline{\mathbf{R}})$ 127
2. Bounds of a Numerical Function 128
3. Upper and Lower Envelopes of a Family of Functions 129

II. Limit Notions Associated with Numerical Functions 131

4. Limits Superior and Inferior of a Function along a Filter Base on E 132
5. Limits Superior and Inferior of a Family of Functions 134
6. Operations on Continuous Functions 135

III. Semicontinuous Numerical Functions 136

7. Semicontinuity at a Point 137
8. Functions, Lower Semicontinuous on the Entire Space 138
9. Construction of Lower Semicontinuous Functions 141
10. Semicontinuous Functions on a Compact Space 141
11. Semicontinuity of Length 142

IV. The Stone-Weierstrass Theorem (Section 12) 146

V. Functions Defined on an Interval of R 150

13. Left and Right Limits 151
14. Monotone Functions 153
15. Theorems of Finite Increase 154
16. Definition of Convex Functions. Immediate Properties 157
17. Continuity and Differentiability of Convex Functions 159
18. Criteria for Convexity 161
19. Convex Functions on a Subset of a Vector Space 163
20. The Mean Relative to a Monotone Function 166

Problems 173

    Numerical Functions Defined on an Arbitrary Set 173
    Numerical Functions Defined on a Topological Space 174
    Semicontinuous Numerical Functions 174
    Stone-Weierstrass Theorem 175
    Theorems of Finite Increase 176
    Convex Functions. 176
    Means and Inequalities 179

DEFINITIONS AND AXIOMS 181

BIBLIOGRAPHY. 182

CHAPTER III

Topological Vector Spaces

I. General Topological Vector Spaces. Examples 183

  1. Definition and Elementary Properties of Topological Vector Spaces 183
  2. Topology Associated with a Family of Seminorms 187
  3. Classical Examples of Topological Vector Spaces 196

II. Normed Spaces 206

  4. Topology Associated with a Norm; Continuous Linear Mappings 202
  5. Stability of Isomorphisms 209
  6. Product of Normed Spaces; Continuous Multilinear Mappings 212
  7. Finite-Dimensional Normed Spaces 214

III. Summable Families; Series; Infinite Products; Normed Algebras . 216

  8. Summable Families of Real Numbers 216
  9. Summable Families in Topological Groups and Normed Spaces 224
 10. Series; Comparison of Series and Summable Families 232
 11. Series and Summable Families of Functions 239
 12. Multipliable Families and Infinite Products of Complex Numbers 243
 13. Normed Algebras. 251

IV. Hilbert Spaces 259

 14. Definition and Elementary Properties of Prehilbert Spaces 260
 15. Orthogonal Projection. Study of the Dual. 268
 16. Orthogonal Systems. 275
 17. Fourier Series and Orthogonal Polynomials 282

Problems 287

    General Topological Vector Spaces 287
    Topology Associated with a Family of Seminorms 289

Topology Associated with a Norm. 292
Comparison of Norms 293
Norms and Convex Functions 294
Linear Functionals on Normed Spaces 296
Topological Dual and Bidual 297
Compact Linear Mappings 298
Complete Normed Spaces 300
Separable Normed Spaces 302
Discontinuous Linear Mappings 303
Products of Normed Spaces and Direct Sums 304
Finite-Dimensional Normed Spaces 304
Summable Families of Real or Complex Numbers 305
Summable Families in Topological Groups and Normed Spaces 306
Series; Comparison of Series and Summable Families 308
Summable Series and Families of Functions 310
Multipliable Families and Infinite Products of Complex Numbers 314
Normed Algebras 316
Elementary Properties of Prehilbert Spaces 317
Orthogonal Projection. Study of the Dual. 321
Orthogonal Systems 326
Orthogonal Polynomials 329

DEFINITIONS AND AXIOMS 331

NOTATION 333

BIBLIOGRAPHY. 334

SUBJECT INDEX 335

TOPOLOGY

CHAPTER I

Topological Spaces and Metric Spaces

INTRODUCTION

General topology has formed a coherent doctrine only for the last half century; it is the outcome of a movement of ideas which goes back to antiquity.

The notions of limit and continuity intruded upon the Greek mathematicians as soon as they tried to make precise the notion of number. It was then necessary to await Cauchy (1821) and Abel (1823) for a clarification of the notions of convergent sequences and series, and the notion of a continuous function.

With Riemann (1851) the scope of the problem broadened; in his inaugural lecture, "On the hypotheses which serve as the foundations of geometry," he outlined a grandiose program: The study of "the general meaning of an entity obtained by a successive increase of dimensionality," by which he meant not only varieties of an arbitrary number of dimensions, but also spaces of functions and of sets.

But such a program could not be carried out without a better understanding of the real line (Dedekind) and of numerical functions (Riemann, Weierstrass), nor, above all, without a language both precise and general; it was Cantor (1873) who created this language and opened the door to a new world.

A heroic and fruitful period then commenced. Despite the opposition of mathematicians who were hostile to new ideas, discoveries followed one another, particularly in France (Poincaré, Hadamard, Borel, Baire, Lebesgue) and in Germany (Klein, Mittag-Leffler). This rapidly led to the study of functions of lines and the creation of a functional analysis (Ascoli, Volterra, Hilbert) which is a first step in the realization of Riemann's program.

But once again the need for a language and a framework adapted to these studies made itself felt: The metric spaces, defined by Fréchet, provided a tool which is essential for the study of uniform continuity and uniform convergence, and is also convenient for the study of topological structures. Finally, Hausdorff succeeded in extracting, from a jungle of axioms, a simple axiomatic system which is the cornerstone of present-day general topology.

We shall begin the study of general topology with an elementary study of the real line, whose importance has not been diminished by modern research. The definitions and statements of properties will be formulated in such a way as to be immediately generalizable to arbitrary topological spaces; it is in this framework that we shall then study most topological properties.

A topological space can be a curve or a surface as well as a space of curves or functions; thus each of the results which we shall formulate summarizes a host of particular results and can be applied to a great number of problems. But it is only gradually that we shall discover the great variety of applications to analysis and geometry.

Numerous examples will illustrate the definitions and theorems; nevertheless certain results will be motivated only subsequently. Thus, the study of general topology requires a certain act of faith from the outset, which however will be made easier by the internal beauty of this theory.

I. TOPOLOGY OF THE LINE R

1. OPEN SETS, CLOSED SETS, NEIGHBORHOODS, BOUNDS OF A SET

1.1. Definition. A SUBSET A OF **R** IS SAID TO BE *OPEN* IF IT IS EMPTY OR IF, FOR EVERY $x \in A$, THERE EXISTS AN OPEN INTERVAL CONTAINING x AND CONTAINED IN A.

In other words an open set in **R** is a set which is the union of open intervals.

The following assertions are an almost immediate consequence of this definition.

O_1 :   Every union (finite or infinite) of open sets is open;
O_2 :   Every *finite* intersection of open sets is open;
O_3 :   The line **R** and the empty set Ø are open sets.

Property O_1 results from the fact that every union of sets, each of which is a union of open intervals, is itself a union of open intervals.

To prove property O_2, it is sufficient to prove it for the intersection of two open sets A, B:

By hypothesis

$$A = \bigcup_i A_i \quad \text{and} \quad B = \bigcup_j B_j ,$$

where the A_i and B_j are open intervals.

Therefore

$$A \cap B = \left(\bigcup_i A_i\right) \cap \left(\bigcup_j B_j\right) = \bigcup_{i,j} (A_i \cap B_j).$$

Since each of the sets $A_i \cap B_j$ is either empty or an open interval, $A \cap B$ is open.

Finally, property O_3 is obvious.

EXAMPLE 1.   Every open interval is an open set.

EXAMPLE 2.   The union of the open intervals $(n, n + 1)$ (where $n \in \mathbf{Z}$) is an open set.

On the other hand, a closed interval $[a, b]$ is not an open set.

Z   It is false that the intersection of an infinite number of open sets is always open. For example, the intersection of the open intervals $(-1/n, 1/n)$ $(n = 1, 2, ...)$ is the set consisting of the point 0, which is not open.

1.2. Definition.   A SUBSET A OF **R** IS SAID TO BE *CLOSED* WHEN ITS COMPLEMENT $\complement_\mathbf{R} A$ IS OPEN.

Each of the properties O_1, O_2, O_3 at once implies a dual property for closed sets. We shall simply state these, as their proof is immediate.

F_1 :   Every intersection of closed sets is closed;
F_2 :   Every finite union of closed sets is closed;
F_3 :   The line **R** and the empty set $\emptyset$ are closed sets.

EXAMPLE.   Every closed interval $[a, b]$ (where $a \leqslant b$) is a closed set. Indeed, the complement of $[a, b]$ is the union of the two open intervals $(-\infty, a)$ and (b, ∞), and is therefore an open set.

Z   It should be observed that a set can be neither open nor closed. This is, for example, the case for **Q**.

1.3. Definition.   ANY SUBSET V OF **R** WHICH CONTAINS AN OPEN SET CONTAINING A POINT x OF **R** IS CALLED A *NEIGHBORHOOD* OF x.

In other words, V is a neighborhood of x if V contains an open interval containing x.

For example, every open set A is a neighborhood of each of its points. Conversely, every set A which is a neighborhood of each of its points is a union of open intervals, and therefore open.

If x and y are two arbitrary distinct points such that $x < y$, there exists a neighborhood V_x of x and a neighborhood V_y of y such that

$V_x \cap V_y = \emptyset$; indeed, if z is an arbitrary point between x and y, it suffices to take

$$V_x = (-\infty, z) \quad \text{and} \quad V_y = (z, \infty).$$

Z The meaning which we have just given to the word "neighborhood" appears different from that which it has in ordinary usage, since for us a point x of **R** has many neighborhoods, and one of them is the space **R** itself.

Indeed, we have rather enriched a notion which has up to now been unprecise, since we can henceforth say that a given point y belongs to a particular neighborhood of x; this neighborhood V, as it were, makes the degree of proximity of y to x more precise.

Accumulation Points of a Set.   *If* A *is a subset of* **R**, *a point* x_0 *of* **R** *is called an* **accumulation point** *of* A *if, in every neighborhood of* x_0, *there exists at least one point of* A *different from* x_0.

There thus exists an infinity of points of A, different from x_0, in every neighborhood of x_0; otherwise there would exist an open interval (a, b) containing x_0 and containing only a finite number of points (x_i) of A.

There would thus exist an interval (a', b') which intersects A at most at the point x_0 (take for a' the largest of the x_i smaller than x_0, if such exist, or otherwise the point a; choose the point b' similarly). But this is excluded by hypothesis.

Z An accumulation point of a set does not necessarily belong to the set. For example, the point 0 is an accumulation point of the set of points $x_n = 1/n$ (n an integer > 0), but does not belong to this set. Again, the points 0 and 1 are accumulation points of $(0, 1)$ without belonging to this interval.

1.4. Proposition.   *Every closed set contains its accumulation points. Conversely, every set which contains its accumulation points is closed.*

Let A be a closed set; if $x \in \complement A$, the open set $\complement A$ is a neighborhood of x and does not contain any point of A. Thus x cannot be an accumulation point of A.

Conversely, if A is such that no point of $\complement A$ is an accumulation point of A, there exists for each $x \in \complement A$ a neighborhood of x not containing any point of A, and therefore contained in $\complement A$; the set $\complement A$ is thus a neighborhood of each of its points, i.e., it is open; in other words, A is closed.

Isolated Points.   *An* **isolated** *point of a set* A *is a point* x *of* A *which* *is not an accumulation point of* A. *In other words, it is a point x of* A *which has a neighborhood* V *such that* $A \cap V = \{x\}$.

EXAMPLE.   Set $A = [0, 1] \cup \mathbf{N}$; the isolated points of A are the integers $n \geqslant 2$.

Existence of the Supremum and Infimum. We have defined in Volume 1, Chapter I what is called the supremum of a subset A of an ordered set E. This supremum does not always exist, even if A is a subset of E which is bounded from above.

For example, if E is the totally ordered set of rationals $\geqslant 0$, the subset A of elements x of E such that $x^2 < 2$ does not have a supremum in E although it is evidently bounded from above.

The definition of **R** given in Volume 1, Chapter III ensures, on the other hand, that this cannot happen in **R**. Because of the great importance of this property, we shall repeat this statement here:

Fundamental Property of **R**.   *Every nonempty subset of* **R** *which is bounded from above (from below) has a supremum (infimum).*

Let A be a nonempty subset of **R** which is bounded from above, and let b be its supremum. The halfline $(-\infty, b]$ contains A and is clearly the smallest closed negative halfline containing A.

For every $x < b$, $[x, b]$ intersects A; therefore either $b \in A$ or b is an accumulation point of A.

In particular, if A is closed, it contains its supremum b; this point is then the greatest element of A.

Similar properties clearly hold for the infimum.

REMARK.   When a set A is not bounded form below (from above), one often says that $-\infty$, $(+\infty)$ is its infimum (supremum). Later we shall give a precise justification of this language.

Bounded Sets.   *A nonempty subset* A *of* **R** *is said to be* **bounded** *if it is bounded from above and from below; in other words, if* A *is contained in a closed interval* $[a, b]$.

By the preceding theorem, in order that A be bounded it is necessary and sufficient that it have an infimum and a supremum; if these are a_0 and b_0, the closed interval $[a_0, b_0]$ is the smallest closed interval containing A.

If A is bounded and closed, a_0 and b_0 belong to A and are the smallest and largest elements of A.

Diameter.   *For every* $A \subset \mathbf{R}$, *we call the supremum* $\delta(A)$ *(finite or* $+\infty$*) of the distances between two points of* A *the* **diameter** *of* A.

If $\delta(A)$ is finite, then for every $x \in A$ the set A is bounded from above and from below by $(x + \delta(a))$ and $(x - \delta(A))$, respectively, and is thus bounded. Conversely, if A is bounded and has a and b $(a \leqslant b)$ as its respective bounds, the diameter of A is finite and equals $(b - a)$.

2. LIMIT OF A SEQUENCE.
THE CAUCHY CRITERION FOR CONVERGENCE

Let (a_i) $(i = 1, 2, ..., n, ...)$ be an infinite sequence of points of **R**. We say that this sequence converges to l, or that l is the limit of this sequence, if for every neighborhood V of l we have $a_i \in V$ except for at most a finite number of values of i (one can obviously take for the neighborhoods V only open intervals containing l).

This limit l is unique; for, let l_1 and l_2 be two distinct points of **R**, and V_1, V_2 disjoint neighborhoods of l_1 and l_2; if, for every i except at most finitely many, one has $a_i \in V_1$, then $a_i \in V_2$ is possible for only a finite number of the a_i; therefore if l_1 is the limit of the sequence, l_2 is not.

2.1. Theorem. *Every increasing (decreasing) sequence which is bounded from above (from below) has a limit.*

Indeed, let us suppose, for example, that the given sequence (a_i) is increasing, and let A be the set of points a_i. This set is nonempty and bounded from above, and therefore has a supremum l. But every open interval V containing l contains at least one point a_{i_0}, and thus also all the a_i with index $i > i_0$. Therefore l is the limit of the sequence.

The Cauchy criterion for convergence

Up to now we have used only the order structure of **R**; we are now, for the first time, going to use its group structure.

To say that the sequence (a_i) converges to l amounts to saying that for every $\epsilon > 0$ there exists an integer n such that

$$(i \geqslant n) \Rightarrow (|a_i - l| \leqslant \epsilon).$$

It follows that

$$(i \quad \text{and} \quad j \geqslant n) \Rightarrow (|a_i - a_j| \leqslant 2\epsilon).$$

The remarkable thing about this inequality is that l does not enter into it; we shall see, conversely, that every sequence having this property is convergent. To be precise:

2.2. Definition. A SEQUENCE (a_i) $(i = 1, 2, ..., n, ...)$ IS CALLED A CAUCHY SEQUENCE IF $| a_i - a_j |$ TENDS TO 0 WHEN i AND j TEND TO $+\infty$, IN OTHER WORDS, IF FOR EVERY $\epsilon > 0$ THERE EXISTS AN INTEGER n SUCH THAT

$$(i \text{ and } j \geqslant n) \Rightarrow (| a_i - a_j | \leqslant \epsilon).$$

It amounts to the same thing to say that if A_n denotes the set of points (a_i) with index $i \geqslant n$, the decreasing sequence of diameters $\delta(A_n)$ has limit 0.

2.3. Theorem (the Cauchy criterion). *Every Cauchy sequence of points of* **R** *is convergent.*

PROOF. We already know that every convergent sequence of points of **R** is a Cauchy sequence; it is the converse which we want to establish.

Let (a_i) be a Cauchy sequence. With the above notation, the sequence $(\delta(A_n))$ tends to 0. Now let α_n and β_n $(\alpha_n \leqslant \beta_n)$ be the infimum and supremum of A_n. Since the sequence (A_n) is decreasing, the sequence of the α_n is increasing and that of the β_n is decreasing.

The increasing sequence of the α_n is bounded from above by β_1; therefore it has a limit α; similarly the β_n have a limit β.

Since α and β belong to every interval $[\alpha_n, \beta_n]$, we have

$$| \beta - \alpha | \leqslant | \beta_n - \alpha_n |$$

and thus

$$\beta - \alpha = 0.$$

Let us put

$$= \alpha = \beta.$$

For every n we have

$$l \in [\alpha_n, \beta_n] \quad \text{and} \quad a_n \in A_n \subset [\alpha_n, \beta_n],$$

therefore

$$| l - a_n | \leqslant \max (| l - \alpha_n |, | l - \beta_n |).$$

Thus $(l - a_n) \rightarrow 0$ as $n \rightarrow \infty$. Therefore the sequence (a_n) converges to l.

We shall frequently use the Cauchy criterion to prove that a sequence is convergent. And we shall extend it to more general spaces than the real line.

3. COMPACTNESS OF CLOSED BOUNDED INTERVALS

One of the most important properties of closed bounded intervals is expressed by the Heine-Borel-Lebesgue theorem which allows the study of open coverings of such an interval to be reduced to the study of finite subcoverings. From this theorem follows immediately another property known as the Bolzano-Weierstrass theorem.

3.1. Definition. A COVERING OF A SET A ON THE LINE BY OPEN SETS IN **R** IS CALLED AN *OPEN COVERING* OF A.

3.2. Theorem (of Heine-Borel-Lebesgue). *Every open covering of a bounded closed interval* $[a, b]$ *has a finite subcovering.*

Explicitly, this means that for every family $(\omega_i)_{i \in I}$ of open sets in **R** such that

$$[a, b] \subset \bigcup_{i \in I} \omega_i ,$$

there exists a finite subset $J \subset I$ such that

$$[a, b] \subset \bigcup_{i \in J} \omega_i .$$

PROOF. Let $(\omega_i)_{i \in I}$ be the family of open sets which covers $[a, b]$ (where $a < b$, as the theorem is obvious if $a = b$).

Let us denote by A the set of points x of $[a, b]$ such that the interval $[a, x]$ can be covered by a finite number of the open sets ω_i; to prove the theorem amounts to showing that $b \in A$. But A is nonempty since it contains a, and it is bounded from above by b. Therefore it has a supremum m belonging to $[a, b]$.

There exists an $i_0 \in I$ such that $m \in \omega_{i_0}$; but ω_{i_0} is a neighborhood of m and there exist points x in A, in this neighborhood, which lie to the left of m and such that $[x, m] \subset \omega_{i_0}$. For such an x, $[a, x]$ has a finite covering by the ω_i; therefore $[a, m] = [a, x] \cup [x, m]$ also has such a covering. But every finite subfamily of the ω_i which covers $[a, m]$ also covers some interval $[a, m']$, where $m' > m$. This is compatible with the fact that m is the supremum of A only if $m = b$.

Z It is essential to note at this point that the assertion of Theorem 3.2 cannot be extended to unbounded intervals, or to intervals which are bounded but not closed. For example, the sequence of open sets $(1/n, 2)$ (where $n \geqslant 2$) covers the semi-open interval $(0, 1]$, but no finite subsequence of this sequence has this property.

3.3. Theorem (of Bolzano-Weierstrass). *Every infinite subset* X *of a closed bounded interval* $[a, b]$ *has an accumulation point in* $[a, b]$.

Equivalent Statement. *Every subset* X *of* $[a, b]$ *which has no accumulation point in* $[a, b]$ *is finite.*

PROOF. If no point x of $[a, b]$ is an accumulation point of X, every x has an open neighborhood V_x containing at most one point of X, namely, x itself. These V_x form an open covering of $[a, b]$; by the preceding theorem, there exists a finite number of these V_x, say $V_{x_i} (i = 1, 2, ..., n)$, which cover $[a, b]$. Thus X contains at most the points x_i $(i = 1, 2, ..., n)$.

Z Here again let us note that the assertion of Theorem 3.3 does not extend either to bounded intervals which are not closed or to unbounded intervals. For example, the infinite sequence of points $1/n$ of the semi-open interval $(0, 1]$ has no accumulation point in $(0, 1]$; in fact its only accumulation point in **R** is the point 0, which does not belong to $(0, 1]$.

We shall not for the moment go further into the study of the topology of the line. Actually, many topological properties of the line are valid for spaces which are much more general than the line, and whose introduction into analysis, far from being artificial, has become indispensable for the proof and the discovery of many properties.

We shall similarly be content to give several definitions concerning the topology of Euclidean spaces and shall then begin the study of general topological spaces. When we begin this study, it would be well to keep in mind the most concrete special cases, which consist of the line **R**, the spaces **R**ⁿ and their subsets. In the sequel, the metric spaces will constitute another rather intuitive subject, from which we shall be able to draw examples and counterexamples.

4. TOPOLOGY OF THE SPACE **R**ⁿ

Let us recall that the space **R**ⁿ is the product of n spaces identical with **R**, and is therefore the set of ordered sequences $(x_1, x_2, ..., x_n)$ of n real numbers; but up to now we have introduced on this set only an algebraic structure (of a vector space). We are now going to put a topological structure on it.

4.1. Definition. LET ω_i $(i = 1, 2, ..., n)$ BE AN OPEN SET IN **R** WHICH IS EITHER AN OPEN INTERVAL (a_i, b_i) OR THE EMPTY SET $\varnothing$. THE SUBSET $\omega_1 \times \omega_2 \times \cdots \times \omega_n$ OF $\mathbf{R}^n$ IS CALLED AN *OPEN INTERVAL* OF $\mathbf{R}^n$ WITH BASES ω_i (IT IS EMPTY IF ONE OF ITS BASES IS EMPTY); WHEN IT IS NON-EMPTY, ITS CENTER IS THE POINT WITH COORDINATES $x_i = (a_i + b_i)/2$.

The intersection of two open intervals with bases (ω_i), $(\omega_i{}')$ is the open interval with bases $(\omega_i \cap \omega_i{}')$.

One could similarly define the *closed intervals* by replacing the open intervals ω_i by closed intervals.

4.2. Definition. EVERY UNION OF OPEN INTERVALS IN $\mathbf{R}^n$ IS CALLED AN OPEN SET IN $\mathbf{R}^n$.

Thus, to say that a set A in $\mathbf{R}^n$ is open is equivalent to saying that for every $x \in$ A there exists an open interval containing x and contained in A (if it is useful, one can require that this interval have x as its center).

EXAMPLES. Every open interval in $\mathbf{R}^n$ is an open set in $\mathbf{R}^n$. On the other hand, a line in $\mathbf{R}^2$ is not an open set in $\mathbf{R}^2$.

Let us verify that the family of open sets in $\mathbf{R}^n$ satisfies properties O_1, O_2, O_3 of Section 1. (In O_3 replace **R** by $\mathbf{R}^n$.) This is immediate for O_1 and O_3 ; let us show it for O_2 :

If A and A′ are open sets, we have

$$A = \bigcup_{i \in I} p_i \quad \text{and} \quad A' = \bigcup_{j \in J} p_j{}'$$

where the p_i and $p_j{}'$ are open intervals.

Thus

$$A \cap A' = \bigcup_{(i,j) \in I \times J} (p_i \cap p_j').$$

But $(p_i \cap p_j')$ is an open interval; therefore $A \cap A'$ is open. This result extends by induction to every finite intersection of open sets.

Closed Sets, Neighborhoods, Accumulation points, etc. In $\mathbf{R}^n$, a set is said to be *closed* if its complement is open; a set is a *neighborhood* of a point x if it contains an open set containing x; a point x is called an *accumulation point* of a set A if, in every neighborhood of x, there exists at least one point of A which is different from x.

We could study the consequences of these definitions in detail, as we have done for **R**. But at this point it is more instructive to carry out this study in a more general context.

II. TOPOLOGICAL SPACES

In the elementary study of **R** and **R**^{n} which we have just carried out, almost all of the concepts have been defined in terms of open sets, and most of the properties have been obtained by using only properties O_1, O_2, O_3 of the open sets. Hence the idea of basing topology on the notion of open set; we shall try to express all of the classical topological notions, such as limit and continuity, in terms of open sets, and to obtain as many as possible of the classical theorems, starting from some simple hypotheses concerning the collection of open sets.

5. OPEN SETS, CLOSED SETS, NEIGHBORHOODS

5.1. Definition. A *TOPOLOGICAL SPACE* IS A PAIR CONSISTING OF A SET E AND A COLLECTION $\mathcal{O}$ OF SUBSETS OF E CALLED *OPEN* SETS SATISFYING THE FOLLOWING THREE PROPERTIES:

O_1 :   EVERY UNION (FINITE OR NOT) OF OPEN SETS IS OPEN;
O_2 :   EVERY *FINITE* INTERSECTION OF OPEN SETS IS OPEN;
O_3 :   THE SET E AND THE EMPTY SET $\emptyset$ ARE OPEN.

One also says that the collection $\mathcal{O}$ of subsets of E defines a topology on E.

One can define several topologies on every set E, except when E contains at most one point. One of these is the *discrete topology*; this is the one for which $\mathcal{O}$ is the collection of all subsets of E. It is the topology which admits the largest possible number of open sets.

Another is the *coarse topology*; this is the one for which $\mathcal{O}$ contains only two elements: $\emptyset$ and E. It is the topology which admits the fewest possible open sets.

However, the interesting topologies are, in general, neither the discrete nor the coarse.

One should observe that the properties O_1, O_2, O_3 are those which we put forward in the study of the topology of the line. It is remarkable that they are sufficient to obtain very rich results. We shall have to supplement them only when we study separated topological spaces and compact spaces.

EXAMPLE. *Topology associated with a totally ordered set.* Let E be an arbitrary totally ordered set; we shall call every union of open intervals in E an *open* set in E; in other words, A is an open set in E if A is empty or if, for every $x \in A$, there exists an open interval containing x and contained in A.

This definition, obviously, simply repeats the procedure used in Section 1 for the case of **R**.

One can easily verify that properties O_1, O_2, O_3 are satisfied.

The topology thus defined on E is called the order topology.

SPECIAL CASE. Let $\bar{\mathbf{R}}$ be the totally ordered set defined as follows:

The points of $\bar{\mathbf{R}}$ are the points of **R** plus two additional points denoted by $-\infty$ and $+\infty$; we shall say that $x \leqslant y$ in $\bar{\mathbf{R}}$ if $x, y \in \mathbf{R}$ with $(y - x)$ positive, or if $x = -\infty$, or if $y = +\infty$.

It is easy to verify that this definition defines a total order on $\bar{\mathbf{R}}$; $-\infty$ is the smallest element, and $+\infty$ is the largest element.

The set $\bar{\mathbf{R}}$ with this order and the associated topology is called the *extended line*.

5.2. Definition. A SUBSET A OF E IS SAID TO BE *CLOSED* WHEN ITS COMPLEMENT $\complement_E A$ IS OPEN.

As in the case of the line, the statements O_1, O_2, O_3 immediately imply three statements F_1, F_2, F_3 which are equivalent to them by duality, and which concern the closed sets in E:

F_1 :   Every intersection (finite or not) of closed sets is closed;
F_2 :   Every *finite* union of closed sets is closed;
F_3 :   The empty set and the space E are closed.

For example, in the discrete topology on E, every subset of E is both open and closed; in the coarse topology on E, the only closed sets are Ø and E; if E is a totally ordered set, every closed interval of E is a closed set in E in the order topology.

Neighborhoods

5.3. Definition. A *NEIGHBORHOOD* OF A POINT x OF E IS A SUBSET OF E CONTAINING AN OPEN SET CONTAINING x.

GENERALLY THE FAMILY OF NEIGHBORHOODS V OF A POINT x IS DENOTED BY $\mathscr{V}(x)$.

A *NEIGHBORHOOD OF A SET* A IN E IS A SUBSET OF E CONTAINING AN OPEN SET CONTAINING A.

Characterization of open sets

It follows from the preceding definition that an open set is a neighborhood of each of its points. *Conversely*, if a set A is a neighborhood of each of its points, it is an open set. In fact, for every $x \in$ A there exists an open set ω_x containing x and contained in A. Therefore

$$A = \bigcup_{x \in A} \omega_x .$$

This is a union of open sets, and is therefore an open set.

Consequence. It follows from this that the open sets in a space are known whenever the neighborhoods of x are known for every x. In other words, two topologies on the same set which admit the same neighborhoods are identical.

Here are several essential properties of neighborhoods which are often taken as a starting point in defining a topological space.

V_0 :   Every point x has at least one neighborhood;

V_1 :   Every neighborhood of x contains x;

V_2 :   Every set containing a neighborhood of x is a neighborhood of x;

V_3 :   The intersection of two neighborhoods of x is a neighborhood of x;

V_4 :   If V is a neighborhood of x, there exists a subneighborhood W of x (that is, $W \subset V$) such that V is a neighborhood of each point in W.

The first three properties are obvious. The fourth follows from the fact that the intersection of two open sets is open.

The fifth is more subtle; it expresses the following vague idea: Every point which is quite close to a point which is quite close to x is close to x. By hypothesis there exists an open set ω such that $x \in \omega$ and $\omega \subset V$. But ω is a neighborhood of each of its points, and *a fortiori* V is a neighborhood of each point in ω. It therefore suffices to take $W = \omega$;

Neighborhood base of a point

To know $\mathscr{V}(x)$, it suffices to know sufficiently many elements of $\mathscr{V}(x)$.

5.4. Definition. We say that a subset $\mathscr{B}$ of $\mathscr{V}(x)$ constitutes a base for $\mathscr{V}(x)$ if every $V \in \mathscr{V}(x)$ contains an element $W \in \mathscr{B}$.

Knowing $\mathscr{B}$, $\mathscr{V}(x)$ is obtained as the collection of all sets V which have a subset W belonging to $\mathscr{B}$.

Example 1. If E is an arbitrary space, for every $x \in$ E the open sets containing x constitute a base for $\mathscr{V}(x)$.

EXAMPLE 2.   If E is the real line **R** (or **R**^{n}), every point $x \in$ E has a neighborhood base consisting of the open intervals with center x and halflength $1/\text{n}$ (n an integer > 0). Thus every point x of E has a countable neighborhood base.

6. CLOSURE, INTERIOR, BOUNDARY

Adherent point, accumulation point, isolated point

6.1. Definition.   LET A BE A SET IN E AND LET $x \in$ E.

WE CALL x AN *ADHERENT POINT* OF A IF EVERY NEIGHBORHOOD OF x CONTAINS A POINT OF A.

WE CALL x AN *ACCUMULATION POINT* OF A IF EVERY NEIGHBORHOOD OF x CONTAINS AT LEAST ONE POINT OF A OTHER THAN x (x ITSELF NEED NOT BELONG TO A).

WE CALL x AN *ISOLATED POINT* OF A IF IT BELONGS TO A BUT IS NOT AN ACCUMULATION POINT OF A, IN OTHER WORDS IF THERE EXISTS A NEIGHBORHOOD OF x WHICH CONTAINS NO POINT OF A OTHER THAN x.

Thus, to say that x is an adherent point of A is equivalent to saying that either x is an accumulation point of A, or x is an isolated point of A.

The set of points of E which are adherent points of A is called the *adherence* of A.

For example, in **R**, the adherence of **Q** is **R** itself; the adherence of an interval (a, b) with distinct endpoints is $[a, b]$; the adherence of the set of points $1/n$ ($n = 1, 2, \ldots$) is this set with the addition of the point 0.

Closure of a set

For every A $\subset$ E there exist closed sets containing A (for example E itself). By property F_1, the intersection of these closed sets is a closed set containing A, and is the smallest such. Hence the definition:

6.2. Definition.   THE SMALLEST CLOSED SET CONTAINING A SET A IS CALLED THE *CLOSURE* OF A, AND IS DENOTED BY $\bar{\text{A}}$.

6.3. Proposition.   *For every set* A, *the adherence and the closure of* A *are identical.*

Indeed, if A is a subset of E and if x denotes an arbitrary point of E, each of the properties

$$(x \notin \bar{\text{A}}) \qquad \text{and} \qquad (x \text{ not adherent to A})$$

implies the existence of an open neighborhood ω of x which does not meet A.

Corollary 1. *The relation* $A = \bar{A}$ *characterizes the closed sets.*

Corollary 2. *In order that* A *be closed, it is necessary and sufficient that it contain its accumulation points.*

PROOF. 1. If A is closed, it is clearly identical with its closure. Conversely, it follows from $A = \bar{A}$ that A is closed since every closure is by definition a closed set.

Let us note here that $\bar{\bar{A}} = \bar{A}$ for every A.

2. Let A' be the set of accumulation points of A. By the definition of the adherence we have $\bar{A} = A \cup A'$. Therefore to say that $A = \bar{A}$ is equivalent to saying that $A = A \cup A'$ or that $A' \subset A$.

Interior of a set

The notion which is dual to closure is that of interior.

6.4 Definition. THE (POSSIBLY EMPTY) UNION OF ALL OPEN SETS CONTAINED IN A SUBSET A OF E IS CALLED THE *INTERIOR* OF A. IT IS THUS THE LARGEST OPEN SET CONTAINED IN A; WE DENOTE IT BY $\overset{\circ}{A}$.

It is immediate that the relation $A = \overset{\circ}{A}$ characterizes the open sets.

Relations between the topological operations $\overset{\circ}{A}$, $\bar{A}$ *and the elementary operations*

1. Duality between closure and interior:

(1) $$\complement \overset{\circ}{A} = \overline{\complement A}.$$

Indeed, by definition

$$\overset{\circ}{A} = \bigcup_{i \in I} \omega_i \,,$$

where $(\omega_i)_{i \in I}$ denotes the family of all open sets contained in A; therefore

$$\complement \overset{\circ}{A} = \bigcap_{i \in I} \complement \omega_i = \bigcap_{i \in I} \varphi_i \,,$$

where $(\varphi_i)_{i \in I}$ denotes the family of all closed sets containing $\complement A$; this is therefore its closure.

(2) $$\complement \bar{A} = \overset{\circ}{\complement A}.$$

This formula is derived from the preceding one by replacing A by $\complement A$.

2. Properties of the closure:

$$(1) \quad \bar{\emptyset} = \emptyset; \qquad (2) \quad A \subset \bar{A};$$

$$(3) \quad \bar{\bar{A}} = \bar{A}; \qquad (4) \quad \overline{A \cup B} = \bar{A} \cup \bar{B}.$$

The first two relations are immediate; the third follows from the fact that the closure of every closed set A is identical with A.

To prove the fourth relation, we observe first that

$$(X \subset Y) \Rightarrow (X \subset \bar{Y}) \Rightarrow (\bar{X} \subset \bar{Y});$$

from this we deduce that $\bar{A}, \bar{B} \subset \overline{A \cup B}$, hence

$$\bar{A} \cup \bar{B} \subset \overline{A \cup B};$$

conversely, $\bar{A} \cup \bar{B}$ is a closed set containing A and B, therefore also $A \cup B$, from which follows

$$\overline{A \cup B} \subset \bar{A} \cup \bar{B}.$$

This important relation evidently carries over to every finite union. On the other hand it does not carry over to infinite unions due to the fact that an arbitrary union of closed sets is not always closed.

There is no analogous relation for intersection, even finite intersection. For example, if E is the line **R** and if A and B denote, respectively, the set of rationals and the set of irrationals, then $\bar{A} \cap \bar{B} = \mathbf{R}$, while $\overline{A \cap B} = \emptyset$. One only has the inclusion $\overline{A \cap B} \subset \bar{A} \cap \bar{B}$.

Similarly, for every family (A_i) of sets in E one has the inclusions:

$$\bigcup \bar{A}_i \subset \overline{\bigcup A_i} \qquad \text{and} \qquad \overline{\bigcap A_i} \subset \bigcap \bar{A}_i.$$

3. Properties of the interior.   These properties are the duals of those of the closure:

$$(1) \quad \mathring{E} = E; \qquad 2) \quad \mathring{A} \subset A;$$

$$(3) \quad \mathring{\mathring{A}} = \mathring{A}; \qquad (4) \quad \mathring{\overline{A \cap B}} = \mathring{A} \cap \mathring{B}.$$

Boundary of a set

6.5. Definition.   THE BOUNDARY A* OF A SUBSET A OF E IS THE SET OF POINTS x, EACH OF WHOSE NEIGHBORHOODS V CONTAINS AT LEAST ONE POINT OF A AND ONE POINT OF $\complement$ A.

Thus

$$A^* = \bar{A} \cap \overline{\complement A}.$$

From this formula it is seen that the boundary of every set is closed and that two complementary sets have the same boundary.

6.6. Proposition. *For every set* A *in* E, $A^* = \bar{A} \div \mathring{A}.$

In fact, we have the relations

$$A^* = \bar{A} \cap \overline{\complement A} \qquad \text{and} \qquad \overline{\complement A} = \complement \mathring{A},$$

from which follows

$$A^* = \bar{A} \cap \complement \mathring{A},$$

which is just the desired relation.

Corollary. *The following equivalences hold for every closed subset* A *of* E:

$$(A = A^*) \Leftrightarrow (\mathring{A} = \varnothing) \Leftrightarrow (\overline{\complement A} = E).$$

Everywhere dense, dense, and nondense sets

On the real line, there are rational points in every nonempty open set.

On the other hand, every nonempty open set in **R** contains a nonempty open subset which does not contain any integer. To make more precise the vague notions suggested by these differences between the distributions of **Q** and of **Z** over **R**, we introduce the following definition.

6.7. Definition. Let A be a subset of a space E.

The set A is said to be *everywhere dense* on E, *dense* on E, or *nondense* on E according as

$\bar{A} = E$; $\bar{A}$ has a nonempty interior; $\bar{A}$ has an empty interior.

For example, on **R**, the set **Q** is everywhere dense; the set **Q** $\cap$ [0, 1] is dense; the set **Z** is nondense, as is the set of numbers $1/n$ (where $n = 1, 2, ...$).

Immediate Properties (*from the corollary of Proposition 6.6*). 1. If A is everywhere dense on E and if $A \subset B \subset E$, B is also everywhere dense on E.

2. (A everywhere dense) ⟺ (Every nonempty open set in E meets A).

3. (A nondense) ⟺ (Ā nondense) ⟺ ($\complement$ Ā everywhere dense) ⟺ (Every nonempty open set in E contains a nonempty open subset which does not intersect A).

4. If A and B are nondense on E, so is the set A ∪ B.

This last property carries over to arbitrary finite unions, but not to infinite unions (take the case of **Q** on **R**).

Z If A is nondense, $\complement$A is everywhere dense, but it can happen that both A and $\complement$A are everywhere dense; this is the case for the subset **Q** of **R**.

The same example shows that A and B may be everywhere dense on E, and A ∩ B empty.

7. CONTINUOUS FUNCTIONS. HOMEOMORPHISMS

In order to be able to speak of the continuity of a mapping f of a set X into a set Y, it is necessary that there be defined on X and Y a notion of neighboring points, in other words, that X and Y be topological spaces.

An analysis of the classical definition of the continuity of a numerical function of a real variable leads to the following definition:

Continuity at a point

7.1. Definition. A MAPPING f OF A TOPOLOGICAL SPACE X INTO ANOTHER TOPOLOGICAL SPACE Y IS SAID TO BE *CONTINUOUS* AT A POINT x_0 OF X IF, FOR EVERY NEIGHBORHOOD V OF $f(x_0)$, THERE EXISTS A NEIGHBORHOOD v OF x_0 WHOSE IMAGE UNDER f IS IN V, THAT IS, SUCH THAT $f(v) \subset V$.

In the notation of symbolic logic, this relation is written as

$$(f \text{ continuous at } x_0) \overset{\text{def}}{\Leftrightarrow} (\forall V, V \in \mathscr{V}(f(x_0)))(\exists v, v \in \mathscr{V}(x_0)): (f(v) \subset V).$$

Clearly an equivalent definition is obtained by requiring that V and v belong to given neighborhood bases of $f(x_0)$ and x_0, respectively.

Here is another convenient form of the continuity of f at x_0 : *For every neighborhood* V *of* $f(x_0)$, $f^{-1}(V)$ *is a neighborhood of* x_0. In fact, let V be a neighborhood of $f(x_0)$; if v is a neighborhood of x_0 such that $f(v) \subset V$, then $v \subset f^{-1}(V)$; therefore $f^{-1}(V)$, which contains a neighborhood of x_0, is also a neighborhood of x_0. Conversely, if $f^{-1}(V)$ is a neighborhood of x_0, we set $v = f^{-1}(V)$; then surely $f(v) \subset V$. Here again we can require only that V belong to a given neighborhood base of $f(x_0)$.

EXAMPLE 1.   If f is a constant mapping of X into Y, then $f^{-1}(V) = X$ for every neighborhood V of $f(x_0)$; thus every constant mapping of X into Y is continuous at every point of X.

EXAMPLE 2.   The identity mapping $x \to x$ of X into X is continuous at every point of X.

Continuity in the entire space

7.2. Definition.   A MAPPING f OF X INTO Y IS SAID TO BE *CONTINUOUS* ON X (OR IN X) IF IT IS CONTINUOUS AT EVERY POINT OF X.

7.3. Theorem.   *To say that f is continuous on X is equivalent to saying that for every open set B in Y, $f^{-1}(B)$ is an open set in X.*

Indeed, suppose f is continuous on X; if B is open in Y, then since B is a neighborhood of each of its points, its inverse image is a neighborhood of each of its points, and is therefore an open set.

Conversely, suppose that $f^{-1}(B)$ is open for every open set B in Y; then for every x_0 and every neighborhood V of $f(x_0)$, the set $f^{-1}(\overset{\circ}{V})$ is an open set containing x_0, therefore *a fortiori* $f^{-1}(V)$ is a neighborhood of x_0. Thus f is continuous at every point x_0 of X.

7.4. Theorem.   *To say that f is continuous on X is equivalent to saying that for every closed set B in Y, $f^{-1}(B)$ is a closed set in X.*

This theorem follows from the preceding one by applying the relation

$$f^{-1}(\mathcomplement B) = \mathcomplement f^{-1}(B).$$

Corollary.   *If f is a continuous mapping of E into* **R**, *the set of points x in E such that $f(x) = 0$ is a closed set in E.*

Analogous statements hold for the solutions of the relations of the form

$$f(x) \geqslant 0, \qquad f(x) \leqslant 0, \qquad f(x) > 0, \qquad f(x) < 0.$$

In particular, if f is a polynomial in n real variables with real coefficients, the corollary shows that the real algebraic variety of solutions of $f(x) = 0$ is a closed set in **R**^{n}; the same result holds in **C**^{n} for polynomials in n complex variables.

Z It is essential to note that the two characterizations of the continuity of f stated in Theorems 7.3 and 7.4 make use of the *inverse* images, and not the direct images, under f.

In fact, the image of an open set in X under a continuous mapping is an open set in Y only in exceptional cases. For example, for the constant mapping $x \to 0$ of $\mathbf{R}$ into $\mathbf{R}$ no nonempty open set in X has an open image.

Similarly, the image of a closed set in X under a continuous mapping may be nonclosed in Y: for example, the mapping $x \to 1/(x^2 + 1)$ of $\mathbf{R}$ into $\mathbf{R}$ carries the closed set $\mathbf{R}$ onto $(0, 1]$, which is not closed in $\mathbf{R}$.

Transitivity of continuous mappings

Let X, Y, Z, be topological spaces, f a mapping of X into Y, g a mapping of Y into Z, and $h = g \circ f$.

Let $x_0 \in X$; we put $y_0 = f(x_0)$ and $z_0 = g(y_0) = g(f(x_0)) = h(x_0)$.

7.5. Proposition. *If f is continuous at x_0 and if g is continuous at y_0, then the composite $h = g \circ f$ is continuous at x_0.*

Indeed, let V be an arbitrary neighborhood of z_0. The continuity of g at y_0 implies that $g^{-1}(V)$ is a neighborhood of y_0; the continuity of f at x_0 implies, therefore, that $f^{-1}(g^{-1}(V)) = h^{-1}(V)$ is a neighborhood of x_0.

In particular, if f is continuous on X and g is continuous on Y, $h = g \circ f$ is continuous on X.

EXAMPLE. The mapping $u \to |u|$ of $\mathbf{R}$ into $\mathbf{R}$ is continuous; therefore for every continuous mapping f of X into $\mathbf{R}$, the mapping $|f|$ of X into $\mathbf{R}$ defined by $x \to |f(x)|$ is also continuous.

Homeomorphisms

It is natural to say that two topological spaces X and Y are isomorphic if there exists a bijection f of X to Y which interchanges their open sets, that is, such that for every open set A in X, $f(A)$ is an open set in Y, and for every open set B in Y, $f^{-1}(B)$ is an open set in X. Such an isomorphism is called a *homeomorphism*.

It is clear that the inverse of a homeomorphism is a homeomorphism, and that the product of two homeomorphisms is a homeomorphism. In particular, the collection of all homeomorphims of a space with itself forms a group.

REMARKS. The notion of a homeomorphism is fundamental in topology, because a homeomorphism is nothing more than an isomorphism of topological structures; it is the basic equivalence relation in topology.

When two topological spaces are homeomorphic, every property which is true for one is true for the other; they can be considered as two representations of the same geometric entity.

When a set E is provided with various structures, one of which is a topological structure (the other structures can be algebraic, metric, etc.), a property of E is said to be topological if it is true for every topological space which is homeomorphic to E: for example, the fact that **R** contains a countable everywhere dense subset is topological. With a little practice one can in general easily recognize whether a property is topological or not; a property is in any case always topological, when it is stated in terms of open sets and derived notions such as closed sets, neighborhoods, accumulation point, everywhere dense, etc.

Here, in Fig. 1, without the trouble of being precise and without proof, is a series of examples intended to convey the intuitive content of homeomorphness; the letters and figures appearing on each line are homeomorphic to one another.

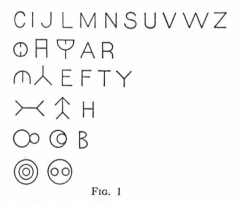

FIG. 1

The lateral surface of a truncated cone is homeomorphic to a circular ring.

A hemisphere is homeomorphic to a closed interval in $\mathbf{R}^2$.

One can get a good idea of homeomorphism, as it applies to surfaces in the space $\mathbf{R}^3$, by imagining that these surfaces are made of rubber; a homeomorphism is then a deformation of these surfaces by stretching and shrinking, without tearing, folding, or gluing. Nevertheless, such recourse to intuition can lead to error, and should never replace an exact argument.

EXAMPLE OF A PROOF OF HOMEOMORPHNESS.   Let X and Y be two isomorphic totally ordered sets, and let f be a bijection of X to Y which is an isomorphism for the order structure (in other words, f is an increasing bijection).

Then f is a homeomorphism for the topologies on X and Y associated with their order.

Indeed, f interchanges the open intervals of X and Y, and therefore their open sets also, since the latter are defined in terms of open intervals.

PARTICULAR CASE.   The mapping $f : x \to x/(1 + |x|)$ is an increasing bijection of **R** to $(-1, 1)$; we complete it to an increasing bijection of $\bar{\mathbf{R}}$ to $[-1, 1]$ by setting

$$f(-\infty) = -1 \quad \text{and} \quad f(+\infty) = 1.$$

Therefore $\bar{\mathbf{R}}$ and $[-1, 1]$, taken with their order topologies, are homeomorphic.

We shall now prove a convenient general criterion for homeomorphness.

7.6. Theorem.   *In order that a bijection f of a space X to a space Y be a homeomorphism, it is necessary and sufficient that it be bicontinuous, that is, that f and f^{-1} be continuous.*

Indeed, to say that f and f^{-1} are continuous is equivalent to saying that the inverse image of every open set in Y is open and that the direct image of every open set in X is open.

EXAMPLE.   The translations of $\mathbf{R}^n$ are homeomorphisms of $\mathbf{R}^n$ to $\mathbf{R}^n$; more generally, the same is true of the *dilations*

$$x \to \lambda x + a \quad (\lambda \neq 0).$$

Z A hurried study of various special cases might lead one to believe that every continuous bijection of a space X to a space Y is also bicontinuous. We shall see later that this is indeed so in certain cases (see the study of compact spaces). But it is not a general fact. Here are some examples:

EXAMPLE 1.   Y is the real line **R**; the elements of X are those of **R**, but its topology is the discrete topology. The mapping f of X onto Y is the identity mapping $x \to x$. It is evidently continuous, but not bicontinuous.

EXAMPLE 2. X and Y are two subsets of **R**, with the topologies induced by the topology of **R** (see Section 9); X consists of the interval [0, 1) and the point 2; Y is the interval [0, 1]. Finally, f is defined by $f(x) = x$ if $x \in [0, 1)$, and $f(2) = 1$.

It is immediate that this mapping is one-to-one and continuous, but that f^{-1} is not continuous at the point 1.

A study of these two examples is enough to show that the lack of continuity of f^{-1} results from the fact that f, while being one-to-one and continuous, brings points "closer together," and that, more precisely, there can exist a set A in X which is not a neighborhood of a point a, while $f(A)$ is a neighborhood of $f(a)$.

8. NOTION OF A LIMIT

Limit of a sequence

8.1. Definition. LET (a_i) $(i = 1, 2, ..., n, ...)$ BE A SEQUENCE OF POINTS OF A SPACE E. WE SAY THAT THIS SEQUENCE *CONVERGES* TO A POINT a OF E, OR THAT a IS THE *LIMIT* OF THIS SEQUENCE, IF FOR EVERY NEIGHBOR-HOOD V OF a THERE EXISTS AN INTEGER i_0 SUCH THAT $a_i \in$ V FOR EVERY $i \geqslant i_0$.

In symbolic notation,

$$(\forall V, V \in \mathscr{V}(a))(\exists i_0, i_0 \in \mathbf{N})(\forall i, i \geqslant i_0): (a_i \in V).$$

This condition can also be expressed as follows: For every neighborhood V of a we have $a_i \in$ V for all except at most finitely many values of i.

It is immediate that if the sequence (a_i) converges to a, every infinite subsequence also converges to a.

If E is an arbitrary space, a sequence can have several limit points; for example, when E has the coarse topology, every point of E is a limit of every sequence $(a_i)_{i\in I}$.

But one can assert that the limit is unique when E is a *separated* space,* in the following sense:

8.2. Definition. A SPACE E IS SAID TO BE *SEPARATED* WHEN ANY TWO DISTINCT POINTS HAVE DISJOINT NEIGHBORHOODS.

The most useful spaces are always separated; for example the line **R** is separated (see Section 1, pp. 3-4).

In a separated space E, every one-point set is closed; in fact, to say that $\{a\}$ is closed is equivalent to saying that $E - \{a\}$ is open, that is,

---

* An equivalent terminology is *Hausdorff* space.

is a neighborhood of each of its points. But this last assertion is true since for every $x \neq a$ there exists by hypothesis a neighborhood of x which does not contain a, and which therefore is contained in $E - \{a\}$.

8.3. Proposition. *Every sequence of points in a separated space has at most one limit.*

The proof is an exact repetition of the proof given for **R**.

Adherent points of a sequence

The sequence of real numbers $a_n = (-1)^n$ is not convergent; nevertheless the numbers 1 and -1 appear as limits in a larger sense. The analysis of this notion leads to the following definition:

8.4. Definition. LET (a_i) $(i = 1, 2, ...)$ BE A SEQUENCE OF POINTS OF A SPACE E. WE SAY THAT A POINT a OF E IS AN *ADHERENT POINT* OF THIS SEQUENCE IF FOR EVERY NEIGHBORHOOD V OF a THERE EXIST ARBITRARILY LARGE INDICES i SUCH THAT $a_i \in V$.

If we denote by A_n the set of points a_i with index $i \geqslant n$, we can say that a is an adherent point when, for every n, the point a belongs to the adherence of A_n.

The set of adherent points of the sequence $(a_i)_{i \in I}$ is thus

$$A = \bigcap_1^\infty \bar{A}_n .$$

This set is closed; it may be empty; for example, the sequence $(a_n = n)$ in **R** has no adherent points.

If all the points a_i of the sequence belong to a closed subset F of E, then $A \subset F$; in fact $A_n \subset F$, hence $\bar{A}_n \subset F$, and $A \subset F$.

In a separated space, if a sequence (a_i) converges to a, this point is the only adherent point of the sequence. In fact, suppose $b \neq a$ and let V_b, V_a be disjoint neighborhoods of these two points. There exists n such that $A_n \subset V_a$; since $A_n \cap V_b = \varnothing$, the point b is not adherent to the sequence.

Z It is, however, false in general, even in a separated space, that if a sequence has a single adherent point, then it converges to this point. For example, the sequence $(1/2, 2, 1/3, 3, ..., 1/n, n, ...)$ in **R** has a single adherent point 0, although it does not converge to 0.

Limit and adherent point along a filter base

Classical analysis does not define the notion of a limit for sequences only: for example, the function $x^2/(x^2 + 1)$ tends to 1 as x tends to ∞; $(1/x^2 + 1/y^2)$ tends to 0 as x and y tend to ∞; $\sin x/x$ tends to 1 as x tends to 0 through values $\neq 0$.

We shall see that all of the limit notions which enter into these examples are special cases of a general concept.

8.5. Definition. LET E BE AN ARBITRARY SET. BY A *FILTER BASE* ON E WE MEAN ANY COLLECTION $\mathscr{B}$ OF SUBSETS OF E SUCH THAT:

1. FOR EVERY B_1, $B_2 \in \mathscr{B}$ THERE EXISTS $B_3 \in \mathscr{B}$ SUCH THAT $B_3 \subset B_1 \cap B_2$;

2. NO ELEMENT B OF $\mathscr{B}$ IS EMPTY.

It follows from this definition that the intersection of a finite number of elements of $\mathscr{B}$ is never empty.

EXAMPLE 1. $E = \mathbf{N}$, and the elements of $\mathscr{B}$ are the subsets of the form $\{n, n + 1, ...\}$.

EXAMPLE 2. $E = \mathbf{N}^2$, and the elements of $\mathscr{B}$ are the subsets B_n of E, where B_n is the family of pairs (p, q) such that $p \geqslant n$ and $q \geqslant n$.

EXAMPLE 3. $E = \mathbf{R}$, and the elements of $\mathscr{B}$ are the intervals $[a, \infty)$ of $\mathbf{R}$.

EXAMPLE 4. E is a topological space, and $\mathscr{B}$ is a neighborhood base of a point a of E.

EXAMPLE 5. E is a topological space; we denote by A a nonempty subset of E, and by a an adherent point of A.

The elements of $\mathscr{B}$ are the sets of the form $A \cap V$, where V is an arbitrary neighborhood of a (we could even require that V belong only to a neighborhood base of a).

8.6. Definition. LET f BE A MAPPING OF A SET X INTO A TOPOLOGICAL SPACE Y; LET $\mathscr{B}$ BE A FILTER BASE ON X, AND LET b BE A POINT OF Y.

WE SAY THAT f CONVERGES TO b (OR HAS LIMIT b) ALONG $\mathscr{B}$ IF FOR EVERY NEIGHBORHOOD V OF b THERE EXISTS A $B \in \mathscr{B}$ SUCH THAT $f(B) \subset V$. WE THEN WRITE $\lim_{\mathscr{B}} f = b$.

IN PARTICULAR, WHEN $X = Y$ AND f IS THE IDENTITY MAPPING OF X INTO X, WE SAY SIMPLY THAT THE FILTER BASE $\mathscr{B}$ CONVERGES TO b.

EXAMPLE 1.   Let (a_n) be a sequence of points of Y; we denote by f the mapping $n \to a_n$ of **N** into Y, and by $\mathscr{B}$ the collection of subsets of **N** whose complements are finite. Then Definition 8.6 coincides with Definition 8.1.

EXAMPLE 2.   If X is a topological space and $\mathscr{B}$ denotes the collection of neighborhoods of a point a of X, to say that $f(a)$ is the limit of f along $\mathscr{B}$ is equivalent to saying that f is continuous at the point a.

We remark that the notation $\lim_{\mathscr{B}} f$ is frequently replaced by $\lim_{\mathscr{B}} f(x)$, in particular when $f(x)$ has a simple expression and a classical notation for f is not available; this is the case for the elementary functions $x \to x^n$ and $x \to |x|$.

8.7. Proposition.   *If Y is a separated space, f can have at most one limit along $\mathscr{B}$.*

In fact, suppose that b and b' are limits of f along $\mathscr{B}$. For any neighborhood V, V' of b, b' there exist B, B' $\in \mathscr{B}$ such that

$$f(\text{B}) \subset \text{V} \qquad \text{and} \qquad f(\text{B}') \subset \text{V}'.$$

Since B $\cap$ B' is nonempty, the same is true of $f(\text{B}) \cap f(\text{B}')$, therefore *a fortiori* of V $\cap$ V'. Since Y is separated, this is possible only if $b = b'$.

8.8. Definition.   LET f BE A MAPPING OF X INTO A TOPOLOGICAL SPACE Y, AND LET $\mathscr{B}$ BE A FILTER BASE ON X.

WE SAY THAT A POINT b OF Y IS AN ADHERENT VALUE OF f ALONG $\mathscr{B}$ IF, FOR EVERY B $\in \mathscr{B}$ AND EVERY NEIGHBORHOOD V OF b, $f(\text{B})$ INTERSECTS V.

This is equivalent to saying that $b \in \overline{f(\text{B})}$ for every B $\in \mathscr{B}$, or again that

$$b \in \bigcap_{\text{B} \in \mathscr{B}} \overline{f(\text{B})}.$$

The set of these b (called the *adherence* of f along $\mathscr{B}$) is therefore the set

$$\bigcap_{\text{B} \in \mathscr{B}} \overline{f(\text{B})};$$

it is clearly closed; we denote it by $\tilde{f}(\mathscr{B})$.

As in the case of sequences, one can verify that if Y is separated, and if f converges to b along $\mathscr{B}$, then b is the only adherent value of f along $\mathscr{B}$.

SPECIAL CASE.   *Limit and adherent values of a function at a point.*

We now assume that X is a topological space; let A be a nonempty subset of X, and $a \in \overline{\text{A}}$; we denote by $\mathscr{B}$ the collection of subsets of X of the form A $\cap$ V, where V is an arbitrary neighborhood of a.

We then say that f has limit b as x tends to a while staying in A, if

$$b = \lim_{\mathscr{B}} f.$$

EXAMPLE. If $X = \mathbf{R}$ and $A = (a, \infty)$, we denote by $f(a_+)$ the possible limit of f along $\mathscr{B}$ (this is the limit *from the right*). The limit from the left $f(a_-)$ is similarly defined.

When $a \in A$ and $\lim_{\mathscr{B}} f$ exists, this limit can only be $f(a)$ when Y is separated.

In the same way, we can define the adherent values of f as x tends to a while staying in A.

9. SUBSPACES OF A TOPOLOGICAL SPACE

Let E be a topological space and A a subset of E.

Among all the topologies which can be defined on A, let us study those which render the identity mapping f of A into E continuous. The inverse image of an open set in E under this mapping is simply the intersection of this open set with A. Therefore, in order than the canonical mapping f be continuous, it is necessary and sufficient that the family of open sets of the topology of A contain all these intersections.

But it is immediate that the traces on A of the open sets in E satisfy the axioms O_1, O_2, O_3. The topology that these traces define on A is the one we shall take.

9.1. Definition. FOR EVERY SUBSET A OF A TOPOLOGICAL SPACE E, THE SET A WITH THE TOPOLOGY WHOSE OPEN SETS ARE THE TRACES ON A OF THE OPEN SETS IN E WILL BE CALLED THE *SUBSPACE* A OF E.

WE ALSO SAY THAT THE TOPOLOGY OF A IS INDUCED BY THAT OF E, OR THAT IT IS THE TRACE OF THAT OF E.

The identity mapping of A into E is then continuous.

Closed sets and neighborhoods in a subspace

The formula

$$A \doteq A \cap \omega = A \cap \complement\omega,$$

where ω is an open set in E, shows that the closed sets in the subspace A are simply the traces on A of the closed sets in E.

Similarly, in a subspace A the neighborhoods of a point a of A are the sets $A \cap V$, where V is a neighborhood of a in E.

Z One should carefully note that an open (closed) set in a subspace
A of E is not necessarily an open (closed) set in E. This remark is
made precise by the following proposition:

9.2. Proposition.   *In order that every open (closed) set in the subspace A of E
be an open (closed) set in E, it is necessary and sufficient that A be open
(closed) in E.*

In fact, if A is open in E, the trace on A of every open set in E is open
in E. Conversely, if the trace on A of every open set in E is open in E,
this is true of the trace of E on A, that is of A itself.

One has a parallel argument upon replacing the word "open" by
"closed."

Transitivity of subspaces

9.3. Proposition.   *Let X be a topological space, Y a subspace of X, and Z
a subspace of Y. The topologies on Z induced by those of X and Y are
identical.*

In fact, the open sets in the subspace Y are the sets of the form $Y \cap \omega$,
where ω is an open set in X. Therefore the open sets in Z, in the topology
induced by that of Y, are the sets of the form $Z \cap (Y \cap \omega)$; but such a
set is simply $Z \cap \omega$; therefore the open sets of the topologies on Z
induced by those of X and Y are identical.

9.4. Proposition.   *Let f be a mapping of a topological space X into a subspace
Y of a topological space Z.*

*To say that f is continuous at a point a of X is equivalent to saying that f,
regarded as a mapping of X into Z, is continuous at a.*

In fact, the neighborhoods of $f(a)$ in Y are the sets $V \cap Y$, where V is
a neighborhood of $f(a)$ in Z; and since $f(X) \subset Y$, we have

$$f^{-1}(V) = f^{-1}(V \cap Y).$$

9.5. Proposition.   *Let f be a mapping of a space X into a space Y. If f is
continuous at the point a, its restriction to every subspace A containing a is
continuous at a.*

In fact, let g be the restriction of f to A; for every neighborhood
V of $f(a)$ in Y, we have

$$g^{-1}(V) = A \cap f^{-1}(V).$$

Thus if $f^{-1}(V)$ is a neighborhood of a in X, $g^{-1}(V)$ is a neighborhood of a in A.

Z   On the other hand, it can happen that g is continuous at a without f being so; for example, if f is the mapping of **R** into **R** which equals 0 on **Q** and 1 on $\complement$ **Q**, f is discontinuous at every point of **R**, while the restriction of f to **Q** is continuous (as is also the restriction of f to $\complement$ **Q**).

There is nevertheless an important case in which the continuity of g at a is equivalent to that of f at a; this is the case in which A is a neighborhood of a. In fact in this case, if $A \cap f^{-1}(V)$ is a neighborhood of a in A, it is also a neighborhood of a in X, therefore *a fortiori* $f^{-1}(V)$ is a neighborhood of a in X.

We state this equivalence by saying that the continuity of a mapping at a point is a *local* property.

9.6. Proposition.   *Every subspace of a separated space is separated.*

In fact, let A be a subspace of a separated space X. For any $x, y \in A$ such that $x \neq y$, there exist disjoint neighborhoods V_x, V_y in X of these points; the sets $A \cap V_x$ and $A \cap V_y$ are neighborhoods of x, y in the subspace A, and they are disjoint.

APPLICATIONS.   The notion of a subspace is a convenient way of defining and studying new topological spaces. Thus every subset A of **R** or **R**^{n}, taken with the induced topology, constitutes a topological space.

For example, the *sphere* S_{n-1} in **R**^{n} defined by $\Sigma x_i^2 = 1$ constitutes a highly interesting topological space.

Every space homeomorphic to S_{n-1} is called a *topological sphere* of dimension $(n - 1)$; in particular, every space homeomorphic to S_1 is called a *simple closed curve*.

Similarly, every space homeomorphic to $(0, 1)$ $([0, 1])$ is called a *simple open* (closed) *arc*.

Z   All the open intervals (a, b) (where $a < b$) in **R** are homeomorphic, since we can pass from one to another by a dilation of the form $x \rightarrow \alpha x + \beta$; and each of them is homeomorphic to **R** since, for example, the bijection $x \rightarrow x/(1 + |x|)$ of **R** to $(-1, 1)$ is a homeomorphism.

It also turns out that the topology induced on each of the intervals (a, b) by that of **R** is identical with the order topology on (a, b). But it should not be assumed that this identity extends to every subset of **R**; for example, these two topologies are distinct on $A = [0, 1) \cup \{2\}$. We shall specify a class of sets for which this identity holds by the following:

9.7. Proposition. *Let* X *be a totally ordered set; for every generalized interval* A *of* X, *the order topology on* A *is identical with the trace on* A *of the order topology on* X.

In fact, every open interval of the ordered set A is of the form (a, b), or $(\leftarrow, a)$, or $(a, \rightarrow)$, or A, where a, b denote points of A. But such a set is the intersection of A with an open interval of X; therefore a union of such sets is simply the intersection of A with an arbitrary open set in X, from which follows the identity of the two topologies.

For example, in **R**, the order topology on $[0, 1]$ or on $(0, 1)$ is identical with the topology induced by that of **R**.

10. FINITE PRODUCTS OF SPACES

We have earlier defined a topology on $\mathbf{R}^n$ derived from that of **R** by using products of open intervals of **R**. This procedure can be extended to the case of arbitrary products of spaces. Here we shall study only finite products of spaces.

Let E_i ($i = 1, 2, ..., n$) be a finite family of topological spaces and let $E = \Pi E_i$ ($i = 1, 2, ..., n$) be the collection of sequences $x = (x_1, x_2, ..., x_n)$ where $x_i \in E_i$. Among all the possible topologies on E we shall take only those for which each of the projections $x \rightarrow x_i = f_i(x)$ of E onto E_i is continuous; this condition amounts to saying that for every open set $\omega_i \subset E_i$, the set $f_i^{-1}(\omega_i)$, which is simply the product

$$E_1 \times \cdots \times E_{i-1} \times \omega_i \times E_{i+1} \times \cdots \times E_n,$$

should be open in E. The same must therefore also be true of every finite intersection of such sets, that is, of every set of the form $\Pi \omega_i$ ($i = 1, 2, ..., n$) and of every union of such sets. If one could show that these sets satisfy axioms O_1, O_2, O_3, it would be natural to take, as the topology on E, the topology which they define.

We are thus led to the following definitions:

10.1. Definition. ANY SET IN $E = \Pi E_i$ OF THE FORM $p = \Pi \omega_i$ ($i = 1, 2, ..., n$), WHERE ω_i IS AN ARBITRARY OPEN SET IN E_i, IS CALLED AN *ELEMENTARY OPEN SET* IN E.

EVERY UNION OF ELEMENTARY OPEN SETS IN E IS CALLED AN OPEN SET IN E.

The family of these open sets clearly satisfies axioms O_1 and O_3. It also satisfies O_2, for if

$$A = \bigcup_{j \in J} p_j \quad \text{and} \quad A' = \bigcup_{k \in K} p_k',$$

then

$$A \cap A' = \bigcup_{(j,k) \in J \times K} (p_j \cap p_k')$$

and each $p_j \cap p_k'$ is easily seen to be an elementary open set.

These open sets therefore define a topology on E. By construction, this topology is that for which the projection of E onto E_i is a continuous mapping for every i. With this topology, E is called the *topological product* of the spaces E_i .

EXAMPLE 1.   We have defined a topology on $\mathbf{R}^n$ in Section 4; we there took for the open sets the unions of open intervals. But since every open set in $\mathbf{R}$ is a union of open intervals, the topology on $\mathbf{R}^n$ defined by means of open intervals is identical with the product topology.

EXAMPLE 2.   The product $S_1 \times \mathbf{R}$ is a topological space called a *cylinder*.

EXAMPLE 3.   The product $(S_1)^n$ is called the *n*-dimensional *torus*.

Product of subspaces

If A_i denotes a subspace of E_i , one can verify that the product topology on $A = \Pi A_i$ is identical with the topology induced by that of ΠE_i on its subset A.

In particular, for every $a_i \in E_i$ $(i = 2, 3, ..., n)$ the space E_1 is homeomorphic to the subspace $E_1 \times \{a_2\} \times \cdots \times \{a_n\}$ of E under the mapping $x_1 \rightarrow (x_1 , a_2 , ..., a_n)$.

Associativity of the topological product.   *If* A, B, *and* C *are topological spaces, the one-to-one canonical correspondence between the spaces* $(A \times B) \times C$ *(respectively,* $A \times (B \times C)$*) and* $A \times B \times C$ *is a homeomorphism.*

It suffices (see Section 5) to show that this correspondence preserves neighborhoods. But every point (a, b, c) of $(A \times B) \times C$ has a neighborhood base consisting of the sets

$$(\omega_a \times \omega_b) \times \omega_c ;$$

and every point (a, b, c) of $A \times B \times C$ has a neighborhood base consisting of the sets $\omega_a \times \omega_b \times \omega_c$ (where $\omega_a , \omega_b , \omega_c$ denote open neighborhoods of a, b, c in A, B, C). But the sets $(\omega_a \times \omega_b) \times \omega_c$ and $\omega_a \times \omega_b \times \omega_c$ are homologous (that is, are carried into each other) by the canonical one-to-one correspondence, which implies the desired property.

This associativity will enable us to simplify certain proofs by carrying them out only for products of two spaces.

Commutativity.   It is easily verified that the topological product is commutative in the sense, for example, that the canonical bijection $(x, y) \to (y, x)$ of A $\times$ B to B $\times$ A is a homeomorphism.

Continuous mappings in a product space.   In general, a mapping $x \to f(x)$ of a space E into a product space F $= \Pi F_i$ is denoted by the coordinate mappings $x \to f_i(x)$ of E into each F_i. The close connection between the continuity of f and that of the f_i is given by the following proposition:

10.2. Proposition.   *In order that the mapping f of E into the finite product F $= \Pi F_i$ be continuous at a, it is necessary and sufficient that each of the coordinate mappings f_i of E into F_i be continuous at a.*

In fact, if f is continuous at a, then since $f_i = \mathrm{pr}_i \circ f$, where pr_i denotes the operation of projection of F onto F_i, the mapping f_i is continuous at a. Conversely, suppose that each f_i is continuous at a; for every elementary open set $\omega = \Pi \omega_i$ in F containing $f(a)$, $f_i^{-1}(\omega_i)$ is a neighborhood of a in E, and therefore $f^{-1}(\omega)$, which is equal to

$$\bigcap_i f_i^{-1}(\omega_i),$$

is also a neighborhood of a. Since every neighborhood V of $f(a)$ in F contains an elementary open set ω containing $f(a)$, then $f^{-1}(V)$, which contains $f^{-1}(\omega)$, is *a fortiori* a neighborhood of a.

EXAMPLE.   Let u_1 and u_2 be continuous mappings of E into F_1 and F_2, respectively, and let $g : (y_1, y_2) \to g(y_1, y_2)$ be a continuous mapping of $F_1 \times F_2$ into a space G.
Then the mapping $x \to g(u_1(x), u_2(x))$ of E into G is continuous.

Mappings of a product space into another space

Let $f : (x, y) \to f(x, y)$ be a mapping of a product X $\times$ Y into a space F.
If f is continuous, its restriction to every subspace of X $\times$ Y is continuous; in particular, for every $a \in$ X the restriction of f to $(a \times$ Y) is continuous; in other words, since the mapping $y \to (a, y)$ of Y onto $(a \times$ Y) is a homeomorphism, the mapping $y \to f(a, y)$ of Y into F is continuous.
In other words, the continuity of f implies that of the partial mappings $x \to f(x, b)$ and $y \to f(a, y)$.

Z But *the converse is false*; in fact, let f be the mapping of $\mathbf{R}^2$ into $\mathbf{R}$ defined by

$$f(0,0) = 0 \quad \text{and} \quad f(x,y) = xy/(x^2 + y^2) \quad \text{if} \quad (x,y) \neq (0,0).$$

It is immediate that all the partial mappings are continuous; at the same time, f is not continuous at $(0,0)$ since, for example,

$$f(x,x) = 1/2$$

for every $x \neq 0$, while

$$f(0,0) = 0.$$

Similar examples can be constructed in which the set of points of discontinuity of f are everywhere dense on $\mathbf{R}^2$.

Limits in a product space

The following result can be proved in the same way as was Proposition 10.2.

10.3. Proposition. *In order that a sequence (a_n) of points of $F = \Pi F_i$ converge to the point $l = (l_i)$ of F, it is necessary and sufficient that for every i, the sequence $(a_n)_i$ converge to l_i .*

More generally, let $\mathscr{B}$ be a filter base on a set E, let $f = (f_i)$ be a mapping of E into the product topological space $F = \Pi F_i$, and let $l = (l_i)$ be a point of F.

One can verify that

$$(l = \lim_{\mathscr{B}} f) \Leftrightarrow (\text{for every } i, \quad l_i = \lim_{\mathscr{B}} f_i).$$

Product of separated spaces

10.4. Proposition. *If the spaces E_i are separated, their product E is separated.*

It clearly suffices to prove this for the product of two spaces E_1 and E_2 .

But if a and b are distinct points of E, with coordinates (a_1, a_2) and (b_1, b_2), then either $a_1 \neq b_1$ or $a_2 \neq b_2$. If for example $a_1 \neq b_1$, the points a_1 and b_1 of E_1 have neighborhoods V_1 and W_1 which are disjoint; the points a and b thus have disjoint neighborhoods $V_1 \times E_2$ and $W_1 \times E_2$.

EXAMPLE. Since $\mathbf{R}$ is separated, so is every space $\mathbf{R}^n$.

Every subspace of $\mathbf{R}^n$ is therefore separated; in particular S_{n-1} is separated.

10.5. Proposition. *For every separated space* E, *the diagonal* Δ *of* E $\times$ E *is closed in* E $\times$ E.

Indeed, let $(a, b) \notin \Delta$; the points a, b of E being distinct, they have disjoint neighborhoods V_a, V_b; the product $V_a \times V_b$ is a neighborhood of (a, b) in E $\times$ E and does not intersect Δ; therefore $(E \times E) - \Delta$ is a neighborhood of (a, b).

Since the complement of Δ is a neighborhood of each of its points and is therefore open, Δ is closed.

Corollary 1. *If f and g are continuous mappings of a space* X *into a separated space* E, *the set of points* x *of* X *such that* $f(x) = g(x)$ *is closed.*

Indeed, let h be the mapping $x \rightarrow (f(x), g(x))$ of X into E $\times$ E; h is continuous, and the set in question is simply $h^{-1}(\Delta)$; this set is closed since Δ is closed.

Corollary 2. *If f is a continuous mapping of a space* E *into a separated space* F, *the graph* Φ *of f is closed in* E $\times$ F.

Indeed, Φ is the set of points (x, y) of E $\times$ F such that $y = f(x)$; but the mappings $(x, y) \rightarrow y$ and $(x, y) \rightarrow f(x)$ of E $\times$ F into F are continuous; therefore Φ is closed by the preceding corollary.

Z It should be noted that the converse of Corollary 2 is false: Even if E and F are separated, the graph of f can be closed without f being continuous.

For example, let f be the mapping of **R** into **R** defined by

$$f(0) = 0, \qquad f(x) = 1/x \qquad \text{if} \qquad x \neq 0.$$

The graph of f is the union of the curve $xy - 1 = 0$ and the set $\{0\}$, and is thus closed; nevertheless f is not continuous at the point 0.

11. COMPACT SPACES

In Section 3 we established an important property of closed bounded intervals of **R**, which was called the theorem of Heine-Borel-Lebesgue; its importance lies in that it allows one to replace certain global studies by a local study.

We have also studied other topological spaces having an analogous property; we shall see, for example, that this is the case for all the closed bounded sets in **R**^{n}.

We shall undertake here a general study of spaces which have this property.

11.1. Definition. A SPACE E IS SAID TO BE *COMPACT* IF IT IS SEPARATED AND IF FROM EVERY OPEN COVERING OF E ONE CAN SELECT A FINITE SUB-COVERING OF E.

The sole purpose, in this definition, of the condition that E be separated is to exclude spaces which have little usefulness, such as spaces with the coarse topology.

EXAMPLES. Every finite separated space is compact. On the other hand, **R** is not a compact space (see Section 3). The theorems which follow will furnish us with huge classes of compact spaces.

It is well to be acquainted with several equivalent forms of the condition of compactness. Here are two others:

11.2. Formulation. E IS SEPARATED, AND FROM EVERY FAMILY OF CLOSED SETS IN E WHOSE INTERSECTION IS EMPTY ONE CAN SELECT A FINITE SUBFAMILY HAVING THE SAME PROPERTY.

This condition is the dual of the preceding one; indeed, if $(G_i)_{i \in I}$ is a family of open sets in E, the formula

$$E = \bigcup_{i \in I} G_i$$

is equivalent to

$$\varnothing = \bigcap_{i \in I} F_i \quad \text{where} \quad F_i = \complement G_i .$$

Let us now say that a family $\mathscr{F}$ of subsets of E has the *finite intersection property* if every finite subfamily of $\mathscr{F}$ has nonempty intersection. Wiht this convention the preceding statement is evidently equivalent to the following:

11.3. Formulation. E IS SEPARATED, AND EVERY FAMILY OF CLOSED SETS IN E WHICH HAS THE FINITE INTERSECTION PROPERTY HAS NONEMPTY INTERSECTION.

In particular we can state:

11.4. Proposition. *In a compact space* E, *every family of nonempty closed sets which is totally ordered by inclusion has a nonempty intersection. For example, every decreasing sequence of nonempty closed sets has a nonempty intersection.*

In fact, every finite subfamily of a totally ordered family of sets has a smallest element, which is therefore the intersection—in the present case nonempty—of this subfamily.

The real line does not have this last property since, for example, the sequence of closed intervals $[n, +\infty)$ $(n = 1, 2, ...)$ has empty intersection.

11.5. Proposition. (1) *In a compact space, every sequence of points has at least one adherent point.*

(2) *If it has a single adherent point, the sequence converges to this point.*

(1) Indeed, with the notation used following Definition 8.4, the set of adherent points is the intersection of the decreasing sequence of nonempty closed sets $\overline{A_n}$.

(2) Let a be the unique element of

$$A = \bigcap_1^\infty \overline{A_n} .$$

For every open neighborhood V of a, the closed sets $\overline{A_n} \cap \complement V$ clearly have empty intersection. Therefore, since they form a decreasing sequence, one of them is empty; in other words, from some n_0 on we have $\overline{A_n} \subset V$ and *a fortiori* $a_n \in V$.

More generally, one can verify that every mapping f of a set X with a filter basis $\mathscr{B}$ into a compact space E has at least one adherent value along $\mathscr{B}$, and that if f has a single adherent value, then f converges along $\mathscr{B}$ to this value.

Z It is not always true, in a compact space, that the *set* A of points of a sequence (a_n) has an accumulation point; it can happen that A is either finite or consists even of a single point, which is the case if all the a_i are identical. In other words, a point can be adherent to a sequence (a_n) either because it is an accumulation point of the set A of the a_n , or because it coincides with infinitely many of the a_n .

11.6. Proposition (analog of the Bolzano-Weierstrass theorem).

(1) *Every infinite subset A of a compact space E has at least one accumulation point in E.*

(2) *Every subset A of E which does not have any accumulation point in E is finite.*

It is clear that these two properties are equivalent; the second is proved exactly as was Theorem 3.3.

Z It is not true that, conversely, every separated space E for which every infinite subset has at least one accumulation point is compact; nevertheless, we shall prove later that this converse is true for metric spaces E.

11.7. Proposition. *Let* A *be a separated subspace of a space* E:

(A *is compact*) ⇔ (*Every family of open sets in* E *which covers* A *contains a finite subfamily which covers* A).

PROOF. 1. If A is compact, and if $(\omega_i)_{i\in I}$ is a family of open sets in E which covers A, the sets $(A \cap \omega_i)_{i\in I}$ constitute an open covering of the compact space A; thus there exists a finite subset J of I such that the sets $(A \cap \omega_i)_{i\in J}$ cover A; *a fortiori* the family $(\omega_i)_{i\in J}$ covers A.

2. Conversely, suppose that A has the second property. Let $(\omega_i')_{i\in I}$ be a family of open sets in A which covers A; every ω_i' is of the form $\omega_i' = A \cap \omega_i$, where ω_i is an open set in E.

The ω_i cover A; therefore there exists a finite subset J of I such that the sets $(\omega_i)_{i\in J}$ also cover A.

But

$$\bigcup_{i\in J} (A \cap \omega_i) = A \cap \left(\bigcup_{i\in J} \omega_i\right) = A,$$

and therefore the finite family $(\omega_i')_{i\in J}$ covers A.

It is therefore true that every covering of A by open sets ω_i' in A has a finite subcovering; therefore A is compact.

11.8. Corollary. *For every* $a, b \in \mathbf{R}$, *the closed interval* $[a, b]$ *is compact.*

This is an immediate consequence of Theorem 3.2, and of Proposition 11.7 which was just proved.

11.9. Corollary. *Let* E *be a separated space and let* (a_n) *be a sequence of points of* E *which converges to a point* a *of* E.

Then the set $A = \{a, a_1, a_2, ...\}$ *is compact.*

Indeed, the set A is, first of all, separated; next, let (ω_i) be a covering of A by open sets in E. There exists an ω_{i_0} which contains a; this open set is a neighborhood of a and therefore contains all the a_n except at most a finite number, say $a_{n_1}, ..., a_{n_p}$. These points are contained, respectively, in certain of the ω_i, say $\omega_{i_1}, ..., \omega_{i_p}$. The open sets $\omega_{i_0}, \omega_{i_1}, ..., \omega_{i_p}$ constitute a finite covering of A. Therefore A is compact.

The next theorem is of fundamental importance.

11.10. Theorem. *In a compact space* E, *every closed subset is a compact subspace.*

Proof.   For a simple proof, we shall use the criterion for compactness which is best suited to the problem, for example criterion 11.3 which is stated in terms of closed sets.

Let A be closed in E, and let $(X_i)_{i \in I}$ be a family of closed sets in the space A, having the finite intersection property. Since A is closed, the X_i are also closed sets in E; therefore since E is compact, the intersection of the X_i is nonempty. Hence A is compact.

11.11. Theorem.   *In every separated space* E, *every compact subspace of* E *is closed in* E.

Let A be a compact subspace of E. We shall show that $\complement A$ is open.

Suppose $x_0 \in \complement A$; for every $y \in A$, let V_y and W_y be two *open disjoint* neighborhoods in E of x_0 and y, respectively. There exists a finite subfamily $(W_{y_i})_{i \in I}$ of the open sets W_y which covers A. The open set

$$V = \bigcap_{i \in I} V_{y_i}$$

is a neighborhood of x_0 and is disjoint from each of the W_{y_i}, hence also from A; in other words, $V \subset \complement A$. Thus $\complement A$ is a neighborhood of each of its points, and is therefore open.

Let us remark that the hypothesis that E is separated is essential. For example, if E has the coarse topology and contains more than one point, every one-point subset of E is a compact subspace, and yet is not closed.

This theorem shows that every compact space can be called "absolutely closed" since it is closed in every space E which contains it (at least if E is separated).

11.12. Corollary (of Theorems 11.10 and 11.11).   *In every compact space* E, *the classes of closed subsets and compact subsets are identical.*

11.13. Corollary.   *The compact subspaces of* **R** *are the subsets of* **R** *which are closed and bounded.*

Indeed, if X is a closed bounded subset of **R**, there exists an interval $[a, b]$ containing X; since X is closed in **R**, it is also closed in the subspace $[a, b]$, and since $[a, b]$ is compact, X is compact.

Conversely if X is a compact subset of **R**, X is closed in **R** since **R** is separated. On the other hand, X is bounded since we can select, from the sequence of open intervals $(-n, n)$ (where $n = 1, 2, ...$), which forms an open covering of X, a finite sequence of intervals which covers X, and the largest among them will contain X.

11.14. Theorem. *In every separated space, the union of two compact sets is compact; every intersection of compact sets is compact.*

PROOF.   Let A and B be compact sets in E.

1. Since E is separated, so is A $\cup$ B.

On the other hand, every open covering of A $\cup$ B is also an open covering of A and of B. We can therefore find two finite coverings, one of A, the other of B; together they constitute a finite covering of A $\cup$ B; therefore A $\cup$ B is compact.

2. If the A_i $(i \in I)$ are compact, each of them is closed in E, and therefore their intersection is closed in E, and *a fortiori* in any member A_{i_0} of $(A_i)_{i \in I}$. This intersection is thus a compact set (Theorem 11.10).

Z   Clearly the union of an infinite family of compact sets is not in general a compact set.

11.15. Theorem. *For every continuous mapping f of a compact space* E *into a separated space* F, *the subspace f(E) of* F *is compact.*

PROOF.   First of all, $f(E)$ is separated because F is. Next, let $(\omega_i)_{i \in I}$ be a covering of $f(E)$ by open sets in $f(E)$. The sets $f^{-1}(\omega_i)$ constitute an open covering of E; one can find a finite covering $(f^{-1}(\omega_i))_{i \in J}$. Since $f(f^{-1}(\omega_i)) = \omega_i$, the $(\omega_i)_{i \in J}$ cover $f(E)$. Therefore $f(E)$ is compact.

11.16. Corollary. *Every continuous bijection of a compact space* E *to a separated space* F *is a homeomorphism.*

It suffices to show that f^{-1} is continuous, hence that for every closed set X in E, $f(X)$ is closed in F.

But X is closed in the compact space E and thus compact; its image $f(X)$ in the separated space F is thus compact, and hence also closed.

This corollary thus gives us an important case in which the continuity of a one-to-one mapping implies its bicontinuity (that is, the continuity of f and f^{-1}).

11.17. Corollary. *Every numerical function which is continuous on a compact space* E *is bounded on* E *and attains its supremum and infimum on* E.

Let f be a continuous mapping of E into **R**; $f(E)$ is compact, therefore closed and bounded in **R**, and hence contains its infimum b_1 and its supremum b_2; thus there exists $x_1 \in E$ such that $f(x_1) = b_1$ and $x_2 \in E$ such that $f(x_2) = b_2$.

In particular, if $f(x) > 0$ on E, there exists $b > 0$ such that $f(x) \geqslant b$ on E.

Z If E is not compact, a continuous numerical function on E need not be bounded, and when it is bounded, need not attain its bounds.

For example, the function $x \rightarrow x$ is not bounded on **R**.

The function $x \rightarrow x/(1 + |x|)$ is bounded on **R** but does not attain either of its bounds.

The function $x \rightarrow 1/x$ is not bounded on $(0, 1]$.

The function $x \rightarrow x$ is bounded on $(0, 1)$ but does not attain either of its bounds on this interval.

11.18. Corollary. *If E is a product of separated spaces* E_i, *the projection of every compact set in E onto each of the* E_i *is compact.*

Indeed, the projection onto each E_i is a continuous mapping.

Product of compact spaces

Theorems 11.10 and 11.15 give us a powerful method for constructing compact spaces. Here is another method, which is particularly convenient for the study of functions of several variables.

11.19. Theorem. *Every finite product of compact spaces is compact.*

PROOF. By the associativity of the product topology, it suffices to prove the theorem for the product of two spaces.

Let $E = X \times Y$ be the product of compact spaces X and Y. Since X and Y are separated, E is separated (Proposition 10.4).

Now let $(\omega_i)_{i \in I}$ be an open covering of E. For every $m = (x, y) \in E$ there exists an $i_m \in I$ such that $m \in \omega_{i_m}$. Therefore there exist open neighborhoods V_m and W_m of x and y in X and Y such that $V_m \times W_m \subset \omega_{i_m}$; we set $U_m = V_m \times W_m$.

But for every $x_0 \in X$, the subset $Y_0 = x_0 \times Y$ of $X \times Y$ is homeomorphic to Y, hence compact.

The U_m, $m \in Y_0$, constitute an open covering of Y_0; we can find a finite subcovering

$$(U_{m_j})_{j \in J}, \qquad \text{where} \qquad m_j = (x_0, y_j).$$

We set

$$V_{x_0} = \bigcap_{j \in J} V_{m_j};$$

this is an open neighborhood of x_0 and it is clear that

$$\bigcup_{j \in J} \omega_{i_{m_j}} \supset V_{x_0} \times Y.$$

The V_{x_0} form an open covering of X; we can find a finite subcovering. With each of the (finitely many) corresponding points x_0 there is associated a (finite) subfamily $(\omega_{i_{m_j}})$ of open set ω_i ; the union of these families is a finite family which covers E.

11.20. Corollary.   *The compact subspaces of* $\mathbf{R}^n$ *are the closed and bounded subsets of* $\mathbf{R}^n$ *(A is said to be bounded in* $\mathbf{R}^n$ *if it is contained in an interval with bounded sides).*

Indeed, if A is a compact set in $\mathbf{R}^n$, it is closed in $\mathbf{R}^n$; on the other hand, the projection of A onto each factor $\mathbf{R}$ is compact, and therefore contained in a bounded interval. Hence A is contained in an interval with bounded sides.

Conversely, if A is closed and bounded, it is a closed subset of a finite product of compact intervals $[a_i , b_i]$; such a product is compact, hence so is A.

EXAMPLE.   The sphere S_{n-1} of $\mathbf{R}^n$ is closed and bounded, therefore compact. It follows that the torus $(S_1)^p$ is also compact.

12. LOCALLY COMPACT SPACES; COMPACTIFICATION

There exist many spaces which, without being compact, behave locally like a compact space; this is the case with $\mathbf{R}$ for example. Precisely:

12.1. Definition.   A SPACE E IS SAID TO BE *LOCALLY COMPACT* IF IT IS SEPARATED AND IF EACH OF ITS POINTS HAS AT LEAST ONE COMPACT NEIGHBORHOOD.

EXAMPLE 1.   Every compact space is locally compact.

EXAMPLE 2.   Every discrete topological space is locally compact (example: $\mathbf{Z}$).

EXAMPLE 3.   The line $\mathbf{R}$ is locally compact; indeed, $\mathbf{R}$ is first of all separated. Next, for every $x \in \mathbf{R}$ there exist $a, b \in \mathbf{R}$ such that $a < x < b$ and $[a, b]$ is a compact neighborhood of x.

We know, by the way, that $\mathbf{R}$ is not compact.

EXAMPLE 4.   The subspace $\mathbf{Q}$ of $\mathbf{R}$ is neither compact nor locally compact; indeed, suppose for example that 0 has, in $\mathbf{Q}$, a compact neighborhood V. The neighborhood V of 0 contains a subneighborhood of the form $\mathbf{Q} \cap [-a, a]$; since this subneighborhood is closed in $\mathbf{Q}$, the set $A = \mathbf{Q} \cap [-a, a]$ would then be compact. But this is clearly false since, for every irrational $x \in [-a, a]$, the decreasing sequence of closed sets $A \cap [x - 1/n, x + 1/n]$ in A has empty intersection.

We now give several results which yield powerful methods for constructing locally compact spaces.

12.2. Proposition. *Every closed subset of a locally compact space is locally compact.*

PROOF.   Let E be a locally compact space, and A a closed subset of E. Every $x \in A$ has, in E, a compact neighborhood V. The set $V \cap A$ is closed in V, hence compact; since it is a neighborhood of x in A, x thus has a compact neighborhood (in A). Finally, A is separated since it is contained in the separated space E; hence it is locally compact.

EXAMPLE.   Every algebraic variety in $\mathbf{R}^n$ is locally compact.

12.3. Proposition. *If* A *and* B *are locally compact subspaces of a separated space, their intersection is also locally compact.*

PROOF.   To begin with, $A \cap B$ is separated; next, for every $x \in A \cap B$ there exist compact neighborhoods V and W of x, in A and B, respectively. The set $V \cap W$ is a neighborhood of x in $A \cap B$, and is compact.

Z   On the other hand, the *union* of A and B need not be locally compact. For example, let A be the subset of $\mathbf{R}^2$ consisting of the points (x, y) such that $x > 0$, and let $B = \{(0, 0)\}$; the set $A \cup B$ is not locally compact because the point $(0, 0)$ does not have any compact neighborhood in $A \cup B$.

12.4. Proposition. *Every finite product of locally compact spaces is locally compact.*

PROOF.   It clearly suffices to prove this for two spaces A, B.
Since A and B are separated, so is $A \times B$. On the other hand, for every $(x, y) \in A \times B$, the points x and y have compact neighborhoods V and W in A and B, respectively. The product $V \times W$ is the desired compact neighborhood of (x, y).

EXAMPLE.   The spaces $\mathbf{R}^n$ and $S_1 \times \mathbf{R}$ are locally compact.

Z   Theorem 11.15 does not have an equivalent for locally compact spaces; in other words, it is false that every separated space which is the image of a locally compact space under a continuous mapping is itself locally compact.

For example, since $\mathbf{Q}$ is denumerable, there is a surjection $n \to f(n)$ of $\mathbf{Z}$ to $\mathbf{Q}$; since $\mathbf{Z}$ is discrete, f is continuous. But $\mathbf{Q}$ is not locally compact, although $\mathbf{Z}$ is.

12.5. Proposition. *Let the space* E *be locally compact but not compact, and let f be a continuous numerical function on* E *such that*

$$\lim_{x \to \infty} f(x) = +\infty$$

(in the sense that for every h > 0, there exists a compact set K ⊂ E *such that f(x) > h outside* K*).*

Then f has a lower bound and attains its infimum.

PROOF.   Let *a* be an arbitrary point of E, and let *h* be a number $> f(a)$. By hypothesis there exists a compact set K ⊂ E such that $f(x) > h$ outside K. The restriction of f to K is continuous, hence has an infimum *m* which is attained at some point *b* of K.

For every $x \notin K$ we have

$$f(x) > h > f(a) \geqslant m.$$

For every $x \in K$ we have

$$f(x) \geqslant m.$$

Therefore *m* is the infimum of f on E; it is attained at the point *b*.

We remark that the set of *x* such that $f(x) = m$ is closed and contained in K; hence it is a compact set.

One can similarly show that every continuous numerical function f on E which tends to a finite limit *l* as $x \to \infty$ (in other words, along the filter base consisting of the complements of the compact sets in E) is bounded and attains each of its bounds which is different from *l*.

EXAMPLE.   Let $P(z)$ be an arbitrary polynomial in z with complex coefficients. The numerical function $z \to |P(z)|$ is continuous in the complex plane **C**; on the other hand, if $P(z) = a_n z^n + a_{n-1} z^{n-1} + \cdots$ (with $a_n \neq 0$), for every $z \neq 0$ we can write

$$|P(z)| = |a_n| \times |z|^n \times |1 + \alpha_1/z + \alpha_2/z^2 + \cdots + \alpha_n/z^n|.$$

Thus

$$|P(z)| \to +\infty \qquad \text{as} \quad z \to \infty.$$

The hypothesis of Proposition 12.5 is satisfied; we can therefore assert that $|P(z)|$ attains its infimum at some point.

This is the basis of one of the proofs of the d'Alembert-Gauss theorem (fundamental theorem of algebra).

Points at infinity and compactification

In the statement of Proposition 12.5, the expression "$x \to \infty$" is only a convenient way of speaking. In fact, we can make it precise by showing that for every space E which is locally compact but not compact, an additional point ω, called the point at infinity, can be adjoined to E and a topology defined on the set $E \cup \{\omega\}$ which makes it a compact space, and whose trace on E is the original topology.

More generally one could set oneself the task of finding the compact spaces $\hat{E}$ of which E is an everywhere dense subspace; the points of $\hat{E} - E$ could then be interpreted as the points at infinity of E. Such a space $\hat{E}$ is called a *compactification* of E.

The particular compactification of interest is dictated by the needs of analysis or of geometry; for example, the compactification of $\mathbf{R}^n$ which is useful in projective geometry is the compact space P^n, called the projective space of dimension n, which can be identified with the set of lines in $\mathbf{R}^{n+1}$ passing through O, taken with a suitable topology.

We shall study two simple examples here.

1. **Compactification of $\mathbf{R}^n$ by a point at infinity.** The inversion f about the pole O and of degree 1 in $\mathbf{R}^{n+1}$, defined by

$$x \to \frac{x}{\| x \|^2} = \frac{x}{\sum x_i^2},$$

is a homeomorphism of $\mathbf{R}^{n+1} - \{O\}$ with itself.

It transforms the hyperplane $x_{n+1} = 1$ of $\mathbf{R}^{n+1}$ into $S - \{O\}$, where S is the sphere of $\mathbf{R}^{n+1}$ with diameter (O, A), calling A the point $(0, 0, ..., 0, 1)$.

Since the canonical mapping $g : (x_1, x_2, ..., x_n) \to (x_1, x_2, ..., x_n, 1)$ of $\mathbf{R}^n$ onto the hyperplane $x_{n+1} = 1$ of $\mathbf{R}^{n+1}$ is a homeomorphism, the bijection $f \circ g$ of $\mathbf{R}^n$ to $S - \{O\}$ is a homeomorphism. If we identify the spaces $\mathbf{R}^n$ and $S - \{O\}$ by this homeomorphism, the sphere S is the desired compactification of $\mathbf{R}^n$; its only point at infinity is the point O.

For $n = 1$, S is a circle.

For $n = 2$, S is a two-dimensional sphere which is called the Riemann sphere when $\mathbf{R}^2$ is identified with $\mathbf{C}$; it is extremely useful in the study of the complex plane, in part due to the fact that the homeomorphism $f \circ g$ preserves angles (one says that it is "conformal").

2. **The extended real line $\bar{\mathbf{R}}$.** We have just compactified $\mathbf{R}$ by a point at infinity. It is also convenient in analysis to use another compactification. We have defined the extended line $\bar{\mathbf{R}}$ in Section 5, and shown in Section 7 that $\bar{\mathbf{R}}$ is homeomorphic to $[-1, 1]$ taken with the order topology.

On the other hand, we have shown (in Section 9.7) that the order topology on $[-1, 1]$ is identical with that induced by the topology of **R**; thus $[-1, 1]$ is compact, and the same is true of $\bar{\mathbf{R}}$.

Moreover, the topology induced by $\bar{\mathbf{R}}$ on its subspace **R** is identical with the original topology of **R**; thus $\bar{\mathbf{R}}$ constitutes a compactification of **R**.

Every nonempty subset X of $\bar{\mathbf{R}}$ has a supremum and infimum, since this is true in $[-1, 1]$; when X is closed, its bounds belong to X.

One neighborhood base of $+\infty$ in $\bar{\mathbf{R}}$ consists of the intervals $[n, +\infty]$ or $(n, +\infty]$ (where $n \in \mathbf{N}$); a similar assertion holds for $-\infty$.

Relatively compact sets in a topological space

We have seen that the compact sets in $\mathbf{R}^n$ are simply the closed bounded subsets of $\mathbf{R}^n$; but every bounded subset of $\mathbf{R}^n$ has a bounded closure. Thus the bounded subsets of $\mathbf{R}^n$ and those subsets of $\mathbf{R}^n$ with compact closure are identical.

More generally, in an arbitrary topological space, the sets which play the role of the bounded sets are those with compact closure; these sets are given a special name.

12.6. Definition. A SUBSET A OF A TOPOLOGICAL SPACE E IS SAID TO BE *RELATIVELY COMPACT* IF ITS CLOSURE $\bar{\mathrm{A}}$ IS COMPACT.

It is evident that this definition is not topological for A, but only for the pair (A, E); for example, the interval (0, 1) is relatively compact in **R**, but not in itself.

Here are some immediate properties:

1. If A is relatively compact in E, so is every subset of A.

2. Every subset of a compact space E is relatively compact in E.

3. If A_1, A_2, ..., A_n are relatively compact in a separated space E, so is their union.

4. Every sequence of points of a relatively compact subset A of E has at least one adherent point in E.

13. CONNECTIVITY

We shall try to make precise the intuitive notion by which we say that a set such as $[0, 1] \cup [2, 3]$ consists of two pieces, while $[0, 1]$ consists of one piece.

It is rather natural to regard two subsets A, B of a topological space E as being clearly separated in E when they are contained in two disjoint closed sets in E; this remark leads us to the following precise definition:

13.1. Definition. A TOPOLOGICAL SPACE E IS SAID TO BE *CONNECTED* IF THERE DOES NOT EXIST ANY PARTITION OF E INTO TWO NONEMPTY CLOSED SETS.

This property is evidently equivalent (by duality) to each of the following:

13.2. THERE DOES NOT EXIST ANY PARTITION OF E INTO TWO NONEMPTY OPEN SETS.

13.3. THE ONLY SUBSETS OF E WHICH ARE BOTH OPEN AND CLOSED ARE E AND $\varnothing$.

A *subset* A of a space E is said to be *connected* if the subspace A of E is connected.

EXAMPLE 1. We shall prove later, in the study of metric spaces, that **R** (as well as every interval of **R**) is connected; we shall for the moment assume this.

EXAMPLE 2. On the other hand, the set **Q** of rationals is not connected; more generally, we shall show that if a subset A of **R** is not an interval, it is not connected. In fact, there then exist two distinct points x, $y \in A$ such that $[x, y] \not\subset A$; therefore there exists a point $a \in [x, y]$ such that $a \notin A$. The nonempty sets $A \cap (-\infty, a)$ and $A \cap (a, \infty)$ are open in A and constitute a partition of A; therefore A is not connected.

To sum up, the only connected subsets of **R** *are the intervals.*

Here are several theorems which often enable one to prove that a set is connected.

13.4. Theorem. *Let* $(A_i)_{i \in I}$ *be a family of connected subsets of* E. *If the intersection of this family is nonempty, its union is connected.*

PROOF. Set

$$A = \bigcup_{i \in I} A_i \,.$$

We consider an arbitrary partition of A into two open sets O_1 and O_2. For every i, $A_i \cap O_1$ and $A_i \cap O_2$ are open relative to A_i; since A_i is connected, one of these sets is empty. Therefore A_i is contained either in O_1 or in O_2. But the A_i have at least one common point x, which belongs to O_1, say. Therefore O_1 contains all the A_i and O_2 is empty. Thus A is connected.

EXAMPLE. Every convex subset X of $\mathbf{R}^n$ is connected; in fact, for every $a \in X$, X is the union of segments containing a, and each of these segments is connected since it is homeomorphic to $[0, 1]$.

In particular $\mathbf{R}^n$, every open or closed interval of $\mathbf{R}^n$, and every open or closed ball of $\mathbf{R}^n$, is connected.

13.5. Theorem. *The closure of every connected set is connected.*

PROOF.　Let A be a connected subset of the space E. To every partition of $\bar{A}$ into two sets O_1 and O_2 which are open in $\bar{A}$, there corresponds the partition of A into two sets $A \cap O_1$ and $A \cap O_2$ which are open in A. Since A is connected, one of these, say $A \cap O_1$, is empty; since A is everywhere dense on $\bar{A}$, the set O_1 is empty. Therefore A is connected.

A similar proof shows that every B such that $A \subset B \subset \bar{A}$ is also connected.

EXAMPLE.　All the spheres of $\mathbf{R}^{n+1}$ are homeomorphic to the sphere S of $\mathbf{R}^{n+1}$ used in Section 12 for the compactification of $\mathbf{R}^n$; but S is the closure of a subspace homeomorphic to $\mathbf{R}^n$. Since $\mathbf{R}^n$ is connected, so is S. Thus every sphere is connected.

13.6. Theorem. *Every continuous image of a connected space is connected.*

PROOF.　Let f be a continuous surjection of a connected space E to F. For every subset X of F which is both open and closed in F, $f^{-1}(X)$ is open and closed in E, and is thus either E or $\varnothing$. But $X = f(f^{-1}(X))$, therefore $X = F$ or $\varnothing$; in other words, F is connected.

13.7. Definition. A COMPACT AND CONNECTED SPACE IS CALLED A *CONTINUUM*.

By Theorems 11.15 and 13.6, every separated space which is the continuous image of a continuum is a continuum.

In studying metric spaces, we shall prove a property of metric continua which makes the notion of connectivity more intuitive.

EXAMPLE 1.　The interval $[-1, 1]$ of $\mathbf{R}$ is a continuum; the same is therefore true of $\bar{\mathbf{R}}$.

EXAMPLE 2.　For every bounded and connected subset X of $\mathbf{R}^n$, $\bar{X}$ is connected and compact, and therefore a continuum.

For example, the graph Γ of the mapping $x \to \sin 1/x$ of $(0, 1]$ into $\mathbf{R}$ is a continuous image of $(0, 1]$, hence a connected subset of $\mathbf{R}^2$; its closure, which is the union of Γ and the interval $0 \times [-1, 1]$, is a continuum.

This continuum is used quite often in topology to construct counterexamples.

13.8. Definition. AN OPEN AND CONNECTED SUBSET D OF A SPACE E IS CALLED A *DOMAIN* OF E.

13.9. Proposition. *In order that an open subset* D *of* $\mathbf{R}^n$ *be a domain, it is necessary and sufficient that any two points p and q belong to a polygonal line whose segments are parallel to a coordinate axis and which is contained in* D.

PROOF. Let $(a_1, a_2, ..., a_p)$ be a sequence of points of $\mathbf{R}^n$ such that each of the segments $[a_i, a_{i+1}]$ (where $i < p$) is parallel to one of the axes of $\mathbf{R}^n$. Using induction, it is immediate from Theorem 13.4 that the polygonal line made up of the union of these segments is connected.

Thus, if for every $p, q \in$ D these points belong to such a line contained in D, then fixing p and letting q range over D, we see that D is the union of polygonal lines containing p; therefore D is connected.

Conversely, suppose that D is connected. For every $x, y \in$ D we write $x \sim y$ if these points are the endpoints of a polygonal line of the preceding type. It is immediate that the relation $\sim$ is an equivalence relation on D, and that each of its classes is open (since for every point y of an open interval containing x and contained in D we have $x \sim y$). There can only be one such class, since otherwise D would admit a partitioning into two nonempty open sets (for example, one such class, and the union of all the others); in other words, for every $x, y \in$ D we have $x \sim y$.

EXAMPLE. In $\mathbf{R}^n$, every open ball, every open interval, the complement of every closed ball and of every closed interval, is a domain.

Connected components of a space

We are now able to study the structure of spaces which are not connected, by making precise the vague notion of a "piece" of such a space.

13.10. Definition. FOR EVERY POINT x OF A SPACE E, THE UNION $C(x)$ OF ALL THE CONNECTED SUBSETS OF E CONTAINING x IS CALLED THE CONNECTED COMPONENT OF x.

By Theorem 13.4, $C(x)$ is a connected set; on the other hand, since $\overline{C(x)}$ is also connected and since by construction $C(x)$ is the largest connected subset of E containing x, we have $C(x) = \overline{C(x)}$; in other words, $C(x)$ is *closed*.

The binary relation on E defined by "$x_1 \sim x_2$ if there is a connected subset of E containing x_1 and x_2" is evidently an equivalence relation. But for every x, $C(x)$ is the equivalence class containing x. Therefore the sets $C(x)$ can also be defined as the equivalence classes associated with the preceding equivalence relation. This is why they are called *connected components* of E.

EXAMPLE 1.   If E is connected, there is only a single connected component, namely E itself.

EXAMPLE 2.   In the space **Q**, every connected component consists of one point; therefore $C(x) = \{x\}$ for every $x \in$ **Q**.

EXAMPLE 3.   In **R** $- \{x\}$, the connected components are $(-\infty, x)$ and (x, ∞).

EXAMPLE 4.   In **R**^{2}, the connected components of **Q** $\times$ **R** are the lines $x \times$ **R** where $x \in$ **Q**.

EXAMPLE 5.   In **R**^{2}, the subspace consisting of the union of the hyperbola $xy = 1$ and its asymptotes has three connected components.

Locally connected spaces

13.11. Definition.   A SPACE E IS SAID TO BE *LOCALLY CONNECTED* AT THE POINT x OF E IF x HAS A NEIGHBORHOOD BASE CONSISTING OF CONNECTED SETS.

WE SAY THAT E IS LOCALLY CONNECTED IF IT IS LOCALLY CONNECTED AT EVERY POINT.

EXAMPLE 1.   **R** and every interval of **R** is locally connected.

EXAMPLE 2.   More generally, every convex subset A of **R**^{n} is locally connected; in fact, every point $x \in$ A has a neighborhood base of convex sets consisting of the intersections of A with the open intervals of **R**^{n} containing x.

EXAMPLE 3.   **Z** is locally connected.

EXAMPLE 4.   **Q**, on the other hand, is not locally connected at any point.

13.12. Proposition.   *To say that* E *is locally connected is equivalent to saying that for every open set ω in* E, *the connected components of ω are open.*

PROOF.   1.   Let E be locally connected, let ω be an open set in E, and let C be a connected component of ω.

For every $x \in$ C, there exists a connected neighborhood V of x contained in ω; evidently V $\subset$ C, and therefore C is a neighborhood of x. Since C is a neighborhood of each of its points, C is open.

2.   Conversely, suppose that every connected component of every open set in E is open. For every $x \in$ E and for every neighborhood V of x, the

connected component C of $\overset{\circ}{V}$ which contains x is open; thus C is the desired connected neighborhood of x contained in V.

EXAMPLE 1. Since **R** is locally connected, for every closed set $F \subset \textbf{R}$ the connected components of $\complement F$ are open, and thus open intervals; each endpoint of such an interval belongs to F.

Since each of these intervals contains at least one rational number, and since they are disjoint, there are finitely or countably many of them.

EXAMPLE 2. The criterion furnished by Proposition 13.12 is often convenient for showing that a space is not locally connected.

For example, let us consider the continuum $\bar{\Gamma}$ defined in Example 2 of Definition 13.7. Let ω be the open set in $\bar{\Gamma}$ defined by $\omega = \bar{\Gamma} \cap (\textbf{R} \times (-1/2, 1/2))$ (see Fig. 2). One of the connected components of ω is the interval $0 \times (-1/2, 1/2)$, which is not open in $\bar{\Gamma}$; therefore $\bar{\Gamma}$ is not locally connected (although it is at every point of Γ).

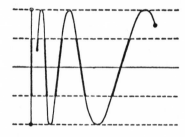

FIG. 2.

Arcwise connectivity

In many branches of mathematics, only connected spaces of a very regular type are used; for example, the spaces used in differential geometry are generally locally homeomorphic to $\textbf{R}^n$ or to a closed halfspace in $\textbf{R}^n$. It is then convenient to use the notion of arcwise connectedness.

13.13. Definition. A SPACE E IS SAID TO BE *ARCWISE CONNECTED* IF FOR EVERY $a, b \in$ E THERE EXISTS A CONTINUOUS MAPPING f OF AN INTERVAL $[\alpha, \beta]$ OF **R** INTO E SUCH THAT $f(\alpha) = a$ AND $f(\beta) = b$.

A SPACE E IS SAID TO BE *LOCALLY ARCWISE CONNECTED* IF EVERY POINT OF E HAS A NEIGHBORHOOD BASE OF ARCWISE CONNECTED SETS.

Since every continuous image of an interval $[\alpha, \beta]$ is connected, it is evident that every arcwise connected space is connected; but the converse is false (one can verify this on the continuum $\bar{\Gamma}$ of Example 2 above).

Similarly, every locally arcwise connected space is locally connected.

The expression "arcwise connected" comes from the fact that if there exists a continuous mapping f of an interval $[\alpha, \beta]$ of **R** into E such that $f(\alpha) = a$ and $f(\beta) = b(a \neq b)$, then there also exists a simple arc in $f([\alpha, \beta])$ with endpoints a, b. But this last property (which, by the way, is not evident) is rarely used, due to the following fact:

Let $\alpha, \beta, \gamma \in$ **R** with $\alpha < \beta < \gamma$, and let f be a mapping of $[\alpha, \gamma]$ into E; if the restrictions of f to $[\alpha, \beta]$ and to $[\beta, \gamma]$ are continuous, then f is continuous. However, if we require in addition that f be one-to-one on $[\alpha, \beta]$ and on $[\beta, \gamma]$, this does not imply that f is one-to-one on $[\alpha, \gamma]$. Thus a definition using connectedness by simple arcs would be awkward.

EXAMPLE 1.   Every domain in $\mathbf{R}^n$ is arcwise connected and locally arcwise connected.

EXAMPLE 2.   The same is true of every convex subset of $\mathbf{R}^n$.

EXAMPLE 3.   Let E be a connected space; if E is locally arcwise connected, it is also arcwise connected (imitate the proof of Proposition 13.9).

This is the case for the locally Euclidean varieties studied in differential geometry.

One can verify the following properties as an exercise:

1.   Every continuous image of an arcwise connected space is arcwise connected.

2.   For every family (E_i) of arcwise connected sets having nonempty intersection, the union of the E_i is arcwise connected.

14. TOPOLOGICAL GROUPS, RINGS, AND FIELDS

The notion of a topological group arose from the study of special cases such as the additive group **R**, or transformation groups depending on a finite number of parameters, such as the group of dilations of $\mathbf{R} : x \rightarrow \lambda x + a$ (where $\lambda \neq 0$). In these various examples, the set under study has both a group structure and a topological structure, and these two structures are compatible in the sense that the group operations are continuous.

More generally, if E is a set having both an algebraic structure defined by several operations, and a topological structure, E is said to be a topological algebraic structure if the algebraic operations in E are continuous for the given topology, in a sense which has to be made precise for each kind of structure.

Topological group

14.1. Definition. A topological group G is a group with a topology for which the functions x^{-1} and (xy) are continuous.

More precisely, it is assumed that the mappings $x \to x^{-1}$ of G onto G and $(x, y) \to xy$ of $G \times G$ onto G are continuous.

When these conditions are satisfied, one also says that the given topology is *compatible with the group structure of* G.

Example 1. The additive group **R** with its ordinary topology is a topological group.

Example 2. Let **R*** be the multiplicative group of real numbers > 0. The topology on **R*** induced by that of **R** is compatible with its group structure.

Example 3. Let T be the quotient group of **R** by the equivalence relation $\langle x_1 \sim x_2$ if $(x_1 - x_2)$ is an integer$\rangle$; in other words (see Volume 1, Chapter II) T is the one-dimensional torus.

For every $c \in T$, we set $| c | =$ the smallest of the absolute values of the representatives of c in **R**. If we then set, for every pair x, y of elements of T,

$$d(x, y) = | x - y |,$$

one can verify that d is a metric on T (see Section 15) which is incidentally invariant under translations of T, and that the topology associated with this metric is compatible with the group structure of T.

The group T, taken with this topology, is the *topological one-dimensional torus*. One can verify that the topological space T is homeomorphic to the circle S_1.

Example 4. The multiplicative group of complex numbers $(a + ib)$ with absolute value 1, with the topology induced by that of the complex plane, is a topological group. One can prove that it is isomorphic to T.

Example 5. If we identify the group of dilations of the line: $x \to \lambda x + a$ (where $\lambda \neq 0$) with the set D of points (λ, a) of the plane **R**^{2} with nonzero abscissa, and give D the topology induced by that of **R**^{2}, D becomes a topological group.

In fact, if $s = (\lambda, a)$, then

$$s^{-1} = (\lambda, a)^{-1} = (1/\lambda, -a/\lambda);$$

thus s^{-1} is a continuous function of s on D. On the other hand, if $s = (\lambda, a)$ and $s' = (\lambda', a')$, then $s \circ s' = (\lambda\lambda', \lambda a' + a)$; thus $s \circ s'$ is a continuous function of the pair (s, s').

EXAMPLE 6.   If G is an arbitrary group, then taken with the discrete topology, G becomes a topological group. It goes without saying that in general this topology is not very interesting.

CONSEQUENCE 1.   The symmetry operation $x \rightarrow x^{-1}$ is continuous and is identical with its own inverse; therefore it is a homeomorphism of G with itself.

CONSEQUENCE 2.   For every $a \in G$, the bijection $x \rightarrow ax$, as well as its inverse $y \rightarrow a^{-1}y$, is continuous.

Similarly, $x \rightarrow xa$, as well as its inverse, is continuous. In other words, every translation is a homeomorphism of G with itself. The same is true, more generally, of every transformation $x \rightarrow axb$.

These two consequences can also be expressed by saying that, for every open set $\omega \in G$, the symmetric set ω^{-1} is open, and every translate $a\omega$ or ωa of ω is open.

Neighborhoods of a point

The fact that every translation is a homeomorphism implies that the set of neighborhoods of a point x_0 can be obtained from the set of neighborhoods of the identity element e by translation by x_0, to the right or left. More precisely, the collection of all neighborhoods of x_0 is identical with the collection of all sets $x_0 V$ or all sets $V x_0$, where V runs through the collection of all neighborhoods of e.

The study of the neighborhoods of a point x_0 of G thus reduces to that of the neighborhoods of e.

Neighborhoods of the identity element

1.   *For every neighborhood V of e, the symmetric set V^{-1} is a neighborhood of e.*

2.   *For every neighborhood V of e, there exists a neighborhood $W \subset V$ of e such that $WW \subset V$.*

The first property follows from the fact that the symmetry operation is a homeomorphism. It follows from this, since $V \cap V^{-1}$ is self-symmetric, that e has a neighborhood base of symmetric sets.

The second property simply expresses the fact that the mapping $(x, y) \rightarrow xy$ of $G \times G$ onto G is continuous at the point (e, e) of $G \times G$.

This property, by the way, is not a consequence of the fact that the symmetry operation and the translations of G are homeomorphisms. In other words, a topology on a group G, for which the symmetry operation and the translations are homeomorphims, does not necessarily define a topological group structure on G.

To define a topology on a group G which is compatible with the group structure of G, the following method is often used: One specifies a family $\mathscr{V}(e)$ of subsets of G containing the identity element e (these elements are intended as neighborhoods of e). For every $x_0 \in G$, one denotes by $\mathscr{V}(x_0)$ the family $x_0\mathscr{V}(e)$ obtained from $\mathscr{V}(e)$ by translation from the left by x_0.

The open sets of G are then defined as those sets ω such that if $x \in \omega$, there exists an element of $\mathscr{V}(x)$ contained in ω.

If the collection of these ω satisfies axioms O_1, O_2, O_3 of a topological space, then a topology has been defined on G; if xy and x^{-1} are continuous in this topology, then it is compatible with the group structure of G. One says that this topology is generated by the family $\mathscr{V}(e)$.

Product of topological groups

Let G_1 and G_2 be topological groups. The product set $G = G_1 \times G_2$ has both a product group structure and a product topology structure.

It is easily verified that the product topology on G is compatible with the product group structure on G; the set G with these two structures defined on it is called the product of the topological groups G_1 and G_2.

The product of any finite number of topological groups is similarly defined.

EXAMPLE 1. The product of n topological groups identical with the additive topological group **R** is called the topological group $\mathbf{R}^n$.

The product of n groups identical with the topological torus T is called the n-dimensional torus.

EXAMPLE 2. The operation $(n, G) \to G^n$ is a special case of a more general procedure for constructing topological groups:

Let E be an arbitrary set and G a topological group: let G^E be the set of all mappings of E into G. A group structure is defined on G^E by defining $h = gf$ by the equality $h(x) = g(x)f(x)$ for every $x \in E$.

For every neighborhood v of e in G, we define V as the set of all elements f of G^E such that $f(x) \in v$ for every $x \in E$. The family $\mathscr{V}$ of sets V generates a topology on G^E according to the procedure described above, and one can verify that this topology is compatible with the group structure of G^E.

EXAMPLE 3. **C*** is isomorphic to the product of the multiplicative group $\mathbf{R}_+^*$ with T. Its subgroup $\mathbf{R}^*$ is isomorphic to the product of $\mathbf{R}_+^*$ with the multiplicative group $\{1, -1\}$.

Isomorphisms. Continuous representations

Let E and F be topological groups and f a representation of E in F (that is $f(xy) = f(x)f(y)$). This representation is said to be continuous if the mapping f is continuous on E.

The equality $f(x) = f(xx_0^{-1})f(x_0)$ shows that if a representation f is continuous at the point e of E, it is continuous at every point x_0 of E.

If f is an algebraic isomorphism of the group E onto the group F, and if f is a homeomorphism, the topological groups E and F are said to be isomorphic.

EXAMPLE 1. *Isomorphisms of the additive group* **R** *onto itself.* Let f be a continuous representation of the additive group **R** into itself. Set $f(1) = a$. We deduce that $f(p/q) = a(p/q)$ for all integers p and q, where $q \neq 0$; in other words, $f(x) = ax$ for every rational number x. Since the mappings f and $x \to ax$ are continuous, this equality extends to all of **R**.

Since the mapping $x \to ax$ is indeed a representation of **R** into **R**, the continuous representations of **R** in itself are the mappings $x \to ax$. Except for $a = 0$, such a representation is always an isomorphism.

We remark that there exist many discontinuous representations of **R** in itself; however, their existence is not evident, and it is not known how to construct them other than by using the axiom of choice.

EXAMPLE 2. It follows from a proposition of Volume 1, Chapter III, that the topological multiplicative group $\mathbf{R}_+^*$ is isomorphic to the topological additive group **R**. Every isomorphism of $\mathbf{R}_+^*$ onto **R** is by definition a logarithm; the isomorphism inverse to a logarithm is an exponential.

EXAMPLE 3. The method of Example 1 easily extends to $\mathbf{R}^n$ and enables one to show that every continuous representation of $\mathbf{R}^n$ in $\mathbf{R}^n$ is a linear mapping of $\mathbf{R}^n$ into $\mathbf{R}^n$; we have already studied these linear mappings.

EXAMPLE 4. *Continuous representations of* T *in itself.* We propose that the reader prove, as an exercise, that every continuous representation of T in itself is of the form $x \to nx$, where n is an arbitrary integer. It follows from this that there exist only two continuous automorphisms of T: the identity and the symmetry operation.

Continuous periodic functions on a topological group

14.2. Definition. LET G BE A COMMUTATIVE GROUP WRITTEN ADDITIVELY, AND LET f BE A MAPPING OF G INTO A SET E. EVERY ELEMENT a OF G SUCH THAT $f(x + a) = f(x)$ FOR EVERY $x \in$ G IS CALLED A *PERIOD* OF f.

It is immediate that the set P of periods of f forms a subgroup of G, called the group of periods of f.

The mapping f is said to be *periodic* if its group of periods does not consist solely of the element O of G.

14.3. Proposition. *The group* P *of periods of a continuous mapping of a topological group* G *into a separated topological space* E *is closed in* G.

In fact, for every $b \in G$ let G_b denote the set of $a \in G$ such that $f(b + a) = f(b)$; since the mapping $\varphi_b : a \to f(b + a)$ of G into E is continuous, and since $\{f(b)\}$ is closed in E, the set $\varphi_b^{-1}(\{f(b)\}) = G_b$ is closed. But by definition

$$P = \bigcap_{b \in G} G_b \, ;$$

therefore P is closed.

Closed subgroups of **R**

The preceding result shows the interest, for the study of periodic functions of a topological group, in studying the closed subgroups of G. We shall only carry out this study for the group **R**.

14.4. Proposition. *Every closed subgroup of* **R** *is either identical with* **R** *or* $\{0\}$, *or is a discrete group of the form* $a\mathbf{Z}$, *where* $a > 0$.

PROOF. Let P be a closed subgroup of **R**. If 0 is an accumulation point of P, for every $\epsilon > 0$ there exist elements x of P such that $x \neq 0$ and $|x| < \epsilon$; in every interval of **R** of length $> \epsilon$ there exists at least one integer multiple of such an x. In other words P is everywhere dense on **R**, and since it is closed, we have P = **R**.

If 0 is an isolated point of P, every point of P is isolated; therefore since P is closed, each of the sets $P \cap [-l, l]$ is compact and discrete, therefore finite. Thus, either $P = \{0\}$, or the set of elements > 0 of P has a smallest member, say a.

The group $a\mathbf{Z}$ of integer multiples of a is contained in P; if $P - a\mathbf{Z}$ were not empty, there would exist an $x \in P$ and an integer n such that $a(n - 1) < x < an$; hence the element $(an - x)$ would satisfy $0 < (an - x) < a$, which is impossible by the choice of a. Therefore $P = a\mathbf{Z}$.

REMARK. Let f be a continuous periodic function on **R**, and let P be the group of periods of f.

If P = **R**, then f is constant on **R**.

If $P = a\mathbf{Z}$, then f is known whenever its restriction to $[0, a)$ or to any one of the intervals $[x_0, x_0 + a)$ or $(x_0, x_0 + a]$ is known.

The period a is called the smallest period of f.

Uniform structure. Uniform continuity

In a topological group G, one can speak not only of points near to a given point, but more generally of the smallness of a set.

In fact, for every neighborhood V of the unit element e of G and for every subset A of G, we can say that A is *small of order* V if $xy^{-1} \in V$ for all $x, y \in A$.

This fundamental fact enables us to introduce the notion of the uniform continuity of a function, a notion which we shall meet with again in a closely related form in the study of metric spaces.

14.5. Definition. LET X AND Y BE TOPOLOGICAL GROUPS WHICH FOR SIMPLICITY WE SHALL ASSUME COMMUTATIVE, AND LET f BE A MAPPING OF X INTO Y. THEN f IS SAID TO BE *UNIFORMLY CONTINUOUS* IF FOR EVERY NEIGHBORHOOD W OF ZERO IN Y THERE EXISTS A NEIGHBORHOOD V OF ZERO IN X SUCH THAT EVERY $A \subset X$ WHICH IS SMALL OF ORDER V HAS AN IMAGE $f(A)$ WHICH IS SMALL OF ORDER W.

This condition can also be expressed by

$$((x_1 - x_2) \in V) \Rightarrow ((f(x_1) - f(x_2)) \in W).$$

EXAMPLES. Let G be a commutative topological group, and let V be an arbitrary symmetric neighborhood of O in G.

1. The relation $-(a + V) = -a - V = -a + V$ shows that every set symmetric to a set which is small of order V is small of order V; therefore the mapping $x \to -x$ of G onto G is uniformly continuous.

2. The continuity of the mapping $f : (x, y) \to (x + y)$ of $G \times G$ onto G at the point (O, O) implies the existence of a neighborhood W of O in G such that $W + W \subset V$.

But for all $a, b \in G$, the set of elements $x + y$ of G such that $x \in a + W$ and $y \in b + W$ is contained in $(a + b) + V$, and is therefore small of order V.

Therefore the mapping f is uniformly continuous.

The topology of the multiplicative group $\mathbf{R}^*$ is the trace on $\mathbf{R}^*$ of the topology of the additive group $\mathbf{R}$; therefore the continuous functions defined on the topological group $\mathbf{R}^*$ or with values in this group are the same as the continuous functions defined on the subspace $\mathbf{R}^*$ of $\mathbf{R}$ or with values in this subspace. For example, x^{-1} and xy are continuous on $\mathbf{R}^*$ in the topology of $\mathbf{R}$. But the situation changes completely when one is concerned with uniform continuity.

For example, the identity mapping $x \to x$ of the multiplicative group $\mathbf{R}^*$ into the additive group $\mathbf{R}$ is not uniformly continuous; in fact, for every neighborhood V of the unit element of $\mathbf{R}^*$, the translates of V are the sets λV and evidently there exists no neighborhood W of O in $\mathbf{R}$ such that all the λV are small of order W.

Similarly, the mapping $x \to x^{-1}$ of $\mathbf{R}^*$ into $\mathbf{R}$ is not uniformly continuous if we put on $\mathbf{R}^*$ the uniform structure associated with its group structure, or even the uniform structure induced by that of $\mathbf{R}$; these conclusions carry over to the mapping $(x, y) \to xy$.

Topological rings

14.6. Definition. A TOPOLOGICAL RING A IS A RING WITH A TOPOLOGY FOR WHICH THE FUNCTIONS $(-x)$, $(x + y)$ AND xy ARE CONTINUOUS.

More precisely, we assume that the mapping $x \to -x$ of G onto G and the mappings $(x, y) \to x + y$ and xy of $G \times G$ into G are continuous. When these conditions are satisfied, the topology on A is said to be compatible with the ring structure of A. In particular, for every topological ring A the topology of A is compatible with the additive group structure of A.

Examples of topological rings

1. For every ring A, if A is given the discrete topology, one obtains a topological ring, which however is in general uninteresting.

2. Let G be a commutative topological group and A the ring of representations of G in itself (recall that $h = g + f$ is defined by $h(x) = f(x) + g(x)$ for every x, and fg by $f \circ g$).

Furthermore let S be a fixed subset of G.

Let 0 be the zero of A, that is, the mapping $x \to O$ of G into itself. For every neighborhood ν of zero of G, let $W(\nu)$ be the set of elements f of A such that $f(x) \in \nu$ for every $x \in S$. One can verify that the sets $W(\nu)$ constitute a neighborhood base of 0 for a topology on A which is compatible with the group structure of A. But it is not compatible, in general, with its ring structure. In order that it be so, one is led to consider only continuous representations, and to take for S some neighborhood of the zero of G with special properties.

3. Let A be a ring on which is defined a function φ with positive real values, and such that

$$\varphi(O) = 0, \qquad \varphi(x) > 0 \quad \text{if} \quad x \neq O$$
$$\varphi(-x) = \varphi(x); \qquad \varphi(x + y) \leqslant \varphi(x) + \varphi(y) \qquad \text{and} \qquad \varphi(xy) \leqslant \varphi(x)\varphi(y).$$

For every $x, y \in A$ we set $d(x, y) = \varphi(x - y)$. It is immediate that d is a metric on A. One can then verify that the topology on A associated with this metric (see Sections 15 and 16) is compatible with the ring structure of A.

Special cases

   a.   A is the ring **R** of real numbers with

$$\varphi(x) = |\, x\, |;$$

   b.   A is the ring of continuous real functions defined on $[0, 1]$ with $\varphi(f) = \sup |\, f(x)|$;
   c.   A is the ring of square matrices of order n with complex elements; if $a_i{}^j$ are the elements of a matrix $m \in A$, we take

$$\varphi(m) = \sum_{i,j} |\, a_i{}^j\, |;$$

   d.   Let A be the ring of polynomials in one variable with complex coefficients. We take the topology on A for which the zero of A has as a neighborhood base the sets $V(\epsilon, n)$ ($\epsilon > 0$, n an integer $\geqslant 0$), where $V(\epsilon, n)$ denotes the set of polynomials $a_0 + a_1 x + \cdots$ such that $|\, a_i\, | \leqslant \epsilon$ for every $i \leqslant n$.

Topological fields

14.7. Definition.   A TOPOLOGICAL FIELD K IS A FIELD WITH A TOPOLOGY WHICH IS COMPATIBLE WITH THE RING STRUCTURE OF K, AND SUCH THAT THE MAPPING $x \to x^{-1}$ OF K^* INTO K IS CONTINUOUS (WHERE K^* DENOTES THE SET OF ELEMENTS OF K DIFFERENT FROM O).

When a topology on a field K satisfies these conditions, one says that it is compatible with the field structure of K.

EXAMPLES OF TOPOLOGICAL FIELDS.   1.   The field **R** of real numbers with the topology of **R**.
   2.   The subfield **Q** of rational numbers of **R**.
   3.   The field **C** of complex numbers, with the topology obtained by carrying over the topology of $\mathbf{R}^2$ to **C** by the correspondence

$$(a + ib) \to (a, b).$$

The fact that this topology is compatible with the field structure of **C** follows from the properties of the absolute value:

$$|-z\, | = |\, z\, |, \qquad |\, z_1 + z_2\, | \leqslant |\, z_1\, | + |\, z_2\, |, \qquad |\, z_1 z_2\, | = |\, z_1\, |\,|\, z_2\, |.$$

We will also give a more general result:

4.   Let K be a field and $|\,x\,|$ a positive real function defined on K, not $\equiv 0$ and not $\equiv 1$, having the following properties:

$$|-x| = |\,x\,|, \qquad |\,x+y\,| \leqslant |\,x\,| + |\,y\,|, \qquad |\,xy\,| = |\,x\,|\,|\,y\,|.$$

It easily follows from these properties that $|\,e\,| = 1$, that $|\,x\,| \neq 0$ for $x \neq O$ and that $|O| = 0$.

Such a function is called an *absolute value* on K. A metric on K is associated with it by setting $d(x, y) = |\,x - y\,|$.

An elementary calculation shows that the topology associated with this metric is compatible with the field structure of K.

When K is the field **C**, the topology associated with the absolute value is identical with the topology defined in Example 3 above.

The quaternion field is another example of a field with an absolute value defined by

$$|\,a + bi + cj + dk\,| = (a^2 + b^2 + c^2 + d^2)^{1/2}.$$

Topological vector spaces

We shall study normed vector spaces, which constitute an important example of topological vector spaces, in Chapter III.

III. METRIC SPACES

In a topological space, the notion of neighborhood allows one to make precise the order of smallness of a set about each point; the notions of convergence and continuity follow from this.

In a topological group, the translations enable us to do better; namely, to specify the order of smallness of a set by comparing it, by translation, to the neighborhoods of the unit element; we can then speak of the uniform continuity of a function.

We shall encounter a similar possibility in metric spaces, whose general definition has been given by M. Fréchet; however in these spaces the proximity of two points is no longer defined by reference to a particular point of the space, but by a number depending on these two points.

15. METRICS AND ECARTS

15.1. Definition. A METRIC SPACE IS A PAIR CONSISTING OF A SET E AND A MAPPING $(x, y) \to d(x, y)$ OF E $\times$ E INTO $\mathbf{R}_+$, HAVING THE FOLLOWING PROPERTIES:

M_1 : $(x = y) \Leftrightarrow (d(x, y) = 0)$;
M_2 : $d(x, y) = d(y, x)$ (SYMMETRY);
M_3 : $d(x, y) \leqslant d(x, z) + d(z, y)$ (TRIANGLE INEQUALITY).

THE FUNCTION d IS CALLED A *METRIC* AND $d(x, y)$ IS CALLED THE DISTANCE BETWEEN THE POINTS x, y.

EXAMPLE 1.   In **R**, the mapping $(x, y) \to |x - y|$ is the usual distance.

EXAMPLE 2.   More generally, let G be a commutative group and let $x \to p(x)$ be a mapping of G into **R**$_+$ such that:

$$(p(x) = 0) \Leftrightarrow (x = O); \qquad p(-x) = p(x); \qquad p(x + y) \leqslant p(x) + p(y).$$

If for every x, $y \in G$ we put $d(x, y) = p(x - y)$, it is immediate that d satisfies axioms M_1 , M_2 ; moreover, the relation

$$(x - y) = (x - z) + (z - y) \quad \text{implies} \quad p(x - y) \leqslant p(x - z) + p(z - y),$$

or

$$d(x, y) \leqslant d(x, z) + d(z, y).$$

Therefore d is a metric on G.

EXAMPLE 3.   Let E be an arbitrary set, and put

$$d(x, y) = 0 \quad \text{if} \quad x = y; \qquad d(x, y) = 1 \quad \text{if} \quad x \neq y.$$

It is immediate that d is a metric on E; it is frequently convenient to use it for the construction of counterexamples.

Z Note that a metric on a set E is a function defined, not on E, but on E^2; one has to remember this when studying the properties of the metric.

Ecart on a set

It is often convenient, and not only in studying metrics, to use the notion of an ecart, which is less restrictive than that of a metric.

15.2. Definition.   AN *ECART* ON A SET E IS A MAPPING f OF $E \times E$ INTO $\bar{\mathbf{R}}_+$ SUCH THAT:

E_1 : $(x = y) \Rightarrow (f(x, y) = 0)$;
E_2 : $f(x, y) = f(y, x)$;
E_3 : $f(x, y) \leqslant f(x, z) + f(z, y)$.

The only difference from the notion of a metric is therefore that f can assume the value $+\infty$, and that two distinct points can have ecart zero. Therefore to see whether an ecart f is a metric, it suffices to determine whether $f(x, y)$ is always finite and whether

$$(x \neq y) \Rightarrow (f(x, y) \neq 0).$$

EXAMPLE.   Let α be a mapping of E into **R**; the function f defined by

$$f(x, y) = |\alpha(x) - \alpha(y)|$$

is an ecart.

For example, if E is the set of numerical functions on $[0, 1]$ and if $a \in [0, 1]$, the function f_a defined by

$$f_a(x, y) = |x(a) - y(a)|$$

is an ecart on E.

Operations on ecarts

The interest in ecarts lies in the great generality of the operations which preserve their properties; this flexibility renders their use very convenient.

1.   The sum of every family of ecarts is an ecart.

In particular, every finite sum of metrics is a metric.

2.   Every limit of ecarts is an ecart.

3.   Every upper envelope of ecarts is an ecart.

Indeed, let $f(x, y) = \sup f_i(x, y)$, where the f_i are ecarts. The mapping of E^2 into $\bar{\mathbf{R}}_+$ clearly satisfies axioms E_1, E_2; moreover, for every i we have

$$f_i(x, y) \leqslant f_i(x, z) + f_i(z, y) \leqslant f(x, z) + f(z, y),$$

from which

$$f(x, y) \leqslant f(x, z) + f(z, y).$$

Therefore f is an ecart. In particular, if there are only finitely many f_i and they are metrics, then f is a metric.

4.   Let α be a mapping of a set E into a set F having an ecart f. For every $x, y \in E$ we put

$$e(x, y) = f(\alpha(x), \alpha(y)).$$

It is immediate that e is an ecart on E; it is called the inverse image of f under the mapping α.

5. We shall say that a mapping φ of $\bar{\mathbf{R}}_+$ into $\bar{\mathbf{R}}_+$ is a *gauge*, if it is increasing and if

$$\varphi(0) = 0 \quad \text{and} \quad \varphi(x + y) \leqslant \varphi(x) + \varphi(y) \quad \text{(subadditivity)}.$$

One can verify that the family of gauges is invariant under the following operations: addition, ordinary passage to the limit, taking upper envelopes, composition: $(\varphi_1, \varphi_2) \to \varphi_1(\varphi_2)$.

Every φ which is increasing and concave and such that $\varphi(0) = 0$ is a gauge; indeed, the concavity of φ implies that

$$\varphi(u + v) - \varphi(0 + v) \leqslant \varphi(u) - \varphi(0),$$

whence $\varphi(u + v) \leqslant \varphi(u) + \varphi(v)$.

In particular, the functions $x/(1 + x)$ and $\inf(x, 1)$ are gauges.

For every gauge φ and every ecart f on a set E, $\varphi(f)$ is also an ecart on E: The properties E_1, E_2 are evident; moreover, let us put, for every $x, y, z \in E$,

$$a = f(x, y); \qquad b = f(x, z); \qquad c = f(y, z).$$

The relation $a \leqslant b + c$ implies $\varphi(a) \leqslant \varphi(b + c) \leqslant \varphi(b) + \varphi(c)$.

The relation $\varphi(a) \leqslant \varphi(b) + \varphi(c)$ proves property E_3.

6. More generally, one can define gauges on $(\bar{\mathbf{R}}_+)^n$. Let us order this set by putting $x \leqslant y$ if $x_i \leqslant y_i$ for every $i = 1, 2, ..., n$; we define $z = x + y$ by $z_i = x_i + y_i$ for every i.

By a *gauge* on $(\bar{\mathbf{R}}_+)^n$ we then mean any mapping φ of this set into $\bar{\mathbf{R}}_+$ which is increasing and such that

$$\varphi(O) = 0 \quad \text{and} \quad \varphi(x + y) \leqslant \varphi(x) + \varphi(y).$$

Every φ which is increasing, convex and positive-homogeneous of degree 1 in $(\bar{\mathbf{R}}_+)^n$ is a gauge of this sort; in fact, the convexity gives

$$\varphi((x + y)/2) \leqslant \tfrac{1}{2}(\varphi(x) + \varphi(y)),$$

from which

$$\varphi(x + y) = 2\varphi((x + y)/2) \leqslant \varphi(x) + \varphi(y).$$

For example, if (x_i) are the coordinates of x, the function

$$x \to \left(\sum x_i^2 \right)^{1/2}$$

has these properties, and is therefore a gauge; the same holds, more generally, for

$$\left(\sum |x_i|^p\right)^{1/p} \qquad (p \geqslant 1).$$

The gauges on $(\bar{\mathbf{R}}_+)^n$ are a convenient means of constructing ecarts. Indeed, if $f_1, ..., f_n$ are ecarts on a set E, and if φ is a gauge on $(\bar{\mathbf{R}}_+)^n$, one can verify as for the case $n = 1$, that $\varphi(f_1, ..., f_n)$ is an ecart on E.

For example, $(\Sigma f_i^2)^{1/2}$ is an ecart.

Applications of operations on ecarts

1. **Classical metrics on $\mathbf{R}^n$.**   Let (x_i) denote the coordinates of a point x of $\mathbf{R}^n$. For every i, we put

$$d_i(x, y) = |x_i - y_i|;$$

this is the inverse image of the distance in $\mathbf{R}$ under the mapping $x \to x_i$;   therefore it is an ecart on $\mathbf{R}^n$.

By the foregoing, the functions

$$d(x, y) = \left(\sum_i (x_i - y_i)^2\right)^{1/2}; \qquad d'(x, y) = \sup_i |x_i - y_i|;$$

$$d''(x, y) = \sum_i |x_i - y_i|$$

are ecarts on $\mathbf{R}^n$; since they are finite and are zero only for $x = y$, they are metrics on $\mathbf{R}^n$. Each of them is invariant under the translations of $\mathbf{R}^n$.

It can be verified that the ratio of any two of these metrics is bounded, and that more precisely we have

$$d' \leqslant d \leqslant d'' \leqslant nd'.$$

2. **Product of metric spaces.**   Let (E_i) be a finite family of metric spaces with metrics d_i.

Each of the functions $(x, y) \to d_i(x_i, y_i)$ is an ecart on the product E of the E_i; therefore, as in the example above, the functions

$$d(x, y) = \left(\sum_i d_i^2(x_i, y_i)\right)^{1/2}; \qquad d'(x, y) = \sup_i d_i(x_i, y_i);$$

$$d''(x, y) = \sum_i d_i(x_i, y_i)$$

are ecarts on E; it is immediate that they are metrics, and that they are comparable, since here again

$$d' \leqslant d \leqslant d'' \leqslant nd'$$

(where n is the number of E_i).

Depending upon the circumstance, one or another of these metrics can be used; the first, d, enters only when the spaces E_i are vector spaces and the metrics d_i are derived from a scalar product; it is called the Cartesian or Euclidean metric, and the space $\mathbf{R}^n$ with this metric is called n-dimensional *Euclidean space*.

3.   Let E be a metric space and d its metric.

The functions $d' = d/(1 + d)$ and $d'' = \inf(d, 1)$ are metrics on E.

We have $d' \leqslant d'' \leqslant 2d'$; thus these metrics are comparable. We shall see that they give E the same topology and the same "uniform structure" as does d, with the often-appreciable advantage that they are $\leqslant 1$.

4.   Let E be the family of mappings of a set A into a metric space B with a metric d.

We know that for every $a \in A$, $d(x(a), y(a))$ is an ecart on E; this ecart measures the proximity of the functions x, y at the point a.

More generally, let us put, for every $X \subset A$,

$$d_X(x, y) = \sup_{a \in X} d(x(a), y(a)).$$

This is an ecart on E, which measures the proximity of the functions x, y on X; in particular d_A is an ecart on E which vanishes only for $x = y$. If in addition, therefore, $d \leqslant 1$, then $d_A \leqslant 1$; hence d_A is a metric.

We shall use these ecarts in the study of uniform convergence.

Most of the concepts which we are now going to introduce extend in an evident way to sets with an ecart; we shall do this explicitly only when it will be useful.

Metric subspaces of a metric space

15.3. Definition. Let E be a metric space defined by a metric d, and let A be a subset of E. The set A with the metric d_A defined by $d_A(x, y) = d(x, y)$ for $x, y \in A$ is called the *metric subspace* A of E.

In other words, d_A is the restriction of d to the subset A^2 of E^2. This definition gives us extensive examples of metric spaces: for example, every subset of $\mathbf{R}^n$ becomes a metric subspace of $\mathbf{R}^n$ when $\mathbf{R}^n$ is taken with one of the metrics defined above.

Isometries

15.4. Definition. Let E and E' be two metric spaces with the metrics d and d'; let $f : x \to x'$ be a bijection of E to E'.

Then f is called an isometry if for all x, $y \in$ E,

$$d(x, y) = d'(x', y').$$

Thus, an isometry is simply an isomorphism for the metric space structures.

EXAMPLE 1. In a commutative group with a metric d of the form $d(x, y) = p(x - y)$, the symmetry operation and every translation is an isometry.

EXAMPLE 2. In the space $\mathbf{R}^n$ with one of its classical metrics, every line is a subspace isometric to the real line $\mathbf{R}$.

EXAMPLE 3. One can prove that the isometries of the Euclidean space $\mathbf{R}^n$ on itself which leave the origin fixed are simply the linear transformations of $\mathbf{R}^n$ which preserve the quadratic form $\sum x_i^2$.

Open and closed balls. Spheres

15.5. Definition. In a metric space E, the set $B(x, \rho)$ of points x of E such that $d(a, x) < \rho$ ($\leqslant \rho$) is called the *open* (*closed*) ball with center a and radius ρ ($\rho \geqslant 0$ or $+\infty$ and $a \in$ E).

When E is the Euclidean plane $\mathbf{R}^2$ the term ball is often replaced by the term *disk*.

The set $S(a, \rho)$ of points of E such that $d(a, x) = \rho$ is called the *sphere* with center a and radius $\rho \geqslant 0$.

When E is the Euclidean plane $\mathbf{R}^2$ the term sphere is often replaced by the term *circle* or circumference.

EXAMPLE. In $\mathbf{R}^n$ with the metric $d'(x, y) = \sup| x_i - y_i |$, the ball $B(a, \rho)$ is a cube with sides parallel to the axes.

It is immediate that every union of open balls with center a is again an open ball with center a; similarly every intersection of closed balls with center a is a closed ball with the same center.

It should be mentioned here that the balls and spheres of a space E do not in general have any of the geometric properties of the balls and spheres of $\mathbf{R}^n$. One can convince oneself of this by taking for E an arbitrary metric subspace of $\mathbf{R}^n$.

Diameter. Distance between two sets

15.6. Definition. The *diameter* of a subset A of a metric space E is the supremum $\delta(A)$ of the distances $d(x, y)$, where $x, y \in$ A.

A SET A IS SAID TO BE *BOUNDED* WHEN ITS DIAMETER IS FINITE.

FOR EVERY MAPPING f OF A SET X INTO A METRIC SPACE E AND EVERY SUBSET Y OF X, THE DIAMETER OF $f(Y)$ IS CALLED THE *OSCILLATION* OF f ON Y.

EXAMPLE 1.   The diameter of a plane triangle is equal to the length of its longest side.

EXAMPLE 2.   The diameter of a ball of $\mathbf{R}^n$ of radius ρ is equal to 2ρ; however, in every metric space of diameter ρ_0, the diameter of every ball of radius $\rho > \rho_0$ is equal to ρ_0.

It is immediate that the bounded subsets of a metric space are simply the subsets of balls with finite radii, that the union of two bounded sets is bounded, and that

$$(A \cap B \neq \emptyset) \Rightarrow (\delta(A \cup B) \leqslant \delta(A) + \delta(B)).$$

15.7. Definition.   LET A AND B BE SUBSETS OF A METRIC SPACE E WITH THE METRIC d. THE *DISTANCE* BETWEEN A AND B IS DEFINED AS THE INFIMUM $d(A, B)$ OF THE DISTANCES $d(x, y)$, WHERE $x \in A$ AND $y \in B$.

IN PARTICULAR, FOR EVERY $x \in E$ THE DISTANCE FROM x TO B IS DEFINED AS THE NUMBER $d(x, B) = d(\{x\}, B) = \inf_{y \in B} d(x, y)$.

EXAMPLE 1.   In the Euclidean plane the distance from a point to a line D is equal to the distance from the point to its projection on D.

EXAMPLE 2.   In $\mathbf{R}$, the distance between $\mathbf{Q}$ and $\complement \mathbf{Q}$ is zero.

EXAMPLE 3.   The distance from a branch of a hyperbola to one of its asymptotes is zero.

Z Despite its name, $d(A, B)$ is not a metric, nor even an ecart, on the set of subsets of E, for the triangle inequality is not satisfied. For example, if

$$A = [0, 1], \qquad B = [1, 2], \qquad C = [2, 3],$$

then

$$d(A, B) = d(B, C) = 0,$$

while

$$d(A, C) = 1.$$

16. TOPOLOGY OF A METRIC SPACE

Among all the topologies which can be defined on a set E having a metric space structure, there is one which is directly related to the metric, and which is called the topology of the metric space E.

16.1. Definition. A SUBSET A OF A METRIC SPACE E IS SAID TO BE OPEN IF IT IS EMPTY OR IF FOR EVERY $x \in$ A THERE EXISTS AN OPEN BALL WITH CENTER x AND NONZERO RADIUS CONTAINED IN A.

It is immediate that the collection of open sets in E satisfies axioms O_1, O_2, O_3 of a topological space; the topology on E defined by these open sets is called the topology of the metric space E.

Every open ball $B(a, \rho)$ is an open set. This is evident if $\rho = 0$. If $\rho \neq 0$, let $x \in B(a, \rho)$; the open ball $B(x, \rho - d(a, x))$ is contained in $B(a, \rho)$, as

$$d(x, y) < \rho - d(a, x) \quad \text{implies} \quad d(a, y) \leqslant d(a, x) + d(x, y) < \rho.$$

It follows that every union of open balls is an open set.

Conversely, the definition of an open set implies that every open set is a union of open balls. The open sets in E and the unions of open balls are thus identical.

16.2. Proposition. *The topology of every metric space is separated.*

Indeed, if x and y are distinct points of E, the open balls $B(x, \rho)$ and $B(y, \rho)$, where $\rho \leqslant d(x, y)/2$, are disjoint neighborhoods of x and y.

Corollary. *A sequence of points of a metric space E (or, more generally, a filter base on E) can have at most one limit point.*

Z Note that the topology on a set E which can be associated with an ecart d on E by a definition analogous to Definition 16.1 is also separated if the condition

$$(d(x, y) = 0) \Rightarrow (x = y)$$

is satisfied.

More generally, for every ecart d, two distinct points x, y such that $d(x, y) \neq 0$ can be separated; on the other hand, if $d(x, y) = 0$, every neighborhood of x contains y, and conversely.

16.3. Proposition. *Every point of a metric space has a countable neighborhood base.*

More precisely, for every sequence (ρ_n) of numbers > 0 tending to 0, the balls $B(a, \rho_n)$, either open or closed, form a neighborhood base of a. Indeed, every open set containing a contains a ball $B(a, \rho)$ where $\rho > 0$, and therefore also contains some ball $B(a, \rho_n)$; on the other hand, every $B(a, \rho_n)$ is a neighborhood of a.

Here are several consequences of this property:

16.4. Proposition. *Let* E *be a metric space and* A *a subset of* E. *Then*

$(a \in \bar{A}) \Leftrightarrow (there\ exists\ a\ sequence\ (x_n)\ of\ points\ of\ A\ which\ converges\ to\ a).$

Indeed, if $a \in \bar{A}$, the set $A \cap B(a, 1/n)$ is nonempty. Let x_n be one of its points. The sequence (x_n) clearly converges to a.

The converse is true in every topological space.

16.5. Proposition. *Let* E *be a metric space and let* (x_n) *be a sequence of points of* E. *Then*

$(a\ is\ an\ adherent\ point\ of\ the\ sequence\ (x_n)) \Leftrightarrow (there\ exists\ a\ subsequence$ $(x_{n_i})\ which\ converges\ to\ a).$

The proof is completely analogous to the preceding proof.

16.6. Proposition. *Let* E *be a metric space,* A *a subset of* E, *and* f *a mapping of* A *into a topological space* F.

For every $a \in \bar{A}$ *and* $b \in$ F, *the following properties are equivalent:*

1. *For every sequence* (x_n) *of points of* A *which tends to* a, $\lim f(x_n) = b$.
2. $\lim_{x \to a} f(x) = b$.

PROOF. We shall show that $(1) \Rightarrow (2)$.

Indeed, if $f(x)$ does not converge to b as x tends to a, there exists a neighborhood V of b such that, for every neighborhood v of a in A, we have $f(v) \not\subset V$; in particular, there exists a point $x_n \in A \cap B(a, 1/n)$ such that $f(x_n) \notin V$; the sequence (x_n) converges to a while $f(x_n)$ does not converge to b. This is excluded by the hypothesis.

The converse $(2) \Rightarrow (1)$ is true in every topological space.

Corollary 1. *To say that a mapping* f *of a metric space* E *into a topological space* F *is continuous at the point* a *is equivalent to saying that for every sequence* (x_n) *of points of* E *which converges to* a, *the sequence* $(f(x_n))$ *converges to* $f(a)$.

This is a special case of the preceding proposition.

Corollary 2. *To say that a mapping* f *of a metric space* E *into a topological space* F *is continuous in* E *is equivalent to saying that the restriction of* f *to every compact set in* E *is continuous.*

In one direction, this is evident. Conversely, suppose that the restriction of f to every compact set is continuous. For every $a \in$ E and every sequence (x_n) which tends to a, the set $\{a, x_1, x_2, ...\}$ is compact; therefore $f(x_n)$ tends to $f(a)$. By the preceding corollary, f is continuous.

Relation between the metric and the topology

We have associated a topology with every metric on a set. It is sometimes convenient to use this metric in studying the topological properties of E; for example, the fact that for every point x of E the balls with center at x constitute a neighborhood base of x implies the following equivalences:

For every sequence (x_n) of points of E,

$$(\lim x_n = a) \Leftrightarrow (\lim d(a, x_n) = 0).$$

For every mapping f of E into a metric space F, the continuity of f at the point a is equivalent to the following condition:

For every $\epsilon > 0$ there exists $\eta > 0$ such that $(d(a, x) < \eta) \Rightarrow (d(f(a), f(x)) < \epsilon)$.

Nevertheless an overusage of the metric frequently complicates proofs and hides the actual causes of phenomena.

This comes in part from the fact that the same topology on a set E may be associated with many different metrics; these metrics do not therefore constitute an intrinsic tool for the study of this topology.

Another reason which tends to limit the use of metrics is that certain topological spaces which are very useful in the study of the most classical kinds of questions are not *metrizable*, that is, cannot be defined starting with a metric.

We shall make precise the connections between the metric and the topology by several results.

16.7. Proposition. *Let d and d' be metrics on a set E, and let φ and φ' be increasing mappings of $\mathbf{R}_+$ into $\bar{\mathbf{R}}_+$, continuous at 0 and such that $\varphi(0) = \varphi'(0) = 0$.*

If for every $x, y \in E$ we have

$$d'(x, y) \leqslant \varphi(d(x, y)) \quad and \quad d(x, y) \leqslant \varphi'(d'(x, y)),$$

then the topologies associated with d and d' are identical.

Indeed, it follows from the hypothesis that the mapping $x \rightarrow x$ of E, with the topology associated with d, onto E with the topology associated with d', is bicontinuous; hence it is a homeomorphism.

EXAMPLE 1.   For every metric d on E, the topologies on E associated with the metrics d, $d/(1 + d)$, $\inf(1, d)$, are identical.

EXAMPLE 2.   Let E be a product of metric spaces E_i with the metrics d_i. The topologies on E associated with the metrics

$$\left(\sum d_i^2\right)^{1/2}, \quad \sup d_i, \quad \sum d_i,$$

are identical; indeed, we know that the ratio of any two of these metrics is bounded.

Z It is false that when the topologies on E associated with two metrics are identical, these metrics satisfy relations of the kind used in Proposition 16.7. For example, the metrics $| x - y |$ and $| 1/x - 1/y |$ on $\mathbf{R}_+^*$ give $\mathbf{R}_+^*$ the usual topology, although $| 1/x - 1/y |$ does not tend to 0 as $| x - y |$ tends to 0.

16.8. Proposition. 1. *Every metric subspace of a metric space* E *has for its topology the topology induced by that of* E.

2. *Every metric space* E *which is the product of a finite number of metric spaces* E_i *has as its topology the product of the topologies of the* E_i .

PROOF. 1. This is immediate since, for every $A \subset E$, the open balls of A are the traces on A of the open balls of E.

2. We already know that the three metrics $(\Sigma d_i^2)^{1/2}$, sup d_i, Σd_i define the same topology on E. Let us for example use the second of these metrics: For every point $a = (a_i)$ of E, the open ball $B(a, \rho)$ is the product of the open balls $B_i(a_i , \rho) \subset E_i$.

Thus these balls constitute a neighborhood base of a, both for the topology associated with the metric of E, and for the product of the topologies of the E_i .

EXAMPLE. In $\mathbf{R}^n$ the product topology used up to now is identical with the topology associated with the Euclidean metric.

17. UNIFORM CONTINUITY

The possibility of speaking of the smallness of a set will enable us, as in the case of topological groups, to speak of the uniform continuity of a function.

17.1. Definition. A MAPPING f OF A METRIC SPACE E INTO A METRIC SPACE F IS SAID TO BE *UNIFORMLY CONTINUOUS* IF, FOR EVERY $\epsilon > 0$, THESE EXISTS AN $\eta > 0$ SUCH THAT

$$(d_E(x, y) \leqslant \eta) \Rightarrow (d_F(f(x), f(y)) \leqslant \epsilon).$$

An equivalent definition, perhaps more suggestive, is the following:

17.2. Definition. f IS SAID TO BE UNIFORMLY CONTINUOUS IF, FOR EVERY $\epsilon > 0$, THERE EXISTS AN $\eta > 0$ SUCH THAT FOR EVERY $X \subset E$,

$$(\delta(X) \leqslant \eta) \Rightarrow (\delta(f(X)) \leqslant \epsilon),$$

WHERE δ DENOTES THE DIAMETER, IN E AND IN F.

REMARK 1.   This definition points up the difference between uniform continuity and continuity at every point.

The continuity of f is expressed by

$$(\forall x \in E)(\forall \epsilon > 0)(\exists \eta > 0) : (d_E(x, y) \leqslant \eta) \Rightarrow (d_F(f(x), f(y)) \leqslant \epsilon).$$

The uniform continuity of f is expressed by

$$(\forall \epsilon > 0)(\exists \eta > 0) : (d_E(x, y) \leqslant \eta) \Rightarrow (d_F(f(x), f(y)) \leqslant \epsilon).$$

In the first case, η depends on the choice of x and ϵ; in the second case, η depends only on the choice of ϵ.

This remark clearly shows that if f is uniformly continuous, it is continuous. But the converse is false. For example, the mapping $x \to x^2$ of **R** into **R** is not uniformly continuous since, for every $\eta > 0$, the oscillation $\omega(a)$ of f on the interval $[a, a + \eta]$ is $\geqslant |2a\eta + \eta^2|$, and $\omega(a)$ is not bounded independently of a.

Similarly the mapping $f : x \to \sin 1/x$ of $(0, 1)$ into $[-1, 1]$ is not uniformly continuous, although it is bounded; indeed, the oscillation of f on each of the intervals $(0, \eta]$ is equal to 2.

We shall see, on the other hand, that when E is compact, the converse is true.

REMARK 2.   One could easily formulate a notion of uniform continuity for a mapping of a topological group into a metric space, or vice versa. This would be another example of a general notion of uniform continuity which can be formulated in terms of a *uniform structure* on a set. Metric spaces and topological groups are two important examples of such uniform structures.

Modulus of continuity. Mappings of Lipschitz class

Let φ be an increasing mapping of $\bar{\mathbf{R}}_+$ into $\bar{\mathbf{R}}_+$, continuous at the point 0, and such that $\varphi(0) = 0$; and let f be a mapping of a metric space E into a metric space F.

Then f is said to admit φ as a *modulus of continuity* if, for all $x, y \in$ E,

$$d(f(x), f(y)) \leqslant \varphi(d(x, y)).$$

Since $\lim_{x \to 0} \varphi(x) = 0$, f is then uniformly continuous.

Conversely, if f is uniformly continuous, let us put for every $u \geqslant 0$

$$\varphi(u) = \sup (d(f(x), f(y)))$$

over all $x, y \in$ E such that $d(x, y) \leqslant u$.

It is immediate that φ is a modulus of continuity for f.

Thus the notion of uniform continuity can be expressed in terms of moduli of continuity.

If f maps E into F, if g maps F into G, and if f and g have φ and γ for moduli of continuity, then the mapping $g \circ f$ has $\gamma \circ \varphi$ for a modulus of continuity.

The most-used moduli of continuity in analysis are the functions φ of the type $u \to ku^\alpha$ ($\alpha > 0$); the case $\alpha = 1$ yields the mappings of Lipschitz class. More explicitly:

17.3. Definition. Let k be a number >0. A mapping f is said to be of *Lipschitz class* with ratio k if, for all $x, y \in$ E,

$$d(f(x), f(y)) \leqslant k\, d(x, y).$$

When $k < 1$, f is said to be a *contractive* mapping.

Example 1. Let f be a numerical function defined and differentiable on an interval of **R**. If f is of Lipschitz class with ratio k, the relation $|\Delta f/\Delta x| \leqslant k$ shows that $|f'| \leqslant k$; conversely, if $|f'| \leqslant k$, the mean value theorem shows that

$$|\Delta| f = |f(x) - f(y)| = |(x - y)f'(z)| \leqslant k|\Delta x|,$$

so that f is of Lipschitz class with ratio k.

Example 2. For every product E of metric spaces E_i, the projection f_i of E on the space E_i is of Lipschitz class with ratio 1 (for any one of the three usual metrics on E).

Example 3. Let E be a metric space, and d its metric. The mapping $(x, y) \to d(x, y)$ of $E \times E$ into **R** is of Lipschitz class with ratio 1 (therefore also continuous) when $E \times E$ is taken with the metric d'' defined by

$$d''((x, y), (x', y')) = d(x, x') + d(y, y').$$

Indeed, the triangle inequality gives

$$d(x', y') \leqslant d(x', x) + d(x, y) + d(y, y')$$

and a similar relation for $d(x, y)$, whence

$$|d(x', y') - d(x, y)| \leqslant d(x, x') + d(y, y') = d''((x, y), (x', y')).$$

For the other two usual metrics, the ratio 1 has to be replaced by $\sqrt{2}$ and 2, respectively.

Similarly, for every $a \in E$, the mapping $x \rightarrow d(a, x)$ is of Lipschitz class with ratio 1.

It follows from the continuity of the metric that for every $A \subset E$ we have $\delta(A) = \delta(\bar{A})$. From it we also deduce the following proposition:

17.4. Proposition. *For any compact sets* A, B $\subset$ E, *there exists* $a \in A$ *and* $b \in B$ *such that* $d(a, b) = d(A, B)$.

PROOF. The function d is continuous on the compact set $A \times B$, and is therefore bounded and attains its infimum at some point (a, b), which is the assertion of the proposition.

Similarly, there exists a point (a', b') at which d attains its supremum; in particular, if $A = B$, $d(a', b')$ is equal to the diameter of A.

Isomorphism of uniform structures. Equivalent metrics

We have defined a notion of isomorphism for topological spaces (homeomorphisms), and then for metric spaces (isometries). We shall see that there exists an intermediate notion which implies a certain preservation of the notion of smallness.

17.5. Definition. LET E AND E′ BE METRIC SPACES, AND LET f BE A BIJECTION OF E TO E′. IF f AND f^{-1} ARE UNIFORMLY CONTINUOUS, f IS SAID TO BE AN ISOMORPHISM OF THE UNIFORM STRUCTURES OF E AND E′.

If d, d' denote the metrics on E, E′, this definition can at once be stated as follows: The bijection $f : x \rightarrow x'$ is an isomorphism if there exist two moduli of continuity φ and φ' such that for all $x, y \in E$,

$$d'(x', y') \leqslant \varphi(d(x, y)) \quad \text{and} \quad d(x, y) \leqslant \varphi'(d'(x', y')),$$

or more briefly, if $d(x, y)$ and $d'(x', y')$ tend to 0 simultaneously.

It is evident that the product of two isomorphisms is an isomorphism.

EXAMPLE 1. Let f be a homeomorphism between a *compact metric* space E and a compact metric space E′. Since f and f^{-1} are continuous and E, E′ are compact, these mappings are uniformly continuous (See Section 18). Therefore f is an isomorphism of the uniform structures of E and E′.

EXAMPLE 2. On the other hand, the mapping $x \rightarrow x/(1 + | x |)$ of **R** onto $(-1, 1)$ is uniformly continuous and is a homeomorphism. But f^{-1} is not uniformly continuous; therefore f is not an isomorphism.

17.6. Definition. TWO METRICS d, d' ON A SET E ARE SAID TO BE *EQUI-VALENT* IF THE IDENTITY MAPPING $x \rightarrow x$ OF E WITH THE METRIC d ONTO E WITH THE METRIC d', AND ALSO ITS INVERSE, IS UNIFORMLY CONTINUOUS.

This is evidently a special case of isomorphism; the condition can be expressed briefly by the assertion that $d(x, y)$ and $d'(x, y)$ tend to 0 simultaneously.

EXAMPLE.   The three usual metrics on a product of metric spaces are equivalent.

It is evident that the notions of continuity and uniform continuity on a metric space do not change when the metric is replaced by an equivalent metric.

18. COMPACT METRIC SPACES

We shall base our study of such spaces on the following fundamental lemma.

18.1. Lemma. *Let* E *be a metric space, and let* K *be a closed set in* E *such that every infinite sequence of points of* K *contains a convergent subsequence.*

For every family $(\omega_i)_{i \in I}$ *of open sets in* E *covering* K, *there exists a number* $\rho > 0$ *such that, for every* $x \in K$, *the open ball* $B(x, \rho)$ *is contained in at least one* ω_i.

PROOF.   It is, in effect, a question of showing that not only do the ω_i cover K, they cover it ρ-uniformly, in a sense made clear by the assertion of the lemma.

Let us suppose that such a ρ does not exist; then for every integer n there exists a point x_n of K such that $B(x_n, 1/n)$ is not contained in any ω_i. The sequence (x_n) contains a convergent subsequence (x_{n_i}); let a be the limit of this subsequence.

Since K is closed, a belongs to K. Therefore there exists an open set ω of the family $(\omega_i)_{i \in I}$ which contains a; let $B(a, \lambda)$ be an open ball with center a which is contained in ω.

The ball $B(x_{n_i}, (\lambda - \epsilon_{n_i}))$, where $\epsilon_{n_i} = d(a, x_{n_i})$, is contained in $B(a, \lambda)$ by the triangle inequality, and therefore *a fortiori* in ω. Since ϵ_{n_i} tends to 0 as $n_i \to \infty$, the ball $B(x_{n_i}, 1/n_i)$ is contained in ω for n_i sufficiently large, contrary to hypothesis.

This contradiction proves the lemma.

Z   It is false that the property stated in the lemma is true for every subset K of a metric space. For example if E = **R** and K = (0, 1), the family (ω_i) consisting of the single open set (0, 1) does not have the stated property. A similar example is obtained with E = K = (0, 1); moreover, here K is closed in E.

This lemma has important consequences, in particular Theorems 18.2 and 18.4 which follow.

18.2. Theorem. *For every metric space* E, *the following four properties are equivalent*:

1. E *is compact.*
2. *Every infinite sequence of points of* E *has at least one adherent point.*
3. *Every infinite sequence of points of* E *has a convergent subsequence.*
4. *Every infinite subset of* E *has at least one accumulation point.*

PROOF.

(1) ⇒ (2)   by Proposition 11.5.

(2) ⇒ (3)   by Proposition 16.5.

(3) ⇒ (4).   Indeed, if A is an infinite subset of E, there exists an infinite sequence (x_n) of *distinct* points of A; this sequence contains a convergent subsequence; if x is its limit, clearly x is an accumulation point of A.

(4) ⇒ (1).   Indeed, suppose that every infinite subset of E has at least one accumulation point.

Let $(\omega_i)_{i \in I}$ be an open covering of E; we shall find a finite subcovering of E, which will prove the compactness of E.

By the preceding lemma, there exists a number $\rho > 0$ such that every open ball $B(x, \rho)$ is contained in some ω_i.

Let x_1 be a point of E; if $B(x_1, \rho)$ does not cover E, there exists a point x_2 such that $d(x_1, x_2) \geqslant \rho$. Suppose, proceeding inductively, that the points $x_1, x_2, ..., x_p$ have mutual distances $\geqslant \rho$. If the union of the $B(x_n, \rho)$ $(n = 1, 2, ..., p)$ does not cover E, there exists a point x_{p+1} such that the distances from x_{p+1} to the x_n $(n \leqslant p)$ are $\geqslant \rho$.

The sequence of x_n cannot be infinite, for otherwise the x_n would form an infinite set of points whose mutual distances are $\geqslant \rho$, which excludes the possibility of having an accumulation point, contrary to hypothesis.

Thus there exists an integer p such that the family of balls $B(x_n, \rho)$ $(n \leqslant p)$ covers E; each of them is contained in some ω_i; these ω_i form the desired finite subcovering.

Corollary.   *Let* X *be a subset of a metric space* E. *To say that* X *is relatively compact in* E *is equivalent to saying that every infinite sequence of points of* X *has a subsequence which converges to a point of* E.

PROOF.   1.   Indeed, if $\bar{X}$ is compact, every infinite sequence of points of X is an infinite sequence of points of $\bar{X}$, and therefore contains a subsequence which converges in $\bar{X}$.

2.   Conversely, we shall show that if this holds, then $\bar{X}$ is compact.

Let (x_n) be a sequence of points of $\bar{X}$; for every n there exists an $x'_n \in X$ such that $d(x_n, x'_n) < 1/n$. The sequence (x'_n) contains a subsequence (x'_{n_i}) which converges to a point a of E; evidently the sequence (x_{n_i}) also converges to a, which is thus adherent to $\bar{X}$, and therefore in $\bar{X}$.

Thus $\bar{X}$ is compact by Theorem 18.2.

One can easily state equivalent criteria in terms of accumulation points, or adherent points of a sequence.

18.3. Proposition. *For every compact metric space* E, *there exists a countable family of open balls of* E *such that every open set in* E *is the union of a subfamily of these balls.*

Proof.   Indeed, for every n the open balls $B(x, 1/n)$ cover E; therefore there exists a finite family $\mathscr{F}_n$ of these balls which covers E. The union of these finite families is the desired family. Indeed, for every open set ω in E, and for every $x \in \omega$, there exist elements B of this family which contain x and have arbitrarily small diameter; one of them, B_x, is therefore contained in ω, and ω is evidently the union of these B_x.

Corollary.   *Every compact metric space contains a countable everywhere dense subset.*

Indeed, if (B_i) is the countable family of balls just constructed, and if x_i denotes an arbitrary point of B_i, the set consisting of these x_i has the required property.

18.4. Theorem. *Every continuous mapping f of a compact metric space* E *into another metric space* F *is uniformly continuous.*

Because of the importance of this theorem, we shall give two proofs of it.

Proof 1.   Let $\epsilon > 0$. Since f is continuous, with every $x \in$ E we can associate an open neighborhood ω_x of x such that the oscillation of f on ω_x is $\leqslant \epsilon$.

Let ρ be the number associated with the family of ω_x by Lemma 18.1. Every ball $B(y, \rho)$ of E is contained in at least one ω_x; therefore the oscillation of f on this ball is $\leqslant \epsilon$. This proves the uniform continuity of f.

Proof 2.   If f is not uniformly continuous, there exists a number $\epsilon > 0$ such that, for every integer $n > 0$, there exist two points $x_n, y_n \in$ E such that

$$d(x_n, y_n) \leqslant 1/n \quad \text{and} \quad d(f(x_n), f(y_n)) \geqslant \epsilon.$$

The sequence (x_n) has a subsequence (x_{n_i}) which converges to some point a of E; since $\lim d(x_n, y_n) = 0$, the sequence (y_{n_i}) also converges to a. Therefore every neighborhood V of a contains pairs (x_n, y_n); the oscillation of f on every V is thus at least ϵ, hence f is not continuous at a. But this contradicts the hypothesis.

One can extend Theorem 18.4 and obtain a result which is slightly more general and very convenient:

18.5. Theorem. *Let* E *be a metric space,* K *a compact set in* E, *and let* f *be a mapping of* E *into a metric space* F. *If* f *is continuous at every point of* K, *then* f *is uniformly continuous about* K *in the sense that for every* $\epsilon > 0$ *there exists a number* $\rho > 0$ *such that for every* $x \in$ K *the oscillation of* f *on the ball* $B(x, \rho)$ *is* $\leqslant \epsilon$.

The proof can be carried out by adapting one or the other of the proofs of Theorem 18.4, for example by applying Lemma 18.1 to the family of open sets ω_x defined as follows: For every $x \in$ K, ω_x is an open neighborhood of x in E on which the oscillation of f is $\leqslant \epsilon$.

Note that the statement of the theorem assumes nothing about the continuity of f outside K.

19. CONNECTED METRIC SPACES

We shall see that for metric spaces one can make the intuitive notion of connectedness more precise.

19.1. Definition. A METRIC SPACE E IS SAID TO BE *WELL-LINKED* IF FOR EVERY PAIR (a, b) OF POINTS OF E AND FOR EVERY $\epsilon > 0$, THERE EXISTS A FINITE SEQUENCE $a_1, ..., a_n$ OF POINTS OF E, WITH $a_1 = a$ AND $a_n = b$, SUCH THAT $d(a_i, a_{i+1}) \leqslant \epsilon$ FOR EVERY $i < n$; IN OTHER WORDS, a AND b CAN BE JOINED BY A CHAIN OF STEPS AT MOST EQUAL TO ϵ.

19.2. Proposition. *Every connected metric space* E *is well-linked.*

PROOF. Let $a \in$ E and let E(a, ϵ) be the set of points x of E which can be joined to a by a chain of steps at most equal to ϵ. This set is not empty, as it contains a; it is open, since if $x \in$ E(a, ϵ), the same is true for every y such that $d(x, y) < \epsilon$; it is closed since if x is an accumulation point of E(a, ϵ), there exist points y of E(a, ϵ) such that $d(x, y) < \epsilon$.

Since E is connected, we have E$(a, \epsilon) =$ E; in other words, every point b of E can be joined to a by a chain of steps at most equal to ϵ. Thus E is well-linked.

Z It is false that, conversely, every well-linked metric space is connected. For example, the set **Q** of rationals is well-linked but not connected. However, this converse holds if E is compact:

19.3. Proposition. *For a compact metric space, the properties of being connected and being well-linked are equivalent.*

PROOF. We have only to show one half of this equivalence. Thus, let E be a compact metric space. If it is not connected, there exists a partition of E into two nonempty closed sets E_1, E_2. Since E_1 and E_2 are compact, the distance δ between them is not zero. A point of E_1 cannot be joined to a point of E_2 by a chain of steps less than $\delta/2$, for if $(a_1, a_2, ..., a_n)$ is such a chain, let i be the smallest index such that $a_i \in E_2$; then $a_{i-1} \in E_1$ and $d(a_{i-1}, a_i) < \delta/2$, in contradiction with

$$d(E_1, E_2) = \delta.$$

In other words, if E is well-linked, it is also connected.

Corollary. *Every compact interval of **R** is connected.*
Indeed, every interval $[a, b]$ is compact and is clearly well-linked (use the points $a + n\epsilon$).
More generally, let E be an arbitrary interval of **R**, and $x_0 \in E$; for every $x \in E$, we have $[x_0, x] \subset E$; therefore E is the union of the compact intervals $[x, x_0]$, hence connected.
Conversely, we have seen during the study of connected topological spaces that a subset of **R** which is not an interval is not connected. To sum up:

19.4. Proposition. *The only connected subsets of **R** are the intervals (open, semi-open, or closed).*

Corollary. *For every continuous numerical function f on a connected topological space* E, *the set f(E) is an interval of **R**.*

Therefore if f takes on positive and negative values on E, it vanishes at one point at least of E.

19.5. APPLICATION. Let f be a continuous and strictly increasing numerical function defined on an interval E of **R**.
Since f is an isomorphism for the order relations of E and $f(E)$, it is also a homeomorphism for the topologies associated with these orders. But f being continuous, $f(E)$ is an interval. Thus the order topology on

$f(E)$ is identical with the topology induced by that of **R**; the same is true for E. Therefore f is a homeomorphism of the intervals E, $f(E)$; hence the inverse function f^{-1} is also continuous and strictly increasing.

Evidently an analogous result holds if f is strictly decreasing.

20. CAUCHY SEQUENCES AND COMPLETE SPACES

During the study of **R**, we defined the notion of a Cauchy sequence, and showed that every Cauchy sequence in **R** is convergent.

The notion of a Cauchy sequence is not a topological notion since, for example, the sequence $(1/n)$, which is a Cauchy sequence in $(0, \infty)$, is transformed by the homeomorphism $x \to x^{-1}$ of $(0, \infty)$ with itself into the sequence (n), which is not a Cauchy sequence.

Therefore we cannot hope to define the notion of a Cauchy sequence in general topological spaces.

However, we shall see that this can easily be done in metric spaces.

20.1. Definition.   Let E be a metric space, and let (x_n) be an infinite sequence of points of E. We say that (x_n) is a *cauchy sequence* if $d(x_p, x_q)$ tends to 0 as p and q tend to $+\infty$; in other words, if for every $\epsilon > 0$ there exists an integer n such that $d(x_p, x_q) \leqslant \epsilon$ for all $p, q \geqslant n$.

Briefly:

$$(\forall \epsilon > 0)(\exists n, n \in \mathbf{N})(\forall p, q \geqslant n) : (d(x_p, x_q) \leqslant \epsilon).$$

An equivalent and perhaps more suggestive definition is obtained by using the set A_n of points x_p such that $p \geqslant n$:

20.2. Definition. (x_n) is a Cauchy sequence if $\lim \delta(A_n) = 0$ (where $\delta(A_n)$ denotes the diameter of A_n).

Every subsequence of a Cauchy sequence is a Cauchy sequence. If a subsequence of a Cauchy sequence converges to a point x, the given sequence also converges to x.

Example 1.   For every metric space E, every sequence (x_n) which converges to a point of E is a Cauchy sequence.

Example 2.   In the metric subspace $E = (0, \infty)$ of **R**, the sequence $(1/n)$ is a nonconvergent Cauchy sequence.

EXAMPLE 3.   More generally, let E be a metric subspace of a metric space F; for every $x \in \bar{E}$ there exists a sequence (x_n) of points of E which converges to x; this sequence is a Cauchy sequence in E; it converges in E only if $x \in E$.

EXAMPLE 4.   Let E be the collection of continuous numerical functions on $[0, 1]$; for every $f, g \in E$ we put

$$d(f, g) = \int_0^1 |f(x) - g(x)| \, dx.$$

One can verify that d is a metric on E. If we put

$$f_n(x) = \inf(n, x^{-1/2}),$$

then (f_n) is a Cauchy sequence in E.

20.3. Proposition.   *Let E and F be metric spaces, and let f be a uniformly continuous mapping of E into F; then the image under f of every Cauchy sequence (x_n) in E is a Cauchy sequence in F.*

Indeed, if A_n and B_n denote, respectively, the set of x_p and of $f(x_p)$ such that $p \geqslant n$, then $f(A_n) = B_n$; but $\lim \delta(A_n) = 0$; thus since f is uniformly continuous, $\lim \delta(B_n) = 0$, that is, $(f(x_n))$ is a Cauchy sequence.

Z If f were only continuous, it would still transform every *convergent* Cauchy sequence into a convergent sequence, and thus into a Cauchy sequence; but Example 2 above showed that f could transform certain nonconvergent Cauchy sequences into sequences which are not Cauchy.

Corollary.   *If f is an isomorphism of the uniform structures of E and F, then f interchanges the Cauchy sequences of E and F.*

In particular, if d and d' are equivalent metrics on a set E, the same sequences are Cauchy sequences for d and d'. The notion of a Cauchy sequence in E is thus related not to the metric structure of E, but to its uniform structure.

20.4. Proposition.   *Let E be a finite product of metric spaces E_i . Let (x_n) be a sequence of points of E and let $(x_{n,i})$ be its projection on E_i . Then*
$((x_n)$ is a Cauchy sequence in E) $\Leftrightarrow$ ($\forall i, (x_{n,i})$ is a Cauchy sequence in E_i).

PROOF.   Let d_i be the metric on E_i ; since the three usual metrics on E are equivalent, the corollary above shows that we can take any one of these metrics on E; we shall take

$$d''(x, y) = \sum d_i(x_i, y_i).$$

The projection $x \to x_i$ of E on E_i is of Lipschitz class with ratio 1, therefore uniformly continuous; hence if (x_n) is Cauchy, so is $(x_{n,i})$. Conversely, if each $(x_{n,i})$ is a Cauchy sequence, the relation

$$d''(x_p, x_q) = \sum_i d_i(x_{p,i}, x_{q,i})$$

shows that (x_n) is a Cauchy sequence.

Complete spaces

Every Cauchy sequence in **R** converges; on the other hand, several of the examples above show that there exist metric spaces in which certain Cauchy sequences do not converge. We are thus led to study the spaces in which every Cauchy sequence converges.

20.5. Definition. A METRIC SPACE E IS SAID TO BE A *COMPLETE SPACE* IF EVERY CAUCHY SEQUENCE OF POINTS OF E IS CONVERGENT IN E.

EXAMPLES. **R**, with the usual metric, is complete. On the other hand, (0, 1) and **Q** are not complete.

20.6. Proposition. *Let* E *be a complete metric space. For every decreasing sequence* (X_n) *of nonempty closed sets in* E *such that* $\lim \delta(X_n) = 0$, *the intersection* X *of the* X_n *contains exactly one point.*

PROOF. We choose an arbitrary point x_n in each X_n. If $p \geqslant n$, then $X_p \subset X_n$, hence $x_p \in X_n$.

Thus the set A_n of x_p such that $p \geqslant n$ is contained in X_n; it follows that $\lim \delta(A_n) = 0$, and so (x_n) is a Cauchy sequence. Since E is complete, (x_n) converges to a point x.

But for every fixed n, x is the limit of the points x_{n+p}, which belong to X_n; since X_n is closed, we have $x \in X_n$ for every n, hence $x \in X$.

Finally, since $\delta(X) \leqslant \delta(X_n)$ for every n, $\delta(X) = 0$; thus X can contain only one point.

Z One might expect that if $\lim \delta(X_n) > 0$, then not only is the intersection of the X_n not empty, but moreover it contains more than one point. This is not so, as the following example shows:

In the complete space **R**, the intervals $[n, \infty)$ form a decreasing sequence of closed sets with infinite diameter, and yet their intersection is empty.

In other words, the fact that a space is complete only manifests itself on the small sets. We shall confirm this fact by a result which completes Proposition 20.6.

20.7. Definition. LET E BE A METRIC SPACE, AND LET $\mathscr{B}$ BE A FILTER BASE ON E. IF FOR EVERY $\epsilon > 0$ THERE EXISTS AN $X \in \mathscr{B}$ SUCH THAT $\delta(X) < \epsilon$, THEN $\mathscr{B}$ IS CALLED A *CAUCHY FILTER BASE.*

For example, for every decreasing sequence (A_n) of nonempty subsets of E, the A_n form a Cauchy filter base if $\lim \delta(A_n) = 0$.

20.8. Proposition. *Every Cauchy filter base on a complete metric space E is convergent.*

PROOF.   Let $\mathscr{B}$ be a Cauchy filter base on E. For every integer n, there exists an $X_n \in \mathscr{B}$ such that $\delta(X_n) < 1/n$. Let x_n be an arbitrary point of X_n .
For all p, q we have

$$X_p \cap X_q \neq \varnothing; \qquad \text{therefore} \qquad \delta(X_p \cup X_q) < 1/p + 1/q;$$

hence

$$d(x_p, x_q) < 1/p + 1/q.$$

Thus (x_n) is a Cauchy sequence; let x be its limit. For every $\epsilon > 0$, there exists an n such that

$$d(x, x_n) < \epsilon/2 \qquad \text{and} \qquad \delta(X_n) < \epsilon/2.$$

Since $x_n \in X_n$, it follows that $X_n \subset B(x, \epsilon)$. This says that $\mathscr{B}$ converges to x.

EXAMPLE.   Let f be a numerical function on a locally compact but noncompact space E. We assume that for each $\epsilon > 0$ there exists a compact set $K \subset E$ such that the oscillation of f on $\complement K$ is $< \epsilon$. Then the sets $f(\complement K)$ form a Cauchy filter base on **R**; this filter base converges to a number l which is called the limit of $f(x)$ as x tends to infinity.

An important class of complete spaces is given by the following theorem:

20.9. Theorem. *Every compact metric space is complete.*

PROOF.   With the notation already used, for every sequence (x_n) of points of E the adherence of this sequence is

$$A = \bigcap \bar{A}_n .$$

If the sequence is a Cauchy sequence, $\lim \delta(A_n) = 0$, hence $\delta(A) = 0$. Moreover, by Proposition 11.5, A is nonempty, and therefore consists of a single point; by the same proposition, the sequence converges to this point.

REMARK.   There are other complete spaces besides the compact metric spaces; the real line **R** is the classical example. The fact that **R** is locally compact might lead one to believe that every locally compact metric space is complete or that every complete space is locally compact; neither of these statements is true. For example, the metric subspace $(0, 1)$ of **R** is locally compact but not complete; while the space $\mathscr{C}([0, 1], \mathbf{R})$ which we shall define in Section 22 is a complete but not locally compact space.

Analogy between complete spaces and compact spaces

One could note, in the preceding proofs, a certain analogy between complete spaces and compact spaces. We shall clarify this by a series of theorems analogous to those previously established for compact spaces. On the other hand, we shall also point out several important differences.

20.10. Theorem.   *Every closed subset* A *of a complete metric space* E *is a complete metric subspace.*

Indeed, let (x_n) be a Cauchy sequence of points in A. This sequence is also a Cauchy sequence of points in E, and therefore converges to a point x of E; but since the points of the sequence belong to A, which is closed, we also have $x \in A$. Therefore the sequence converges to a point of A.

20.11. Theorem.   *Every complete metric subspace* A *of a metric space* E *is a closed subset of* E.

We shall show that A contains its accumulation points. Let x be such a point; then x is the limit of a sequence (x_n) in A. This sequence being convergent, it is a Cauchy sequence; by hypothesis it converges to a point of A. Therefore $x \in A$.

Corollary.   *In every complete metric space* E, *the closed subsets of* E *and the complete subspaces of* E *are identical.*

20.12. Theorem.   *In every metric space* E, *the union of two complete subspaces is complete; every intersection of complete subspaces is complete.*

1.   Let A and B be complete subspaces of E, and let (x_n) be a Cauchy sequence in A ∪ B; every subsequence of this sequence is a Cauchy sequence. But one or the other at least of A and B contains a subse-

quence of (x_n); since both A and B are complete, this subsequence converges to a point of A or of B; the sequence (x_n) converges to the same point.

2.   If the $(A_i)_{i \in I}$ are complete, each of them is closed in E; therefore their intersection is closed in E and *a fortiori* in any one of the A_i, all of which are complete. By Theorem 20.10, this intersection is a complete space.

Z   Let E and F be metric spaces, and let f be a continuous surjection of E to F. It is false that if E is complete, then F is necessarily complete, even in the case where f is uniformly continuous and is a homeomorphism.

Indeed, the mapping $x \to x/(1 + |x|)$ of **R** onto $(-1, 1)$ has these properties, and $(-1, 1)$ is not complete although **R** is.

However, if f is an isomorphism of the uniform structures of E and F, these two spaces are simultaneously complete or incomplete; in particular, if d and d' are equivalent metrics on a set E, the associated metric spaces are simultaneously complete or incomplete.

More generally, let f be a homeomorphism between E and F; if f is uniformly continuous and if F is complete, then E is complete.

20.13. Theorem.   *Every finite product of complete metric spaces is complete.*

PROOF.   Let E_i be a finite family of complete metric spaces. For every Cauchy sequence (x_n) in $E = \Pi E_i$, the projection of (x_n) on E_i is a Cauchy sequence (Proposition 20.4); let a_i be its limit. The sequence (x_n) converges in E to $a = (a_i)$ (Proposition 10.3); therefore E is complete.

EXAMPLE.   Since **R** is complete, so is $\mathbf{R}^n$. Every closed set in $\mathbf{R}^n$ is therefore complete.

Extension of uniformly continuous functions

If f denotes a continuous mapping of a metric space E into another metric space F, the restriction of f to every $X \subset E$ is continuous; conversely, given a continuous mapping of X into F, the question arises whether f can be extended to E, that is, whether f is the restriction to X of a continuous mapping of E into F.

We shall examine here only a highly useful special case of this question.

20.14. Theorem.   *Let X be an everywhere dense subset of a metric space E, and let f be a uniformly continuous mapping of X into a complete metric* *space* F. *Then there exists a unique continuous mapping g of* E *into* F *whose restriction to* X *is* f; *this mapping g is uniformly continuous.*

PROOF.   If g is such an extension, then for every $a \in$ E we have

$$g(a) = \lim_{x \in X, x \to a} f(x).$$

This relation shows, on the one hand, that if g exists it is unique, and, on the other hand, gives the possible value of $g(a)$ for every $a \in$ E.

Since f is uniformly continuous, the diameter of $f(\mathrm{B}(a, \rho))$ tends to 0 with ρ; therefore for every $a \in$ E the sets $f(\mathrm{B}(a, \rho))$ form a Cauchy filter base on F, and since F is complete, this filter base converges (Proposition 20.8) to a point of F which we denote by $g(a)$.

If $a \in$ X, then $f(a) \in f(\mathrm{B}(a, \rho))$, hence $f(a) = g(a)$; thus if we show that g is uniformly continuous, g will be the desired extension of f.

By hypothesis, for every $\epsilon > 0$ there exists an $\eta = \varphi(\epsilon) > 0$ such that $d(f(x), f(y)) \leqslant \epsilon$ for all $x, y \in$ X satisfying $d(x, y) < \eta$.

Let then $a, b \in$ E be such that $d(a, b) < \eta$; there exist two sequences (a_n), (b_n) of points of X which converge to a and b, respectively, and such that $d(a_n, b_n) < \eta$ for all n. The relations

$$g(a) = \lim f(a_n); \qquad g(b) = \lim f(b_n); \qquad d(f(a_n), f(b_n)) \leqslant \epsilon$$

imply $d(g(a), g(b)) \leqslant \epsilon$ since the metric d is a continuous function.

Thus g is uniformly continuous; and the proof even shows that if a modulus of continuity φ for f is continuous, it is also a modulus of continuity for its extension g; in particular, if f is of Lipschitz class with ratio k, the same is true of g.

21. IDEA OF THE METHOD OF SUCCESSIVE APPROXIMATIONS

One of the most powerful methods for proving the existence of solutions of an equation, be it numerical, differential, partial differential, or integral, and often also for effectively calculating this solution, is the so-called method of successive approximations, which was systematically used for the first time by Emile Picard. In many cases this method can be reduced to a scheme which we shall make specific by the following theorem:

21.1. Theorem.   *Let* E *be a* **complete** *metric space and let* f *be a contractive mapping of* E *into itself.*

For every $x_0 \in$ E, *the sequence of successive transforms* $x_n = f^n(x_0)$ *of the point* x_0 *converges to a point* a *which is a solution of the equation* $x = f(x)$. *This solution* a *is the only solution of this equation.*

PROOF. By hypothesis f is of Lipschitz class with ratio $k < 1$. Put $x_1 = f(x_0)$, and more generally $x_{n+1} = f(x_n)$. For every n, the transform of the pair (x_{n-1}, x_n) is the pair (x_n, x_{n+1}), We therefore have

$$d(x_n, x_{n+1}) \leqslant k\, d(x_{n-1}, x_n).$$

We conclude from the first n relations of this form that

$$d(x_n, x_{n+1}) \leqslant k^n\, d(x_0, x_1),$$

from which

$$d(x_n, x_{n+p}) \leqslant \sum_{n}^{n+p-1} d(x_i, x_{i+1}) \leqslant d(x_0, x_1) \sum_{n}^{\infty} k^p$$
$$= d(x_0, x_1) k^n/(1 - k).$$

Since $0 \leqslant k < 1$, the sequence (x_n) is thus a Cauchy sequence. Let a be its limit; since f is continuous, $\lim f(x_n) = f(a)$. The relation $x_{n+1} = f(x_n)$ therefore has the limit $a = f(a)$.

This solution a is the only solution of the equation $x = f(x)$, since for every solution x of this equation we have

$$d(x, a) = d(f(x), f(a)) \leqslant k\, d(x, a),$$

which implies $d(x, a) = 0$, hence $x = a$.

Let us remark that the method used constitutes an effective calculational procedure, since the series with general term $d(x_n, x_{n+1})$ converges at least as fast as a geometric series with ratio k. More precisely,

$$d(x_n, a) = \lim_{p \to \infty} d(x_n, x_{n+p}) \leqslant d(x_0, x_1) k^n/(1 - k).$$

It can happen that the convergence is still more rapid, for example when the restriction of f to a neighborhood V of a is contractive with ratio $k(V)$ and $k(V)$ tends to 0 with the diameter of V.

Z 1. Every contractive mapping f of E into itself is such that for all $x, y \in E$ $(x \neq y)$, $d(f(x), f(y)) < d(x, y)$; but the converse is false. It can even happen that f is strictly distance decreasing in this sense, and that E is complete, without f having a fixed point; this is the case for the mapping $x \to (x^2 + 1)^{1/2}$ of $\mathbf{R}_+$ into itself.

2. When E is not complete, a contractive mapping of E into E may have no fixed point; for example, the mapping $x \to x/2$ of $(0, 1]$ into itself has no fixed point.

REMARK 1.   Let f be a contractive mapping with ratio k of E (complete) into itself; let a be the fixed point of E.

For every number $\rho > 0$,

$$f^n(B(a, \rho)) \subset B(a, k^n \rho).$$

In particular, if E is bounded the decreasing sequence $\delta(f^n(E))$ has limit 0; the sequences $(f^n(x))$ therefore converge to a uniformly.

REMARK 2.   It can happen that f is not contractive, but that a suitable power f^p of f is; we set $f^p = g$.

We can apply Theorem 21.1 to g. If a is the fixed point of g, the relation $g(a) = a$ gives

$$f(g(a)) = f(a); \quad \text{but} \quad f^{p+1} = f(g) = g(f);$$

therefore

$$g(f(a)) = f(a).$$

Hence $f(a)$ is a fixed point of g; the uniqueness of this point shows that $f(a) = a$; in other words, a is also a fixed point of f.

For every $x_0 \in E$, the $g^n(x_0)$ ($\equiv f^{np}(x_0)$) converge to a; since f is continuous, the same is true of the sequence $(f^{np+1}(x_0))_{n \in \mathbb{N}}$, and more generally of $(f^{np+i}(x_0))_{n \in \mathbb{N}}$ (where $i \leqslant p$); therefore the sequence $(f^n(x_0))$ also converges to a.

EXAMPLE 1.   E is a Euclidean space $\mathbf{R}^n$ and f is a similarity transformation (a transformation which multiplies distances by a constant factor) with ratio $k < 1$. The fixed point a is called the center of the similarity transformation.

EXAMPLE 2.   Let f be a differentiable numerical function on a bounded closed interval $E = [a, b]$, such that the set of its values is also contained in E, and such that $|f'| \leqslant k$ where $k < 1$.

The mapping f of $[a, b]$ into itself is thus contractive with ratio k and the theorem applies.

This is one of the well-known methods for solving numerical equations.

For example, let f be the mapping $x \to x/2 + 1/x$ of $[1, \infty)$ into itself; f is contractive with ratio $1/2$ and its fixed point is $\sqrt{2}$. The fact that $f'(\sqrt{2}) = 0$ renders the convergence of the procedure particularly rapid.

We shall see other applications of this theorem to the theory of implicit functions, and to the solution of differential equations; nevertheless it is convenient, for these applications, to strengthen Theorem 21.1 by introducing a parameter:

21.2. Theorem. *Let* L *be a topological space,* E *a complete metric space, and* f *a continuous mapping of* L $\times$ E *into* E *such that, for every* $\lambda \in$ L, *the mapping* $x \to f(\lambda, x)$ *of* E *into* E *is contractive with ratio* k *(where* k < 1 *does not depend on* λ*).*

If for every λ *we denote by* a_λ *the point* x *of* E *such that* $x = f(\lambda, x)$, *then the mapping* $\lambda \to a_\lambda$ *of* L *into* E *is continuous.*

PROOF.   Let $\lambda_0 \in$ L; we shall show that the mapping $\lambda \to a_\lambda$ is continuous at the point λ_0.

Let $\epsilon > 0$; since f is continuous, there exists a neighborhood V of λ_0 such that, for every $\lambda \in$ V,

$$d(f(\lambda, a_{\lambda_0}), f(\lambda_0, a_{\lambda_0})) \leqslant \epsilon.$$

But the triangle inequality gives

$$d(a_\lambda, a_{\lambda_0}) = d(f(\lambda, a_\lambda), f(\lambda_0, a_{\lambda_0}))$$
$$\leqslant d(f(\lambda, a_\lambda), f(\lambda, a_{\lambda_0})) + d(f(\lambda, a_{\lambda_0}), f(\lambda_0, a_{\lambda_0}))$$
$$\leqslant k\, d(a_\lambda, a_{\lambda_0}) + \epsilon,$$

from which

$$d(a_\lambda, a_{\lambda_0}) \leqslant \epsilon/(1 - k) \qquad \text{for all} \quad \lambda \in V.$$

REMARK.   We have, in fact, used only the partial continuity of f with respect to λ. But this remark does not allow us to weaken the hypotheses, as every mapping f of L $\times$ E into E which is partially continuous with respect to λ and of Lipschitz class with ratio k with respect to x is continuous on L $\times$ E; this is immediate from the inequality

$$d(f(\lambda, x), f(\lambda_0, x_0)) \leqslant d(f(\lambda, x), f(\lambda, x_0)) + d(f(\lambda, x_0), f(\lambda_0, x_0))$$
$$\leqslant k\, d(x, x_0) + d(f(\lambda, x_0), f(\lambda_0, x_0)).$$

The last expression evidently tends to 0 as $x \to x_0$ and $\lambda \to \lambda_0$.

22. POINTWISE CONVERGENCE AND UNIFORM CONVERGENCE

The most useful topological spaces in analysis are the function spaces, that is, spaces whose elements are functions. One can, in such spaces, speak of the convergence of functions to another function, in a sense defined by the topology of the space. Conversely, when one wishes to study certain given aspects of given functions, it is often convenient to put on this set of functions a topology adapted to the study of these aspects.

Here are some examples of such situations:

Let E be the collection of numerical functions on [0, 1] which have derivatives of all orders. This is a vector space; if one wishes to study properties related to this vectorial structure, one should require of the topology of E that it be compatible with the vector space structure. In particular, if one seeks a topology defined by a metric, this metric ought to be invariant under the translations of E; it suffices therefore to define the distance between the element O of E and an arbitrary element f; we will denote this distance by $p(f)$.

1. If we now wish to say that the function $x \rightarrow f(x)$ is close to O when it is small for every x, we can put

$$p(f) = \sup_{x \in E} |f(x)|.$$

2. If, on the other hand, we only wish to say that f is small "on the average," we can put

$$p(f) = \int_0^1 |f(x)| \, dx$$

or, if we wish to avoid large values of $f(x)$,

$$p(f) = \left(\int_0^1 f^2(x) \, dx \right)^{1/2}.$$

3. We might want, on the other hand, to express the fact that f is not only small, but does not oscillate too much.

Depending on the circumstance, we can put

$$p(f) = |f(0)| + \text{Total variation of } f \text{ on } [0, 1]$$

or

$$p(f) = |f(0)| + \sup |f'(x)|.$$

4. If we wish to express the fact that the derivatives up to order n are small, we can put

$$p(f) = |f(0)| + |f'(0)| + \cdots + |f^{(n-1)}(0)| + \sup |f^{(n)}(x)|.$$

We shall discuss these procedures in detail in the study of normed spaces. For the moment we shall only briefly study two of the most used modes of convergence.

Pointwise convergence

Let X be a set, with or without a topology, and let Y be a topological space. Let f be a mapping of X into Y, and let (f_n) be a sequence of mappings of X into Y.

22.1. Definition. THE SEQUENCE (f_n) IS SAID TO *CONVERGE POINTWISE* TO f IF, FOR EVERY $x \in X$, THE SEQUENCE $(f_n(x))$ CONVERGES TO $f(x)$.

EXAMPLE 1.   Let f_n be the mapping $x \to x^n$ of $[0, 1]$ into **R**. This sequence converges pointwise to the function f defined by

$$f(x) = 0 \quad \text{if} \quad x \neq 1; \quad f(1) = 1.$$

EXAMPLE 2.   Let f_n be the mapping $x \to nx/(1 + |nx|)$ of **R** into **R**. This sequence converges pointwise to the function f defined by

$$f(x) = -1 \quad \text{if} \quad x < 0; \quad f(x) = 1 \quad \text{if} \quad x > 0; \quad f(0) = 0.$$

EXAMPLE 3.   Let f_n be the mapping $x \to 1/[1 + (x - n)^2]$ of **R** into **R**. This sequence converges pointwise to $f = 0$.

More generally, it is convenient to be able to speak of the pointwise convergence of a family of functions:

22.2. Definition. LET $(f_i)_{i \in I}$ BE A FAMILY OF MAPPINGS OF X INTO Y, AND LET $\mathscr{B}$ BE A FILTER BASE ON I. THE FAMILY $(f_i)_{i \in I}$ IS SAID TO CONVERGE POINTWISE TO f ALONG $\mathscr{B}$ IF, FOR EVERY $x \in X$, $f_i(x)$ CONVERGES TO $f(x)$ ALONG $\mathscr{B}$.

EXAMPLE 1.   One can take the preceding examples after replacing the integer n by an arbitrary number, and taking for $\mathscr{B}$ the filter base on **R** consisting of the intervals $[\alpha, \infty)$.

EXAMPLE 2.   Let f be a differentiable numerical function defined on **R**. The family (g_α) (where $\alpha \in \mathbf{R}^*$) of functions defined by

$$g_\alpha(x) = (f(x + \alpha) - f(x))/\alpha$$

converges pointwise to the derivative f' as α tends to 0 (in other words, along the filter base $\mathscr{B}$ consisting of the traces on $\mathbf{R}^*$ of the neighborhoods of 0 in **R**).

EXAMPLE 3.   Let $f_{p,q}$ be the mapping of $\mathbf{R}^2$ into **R** defined by

$$f_{p,q}(x, y) = \exp(-px^2 - qy^2) \quad (\text{where } p, q \in \mathbf{N}).$$

The doubly indexed sequence $(f_{p,q})$ converges pointwise to the function f (where $f = 1$ at the origin and 0 everywhere else) as $p, q \to \infty$.

Z We have defined pointwise convergence without using a topology on the family of mappings of X into Y; in fact there is an underlying topology on this family (see Problem 107) called the topology of pointwise convergence, but we shall not have occasion to use it explicitly.

It is useful to note here that this topology cannot in general be defined by a metric: Let (f_n) be a sequence of numerical functions on $[0, 1]$ which converges pointwise to f; when each f_n is itself the pointwise limit of a sequence $(f_{n,p})$, one might think that f is the pointwise limit of a suitable chosen sequence of functions among the $f_{n,p}$. It is immediate that this would be the case if the topology of pointwise convergence were metrizable (see Problem 67); but simple examples show that this is not the case; therefore this topology is not metrizable (see also Problem 107).

Uniform convergence

Again let X be an arbitrary set, with or without a topology, and let Y be a space which we shall now suppose *metric*; f and f_n again denote mappings of X into Y.

22.3. Definition. THE SEQUENCE (f_n) IS SAID TO *CONVERGE UNIFORMLY* TO f (OR, f IS THE UNIFORM LIMIT OF THE f_n) IF FOR EVERY $\epsilon > 0$ THERE EXISTS AN INTEGER n_0 SUCH THAT $d(f_n(x), f(x)) \leqslant \epsilon$ FOR EVERY $n \geqslant n_0$ AND FOR EVERY $x \in X$.

We can similarly define the uniform convergence of a family (f_i) to f along a filter base $\mathscr{B}$; however, this definition will become superfluous once we have defined the topology of uniform convergence.

Z Every sequence (f_n) which converges uniformly to f converges pointwise to f, but it is important to note that the converse is incorrect. Here are several examples:

1.   Let f_n be the continuous numerical function (see Fig. 3) defined on $X = [0, 1]$ by

$$f_n(x) = n^2x(1 - nx) \quad \text{on} \quad [0, 1/n],$$
$$f_n(x) = 0 \quad \text{on} \quad [1/n, 1].$$

It is easily verified that the sequence (f_n) converges pointwise to the function $f = 0$, but this convergence is not uniform, as

$$\sup |f_n(x) - f(x)| = n/4$$

which, far from tending to 0, tends to $+\infty$.

2.   In each of the three examples which illustrate pointwise convergence, the convergence is nonuniform; this is particularly clear in the first two, from the fact that the limit f is not continuous; in the third example, there is uniform convergence on every bounded interval, but not on all of **R**.

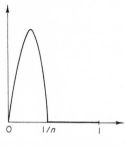

FIG. 3.

Metric and topology of uniform convergence

The study of uniform convergence can be simplified by introducing an ecart on the set $\mathscr{F}(X, Y)$ of mappings of X into Y.

Let f and g be mappings of a set X into a metric space Y, and put

$$d(f, g) = \sup_{x \in X} d(f(x), g(x)).$$

This is either a finite number or $+\infty$; by the previous study of ecarts on a set, for every $x \in X$

$$d_x(f, g) = d(f(x), g(x))$$

is an ecart on $\mathscr{F}(X, Y)$, and

$$d(f, g) = \sup d_x(f, g)$$

is also an ecart. Moreover

$$(f \neq g) \Rightarrow (d(f, g) \neq 0).$$

When the diameter of Y is finite, $d(f, g)$ is always finite, therefore d is a metric on $\mathscr{F}(X, Y)$; when Y is arbitrary, it is often convenient to replace the ecart d by $d/(1 + d)$, which is a metric and which defines the same topology and the same uniform structure on $\mathscr{F}(X, Y)$ as does d.

The topology on $\mathscr{F}(X, Y)$ associated with the ecart d is called the *topology of uniform convergence* (sometimes, *uniform topology*); this terminology is justified by the following result:

22.4. Proposition. *To say that a sequence* (f_n) *of mappings of* X *into* Y *converges uniformly to a mapping f is equivalent to saying that in the space* $\mathscr{F}(X, Y)$ *with the topology of uniform convergence, the sequence of points* f_n *converges to the point f.*

Indeed, to say that the sequence of functions f_n converges uniformly to f is equivalent to saying that for every $\epsilon > 0$ we have, for n sufficiently large,

$$d(f(x), f_n(x)) \leqslant \epsilon \qquad \text{for all} \qquad x \in X,$$

which is equivalent to saying that $d(f, f_n) \leqslant \epsilon$.

Interpretation of uniform convergence by means of the graphs

The use of the graphs of mappings f of X into Y gives a convenient and intuitive interpretation of uniform convergence (Fig. 4):

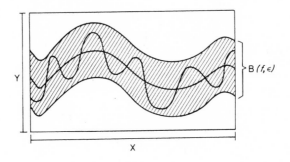

FIG. 4.

Let $B(f, \epsilon)$ be the set of points (x, y) of $X \times Y$ such that

$$d(y, f(x)) \leqslant \epsilon;$$

this set forms a sort of *tube* of radius ϵ about the graph of f.
To say that $d(f, g) \leqslant \epsilon$ is equivalent to saying that

$$d(f(x), g(x)) \leqslant \epsilon$$

for every $x \in X$, or that the graph of g is contained in $B(f, \epsilon)$.

To say that the sequence (f_n) converges uniformly to f amounts to saying that for every $\epsilon > 0$, all the f_n from some n_0 on have their graphs in B(f, ϵ).

One can now better see the reason why, in Example 1 above, the f_n do not converge uniformly to 0: For every $\epsilon < 1/4$, the graph of no one of the f_n is contained in B(0, ϵ).

Case of complete spaces

The introduction of the ecart d on $\mathscr{F}(X, Y)$ allows us to speak of Cauchy sequences of mappings, and to state the following theorem:

22.5. Theorem.   *When the metric space* Y *is complete, the space* $\mathscr{F}(X, Y)$ *is also complete.*

PROOF.   Let (f_n) be a Cauchy sequence in $\mathscr{F}(X, Y)$. For every $x \in X$, the inequality $d(f_p(x), f_q(x)) \leqslant d(f_p, f_q)$ shows that the sequence ($f_n(x)$) of points of Y is a Cauchy sequence. Since Y is complete, this sequence has a limit which we denote by $f(x)$.

But since (f_n) is a Cauchy sequence, for every $\epsilon > 0$ there exists an integer $n(\epsilon)$ such that for all $p, q \geqslant n(\epsilon)$ and every $x \in X$,

$$d(f_p(x), f_q(x)) \leqslant \epsilon.$$

If in this inequality we fix x and p and let $q \to \infty$, then $f_q(x)$ tends to $f(x)$, and we obtain the inequality

$$d(f_p(x), f(x)) \leqslant \epsilon \qquad \text{for all} \quad p \geqslant n(\epsilon).$$

It follows from this inequality that $d(f_p, f) \leqslant \epsilon$, and therefore the sequence (f_n) converges to f in the space $\mathscr{F}(X, Y)$ taken with the ecart d. Hence this space is complete.

Preservation of continuity by uniform convergence

We now assume that X is a topological space, with Y still a *metric* space. One can then speak of the continuity of a mapping of X into Y. We shall see that this property is preserved by uniform convergence.

22.6. Theorem.   *Let* (f_n) *be a sequence of mappings of* X *into* Y *which converges uniformly to* f, *and let a be a point of* X.

If all the f_n *are continuous at a, then f is continuous at a.*

PROOF.   Let $\epsilon > 0$. Since the convergence of the f_n is uniform, there exists an integer n_0 such that

$$d(f(x), f_{n_0}(x)) \leqslant \epsilon \qquad \text{for every} \quad x \in X.$$

Since f_{n_0} is continuous at a, there exists a neighborhood V of a such that

$$d(f_{n_0}(x), f_{n_0}(a)) \leqslant \epsilon \qquad \text{for every} \quad x \in V.$$

It follows that for every $x \in V$ we have

$$d(f(x), f(a)) \leqslant d(f(x), f_{n_0}(x)) + d(f_{n_0}(x), f_{n_0}(a)) + d(f_{n_0}(a), f(a)) \leqslant 3\epsilon.$$

Since ϵ is arbitrary, this inequality proves the continuity of f at a.

Corollary 1. *If the f_n are continuous in* X *and converge uniformly to f, then f is continuous in* X.

Corollary 2. *Let (f_n) be a sequence of continuous mappings of a metric space* X *into a metric space* Y. *If for every compact* K *in* X *the restrictions of the f_n to* K *converge uniformly, then the sequence (f_n) converges on* X *and its limit f is continuous.*

This is an immediate consequence of the preceding theorem and of Corollary 2 of Proposition 16.6.

We shall often have use of this corollary.

Z Theorem 22.6 and its corollaries extend immediately to the uniform limit of a family of continuous functions along a filter base.

However, it should be observed here that Theorem 22.6 does not extend to pointwise convergence:

When a sequence (f_n) of continuous functions converges pointwise to a function f, then f has a certain degree of regularity but is not always continuous. For example, the sequence of monomials $f_n(x) = x^n$ converges pointwise on $[0, 1]$ to the function f equal to 0 on $[0, 1)$ and to 1 for $x = 1$.

The space $\mathscr{C}(X, Y)$

We shall denote by $\mathscr{C}(X, Y)$ the subspace of $\mathscr{F}(X, Y)$ consisting of the continuous mappings of the topological space X into the metric space Y. It follows from the preceding theorem that $\mathscr{C}(X, Y)$ is a *closed* subset of $\mathscr{F}(X, Y)$ taken with the topology of uniform convergence; when $\mathscr{F}(X, Y)$ is complete, then $\mathscr{C}(X, Y)$ is also complete. We can therefore state:

22.7. Theorem. *When* Y *is complete, the subspace* $\mathscr{C}(X, Y)$ *of* $\mathscr{F}(X, Y)$ *consisting of the continuous mappings of* X *into* Y *is complete with respect to the ecart of uniform convergence.*

REMARK. Even if very restrictive regularity hypotheses are imposed on X and Y, the space $\mathscr{C}$(X, Y) is in general noncompact.

For example, suppose that X and Y are identical with the compact interval [0, 1]. The set $\mathscr{C}$(X, Y) is then simply the set of continuous numerical functions defined on [0, 1] with values in [0, 1].

With the metric chosen on $\mathscr{C}$(X, Y), this space is complete, but not compact or even locally compact. For example, the element O of this space does not have any compact neighborhood, since for every $k > 0$ the sequence (f_n) defined by $f_n(x) = k \sin^2 nx$ has no convergent subsequence.

Uniform convergence on a collection of subsets

The sequence of numerical functions $x \to 1/[1 + (x - n)^2]$ converges pointwise to the function O; but this convergence is not uniform. However, for every interval [a, b] of **R**, the restrictions of these functions to [a, b] converge uniformly to 0.

More generally, Corollary 2 of Theorem 22.6 shows the interest of uniform convergence on every compact set.

The latter is a special case of an important general notion.

22.8. Definition. LET X BE AN ARBITRARY SET; LET Y BE A METRIC SPACE, AND LET $\mathscr{A}$ BE A COLLECTION OF SUBSETS OF X. WE DENOTE BY f, f_n MAPPINGS OF X INTO Y.

THE SEQUENCE (f_n) IS SAID TO CONVERGE UNIFORMLY TO f ON EVERY $A \in \mathscr{A}$ IF FOR EVERY $A \in \mathscr{A}$ THE RESTRICTIONS OF THE f_n TO A CONVERGE UNIFORMLY TO THE RESTRICTION OF f TO A.

EXAMPLE 1. If X is the only element of $\mathscr{A}$, we are back to uniform convergence.

EXAMPLE 2. If $\mathscr{A}$ is the collection of one-point subsets of X, we are back to pointwise convergence.

EXAMPLE 3. If $\mathscr{A}$ is the collection of compact sets in the topological space X, we obtain uniform convergence on every compact set.

Relation between uniform convergence and pointwise convergence

Several examples have shown us that the pointwise convergence of a sequence of functions does not necessarily imply its uniform convergence. Here, however, is an important case in which this implication is true:

22.9. Theorem   (of Dini). *Let* X *be a compact space, and let* (f_n) *be a sequence of continuous numerical functions on* X *which converges pointwise to a numerical function f.*

If the sequence (f_n) is increasing, *that is if* $(p \leqslant q) \Rightarrow (f_p \leqslant f_q)$, *and if f is* continuous, *the convergence of the f_n to f is uniform.*

PROOF.   We take an $\epsilon > 0$. For every $x \in X$, there exists an integer p_x such that

$$f_{p_x}(x) > f(x) - \epsilon.$$

Let ω_x denote the set of y such that

$$f_{p_x}(y) > f(y) - \epsilon.$$

Since f and f_{p_x} are continuous, ω_x is open; by hypothesis ω_x contains x, and therefore the ω_x form an open covering of X, which is compact. Therefore there exists a finite set of points x_i of X such that the ω_{x_i} cover X. We put

$$p = \sup_i p_{x_i}.$$

Since the sequence (f_n) is increasing, we have

$$f_p(x) > f(x) - \epsilon$$

for all $x \in \bigcup \omega_{x_i}$, hence everywhere. We thus have, for all $q \geqslant p$,

$$f - \epsilon \leqslant f_q \leqslant f;$$

therefore the convergence is uniform.

Of course, an analogous result holds for *decreasing* sequences.

Z   It is the sequence (f_n) which is increasing, and not each of the f_n ; however, this last interpretation could be meaningful only if X had an order relation, for example if $X = [0, 1]$.

All the same this confusion would not lead to error; it can in fact be verified that if an arbitrary sequence of monotone numerical functions on an interval $[a, b]$ converges pointwise to a continuous function, the convergence is uniform (see Problem 85).

23. EQUICONTINUOUS SPACES OF FUNCTIONS

Despite the interest presented by complete spaces, as evidenced by the preceding theorems, it is often valuable to be able to deal with compact spaces of functions. The notion of *equicontinuity* will give us an important class of such spaces.

23.1. Definition.   LET E BE A FAMILY OF MAPPINGS OF A METRIC SPACE X INTO A METRIC SPACE Y. WE SAY THAT E IS *EQUICONTINUOUS* IF, FOR

EVERY $\epsilon > 0$, THERE EXISTS AN $\eta > 0$ SUCH THAT $d_Y(f(x_1), f(x_2)) \leqslant \epsilon$ FOR EVERY $f \in E$ AND FOR ALL x_1, $x_2 \in X$ SUCH THAT $d_X(x_1, x_2) \leqslant \eta$.

It follows from this definition that every $f \in E$ is not only continuous, but also uniformly continuous. The equicontinuity of E says that in addition this uniform continuity is of the same type for all the $f \in E$, or more precisely, that $\eta(\epsilon)$ does not depend on f.

EXAMPLE 1.   The set E of numerical functions x^n defined on $[0, 1]$ *is not equicontinuous*, although each of these functions is uniformly continuous on X.

EXAMPLE 2.   For any metric spaces X and Y, the collection E_k (where $k > 0$) of mappings of Lipschitz class with ratio k of X into Y is equicontinuous.

Interpretation of equicontinuity

It is convenient to express Definition 23.1 by again using the notion of modulus of continuity which was already used in studying uniform continuity:

To say that E is an equicontinuous set of functions is equivalent to saying that there exists a common modulus of continuity φ for all the $f \in E$.

Let $\alpha > 0$ be arbitrary, and let A be a subset of X which is α-dense in the sense that $d(x, A) < \alpha$ for every $x \in X$. For every $f \in E$, the relation $d(x_1, x_2) \leqslant \alpha$ implies

$$d(f(x_1), f(x_2)) \leqslant \varphi(\alpha);$$

therefore knowing the restriction of f to A entails a knowledge of f on X up to an accuracy $\varphi(\alpha)$.

In other words, the functions f of E have a certain "rigidity" which is measured by their modulus of continuity φ.

For example, a numerical function which is of Lipschitz class with ratio k on $[0, 1]$ is known everywhere with an accuracy k/n whenever $f(1/n), f(2/n), ..., f(p/n), ...$ are known.

All the consequences of equicontinuity follow from this "rigidity."

23.2. Theorem   (of Ascoli).   *Let X and Y be compact metric spaces and let E be a subset of the space $\mathscr{C}(X, Y)$ taken with the topology of uniform convergence.*

To say that E is equicontinuous is equivalent to saying that E is relatively compact in $\mathscr{C}(X, Y)$.

PROOF. 1. Suppose that E is equicontinuous; to show that $\bar{E}$ is compact it suffices, by the corollary of Theorem 18.2, to prove that every infinite sequence S of elements of E contains a subsequence which converges in $\mathscr{C}(X, Y)$; as $\mathscr{C}(X, Y)$ is complete (since Y is), it suffices to prove that S contains a Cauchy subsequence.

Let φ be a common modulus of continuity for all the $f \in E$. For every $\epsilon > 0$ there exists a finite covering of X by open balls of radius ϵ with centers x_i $(i = 1, 2, ..., n)$.

Since Y is compact, we can find a subsequence $S_1(\epsilon)$ of S such that, for all $f, g \in S_1(\epsilon)$,

$$d_Y(f(x), g(x)) \leqslant \varphi(\epsilon) \qquad \text{at the point} \quad x = x_1 . \tag{1}$$

We can find a subsequence $S_2(\epsilon)$ of the sequence $S_1(\epsilon)$ having the same property at the point x_2, and so on. After n operations we will have constructed a subsequence $S_n(\epsilon)$ satisfying inequality (1) at each of the points x_i $(i = 1, 2, ..., n)$; we denote $S_n(\epsilon)$ by $S(\epsilon)$.

But by construction, for every $x \in X$ there exists a point x_i such that

$$d_X(x, x_i) \leqslant \epsilon,$$

which implies that

$$d_Y(f(x), f(x_i)) \leqslant \varphi(\epsilon) \qquad \text{for every} \quad f \in S.$$

For all $f, g \in S(\epsilon)$ we therefore have

$$d_Y(f(x), g(x)) \leqslant d_Y(f(x), f(x_i)) + d_Y(f(x_i), g(x_i)) + d_Y(g(x_i), g(x)) \leqslant 3\varphi(\epsilon),$$

in other words

$$d(f, g) \leqslant 3\varphi(\epsilon). \tag{2}$$

We have thus exhibited a procedure which associates with every sequence S a subsequence $S(\epsilon)$ every two elements f, g of which satisfy the relation (2).

It suffices to iterate this procedure, giving ϵ the successive values $(1, 1/2, ..., 1/n, ...)$, to obtain successive sequences

$$S, \quad S(1), \quad S(1, 1/2), ..., S(1, 1/2, ..., 1/n), ...$$

each of which is a subsequence of the preceding.

Since the sequence $(\varphi(1/n))$ has limit 0, the diagonal of this sequence of sequences is a Cauchy sequence. This is the desired sequence.

2. Let E be a compact subset of $\mathscr{C}(X, Y)$.

For every $\epsilon > 0$ there exists a finite sequence $(f_1, f_2, ..., f_n)$ of points of E such that the open balls $B(f_i, \epsilon)$ form an open covering of E. For each of these f_i there exists an $\eta_i > 0$ such that the inequality

$$d_X(x_1, x_2) < \eta_i$$

implies

$$d_Y(f_i(x_1), f_i(x_2)) < \epsilon.$$

Let η be the smallest of the η_i; for every $f \in E$ we therefore have, noting that f belongs to some ball $B(f_i, \epsilon)$,

$$d_Y(f(x_1), f(x_2)) \leqslant 3\epsilon$$

whenever

$$d_X(x_1, x_2) \leqslant \eta.$$

In other words, E is an equicontinuous family.

Z Theorem 23.2 does not extend to the case where either X or Y is locally compact but not compact.

For example, the collection E of constant mappings of $[0, 1]$ into **R** is clearly equicontinuous; nevertheless it is not compact.

Similarly, the family of mappings $x \to 1/[1 + (x - n)^2]$ of **R** into $[0, 1]$ is equicontinuous but not compact.

EXAMPLES. The family of mappings of Lipschitz class with ratio k of the interval $[0, 1]$ into an interval $[a, b]$ is compact in the topology of uniform convergence.

An important example of equicontinuity is given by the following proposition, which will be useful in the theory of integration.

23.3. Proposition. *Let* X *and* Y *be compact metric spaces; let* f *be a mapping of* X $\times$ Y *into another metric space* Z, *and for every* $x \in$ X *let* f_x *denote the partial mapping* $y \to f(x, y)$.

If f *is continuous, the mapping* $x \to f_x$ *of* X *into* $\mathscr{C}(Y, Z)$ *is continuous, and the* f_x *form an equicontinuous family.*

PROOF. Since X $\times$ Y is compact, f is uniformly continuous; thus for every $\epsilon > 0$ there exists an $\eta > 0$ such that

$$(d(x_1, x_2) < \eta \quad \text{and} \quad d(y_1, y_2) < \eta) \Rightarrow (d(f(x_1, y_1), f(x_2, y_2)) < \epsilon).$$

In particular, $d(x_1, x_2) < \eta$ implies for every y the inequality

$$d(f(x_1, y), f(x_2, y)) < \epsilon,$$

in other words,

$$d(f_{x_1}, f_{x_2}) < \epsilon.$$

Therefore the mapping $x \to f_x$ is continuous.

It follows from this, since X is compact, that the family of the f_x is a compact set in $\mathscr{C}(Y, Z)$; hence by Theorem 23.2 it is an equicontinuous family. This can also be obtained directly. By the foregoing, $d(y_1, y_2) < \eta$ implies, for every x, the inequality

$$d(f_x(y_1), f_x(y_2)) < \epsilon,$$

from which the desired equicontinuity follows.

24. TOTAL VARIATION AND LENGTH

The notions which we have studied up to now, continuity, uniform continuity, uniform convergence, do not have a metric character, even though it is convenient to make use of a metric in studying them.

On the other hand, the total variation which we are going to define has an essentially metric character.

Let T be a totally ordered set (which will play the role of a parameter set) and let f be a mapping of T into a metric space E; to simplify the notation, we shall denote the distance between two points $x, y \in$ E by $| xy |$.

24.1. Definition. For every finite subset σ of T, the number

$$V_\sigma = \sum_i | f(t_i)f(t_{i+1}) |,$$

where the t_i $(t_1 < t_2 \cdots < t_n)$ denote the points of σ, is called the total variation of f on σ.

The triangle inequality shows at once that $(\sigma \subset \sigma') \Rightarrow (V_\sigma \leqslant V_{\sigma'})$; in other words, V is an increasing function of σ. It is therefore natural to introduce the following definition:

24.2. Definition. For every $A \subset T$, the positive, finite or infinite number V_A defined by

$$V_A = \sup V_\sigma \qquad \text{(over all the finite subsets } \sigma \text{ of A)}$$

is called the total variation of f on A. When $V_A < \infty$, f is said to have bounded variation (or to be of bounded variation) on A.

It is evident that V_A is an increasing function of A.

In particular, if T has a first point α and a last point β, then

$$V_T \geqslant V_{\{\alpha,\beta\}}, \qquad \text{that is,} \qquad V_T \geqslant |\, f(\alpha) f(\beta)\,|.$$

EXAMPLE 1.   Let f be an *increasing* mapping of T into **R**. The relation

$$V_\sigma = \sum (f(t_{i+1}) - f(t_i)) = f(t_n) - f(t_1)$$

shows that if T has a first point α and a last point β, then

$$V_T = f(\beta) - f(\alpha).$$

If f is decreasing, then $V_T = |\, f(\beta) - f(\alpha)\,|$.

EXAMPLE 2.   Let f be a mapping of Lipschitz class with ratio k of the interval $[a, b]$ of **R** into a metric space E.

For every $\sigma = \{t_i\} \subset [a, b]$ we have

$$V_\sigma \leqslant k \sum (t_{i+1} - t_i) \leqslant k(b - a).$$

Therefore

$$V_{[a,b]} \leqslant k(b - a).$$

24.3. Proposition.   *The total variation is additive in the sense that, for for every $x \in$ T, if we set*

$$T_1 = (-\infty, x] \cap T \qquad and \qquad T_2 = [x, \infty) \cap T,$$

then

$$V_T = V_{T_1} + V_{T_2}.$$

Indeed, since V_σ is an increasing function of σ, we also have

$$V_T = \sup V_\sigma \qquad \text{over all finite } \sigma \text{ containing } x.$$

But such a σ is simply the union of an arbitrary σ_1 of T_1 containing x and an arbitrary σ_2 of T_2 containing x. But

$$V_\sigma = V_{\sigma_1} + V_{\sigma_2};$$

therefore

$$V_T = \sup V_\sigma = \sup (V_{\sigma_1} + V_{\sigma_2}) = \sup V_{\sigma_1} + \sup V_{\sigma_2} = V_{T_1} + V_{T_2}.$$

24.4. Definition. Let T and T′ be totally ordered sets, and let f and $f′$ be mappings of T and T′, respectively, into E. Then f and $f′$ are said to be equivalent if there exists an increasing bijection φ of T′ to T such that $f′ = f \circ \varphi$.

Such a relation is clearly reflexive, symmetric, and transitive; hence it is an equivalence relation.

24.5. Proposition. *If f and $f′$ are equivalent, the total variations* V, V′ *of f and $f′$ on* T *and* T′, *respectively, are equal.*

Indeed, for all $x′, y′ \in T′$ we have

$$|f′(x′)f′(y′)| = |f(\varphi(x′))f(\varphi(y′))|;$$

therefore for every $\sigma′ \subset T′$, the total variation of $f′$ on $\sigma′$ is equal to the total variation of f on $\sigma = \varphi(\sigma′)$.

It follows that $V′ \leqslant V$; in the same way $V \leqslant V′$, from which the equality follows.

Parametrized curves

From now on we shall consider only the case where T is an interval $[a, b]$ of **R** and where f is continuous; in this case the pair (T, f) is called a *parametrized curve* or a *path*, and V_T is called the *length* of this curve; when this length is finite, we say that the curve is *rectifiable*.

For every finite subset σ of T, with

$$\sigma = \{t_1, t_2, ..., t_n\} \quad \text{where} \quad a = t_1 < t_2 < \cdots < t_n = b,$$

the number

$$\mu(\sigma) = \sup_i |t_{i+1} - t_i|$$

is called the *modulus of σ*.

24.6. Theorem. *For every parameterized curve* (T, f), V_T *is the limit of the V_σ as the modulus $\mu(\sigma)$ tends to* 0.

In other words (assuming $V_T < \infty$ for definiteness), for every $\epsilon > 0$ there exists an $\eta > 0$ such that

$$(\mu(\sigma) < \eta) \Rightarrow (V_T - V_\sigma < \epsilon).$$

This theorem is sometimes stated in the following form: The length of the curve is the limit of the lengths of *polygons inscribed* in the curve, where by an inscribed polygon is meant a pair (σ, f), with σ a finite subset of T containing a and b.

PROOF.　We shall assume $V_T < \infty$; the proof is completely analogous if $V_T = \infty$.

By the definition of V_T, for every $\epsilon > 0$ there exists a finite σ_0, $\sigma_0 = \{t_1, t_2, \cdots, t_{n_0}\}$, such that

$$V_T - V_{\sigma_0} \leqslant \epsilon.$$

Since f is uniformly continuous on T, there exists a number $\eta > 0$ such that $|u - v| < \eta$ implies

$$|f(u)f(v)| < \epsilon/n_0 \, ;$$

we shall assume in addition that η is smaller than the length of the smallest of the intervals $[t_i, t_{i+1}]$ associated with σ_0.

Now let us take any σ with modulus $\mu(\sigma) < \eta$. Each of the intervals $[t_i, t_{i+1}]$ of σ_0 contains at least one point of σ distinct from t_i and t_{i+1}; we denote by t_i' (t_i'') the largest (smallest) of the points t of σ such that $t < t_i$ ($t > t_i$) (see Fig. 5), and put

$$f(t_i) = m_i \, ; \qquad f(t_i') = m_i'; \qquad f(t_i'') = m_i'' \, .$$

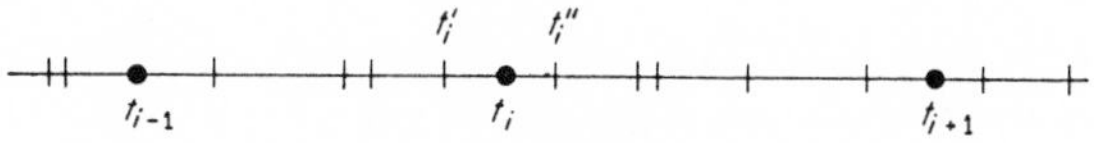

FIG. 5.

We have

$$V_{\sigma \cup \sigma_0} - V_\sigma = \sum_i (|m_i'm_i| + |m_im_i''| - |m_i'm_i''|) \leqslant \sum_i (|m_i'm_i| + |m_im_i''|)$$

$$\leqslant 2(\epsilon/n_0)n_0 = 2\epsilon,$$

where the summation is over only those i for which $t_i \notin \sigma$.

Adding the relations

$$V_T - V_{\sigma_0} \leqslant \epsilon$$

$$V_{\sigma_0} \leqslant V_{\sigma \cup \sigma_0}$$

$$V_{\sigma \cup \sigma_0} - V_\sigma \leqslant 2\epsilon$$

yields

$$V_T - V_\sigma \leqslant 3\epsilon;$$

this is the desired inequality, up to replacement of ϵ by 3ϵ.

Corollary 1. *If* $V_T < \infty$, *the mapping* $t \to V_{[a,t]}$ *of* T *into* **R** *is increasing and continuous.*

PROOF. Given $\epsilon > 0$, there exists an $\eta > 0$ such that

$$(\mu(\sigma) < \eta) \Rightarrow (V_T - V_\sigma < \epsilon)$$

and

$$(|y - x| < \eta) \Rightarrow (|f(x)f(y)| < \epsilon).$$

Now let x, y be arbitrary points of $[a, b]$ such that $0 \leqslant y - x \leqslant \eta$.

There exists a σ containing x, y but no other points of $[x, y]$, and with modulus $\mu(\sigma) < \eta$; let σ_1 and σ_2 denote the traces of σ on $[a, x]$ and $[y, b]$.

The relation $V_T < V_\sigma + \epsilon$ can be written as

$$V_{[a,x]} + V_{[x,y]} + V_{[y,b]} = V_{[a,b]} \leqslant V_\sigma + \epsilon$$
$$= V_{\sigma_1} + |f(x)f(y)| + V_{\sigma_2} + \epsilon \leqslant V_{[a,x]} + \epsilon + V_{[y,b]} + \epsilon,$$

from which $V_{[x,y]} < 2\epsilon$ for all x, y such that $|y - x| < \eta$.

Corollary 2. *If* E *is the Euclidean space* $\mathbf{R}^n$ *and if the mapping* $f = (f_p)$ *of* $[a, b]$ *into* E *has a continuous derivative, the length of the curve defined by* f *is equal to*

$$\int_a^b \left(\sum_p f_p'^2(t)\right)^{1/2} dt.$$

PROOF. To simplify the notation we shall carry out the proof only for $n = 2$; we denote f_1 and f_2 by g and h. Let σ_n be the finite subset of $[a, b]$ consisting of the points

$$t_i = a + i(b - a)/n \qquad (\text{where} \quad i \leqslant n).$$

We set

$$\Delta x_i = g(t_{i+1}) - g(t_i); \qquad \Delta y_i = h(t_{i+1}) - h(t_i); \qquad \Delta t_i = t_{i+1} - t_i.$$

Then

$$\Delta x_i = g'(\tau_i^1)\,\Delta t_i \qquad \text{and} \qquad \Delta y_i = h'(\tau_i^2)\,\Delta t_i$$

where

$$\tau_i^1, \tau_i^2 \in [t_i, t_{i+1}];$$

therefore

$$V_{\sigma_n} = \sum_i (\Delta^2 x_i + \Delta^2 y_i)^{1/2} = \sum_i (g'^2(\tau_i^1) + h'^2(\tau_i^2))^{1/2}\,\Delta t_i.$$

This expression is the integral of the step function φ_n, whose value on each $[t_i, t_{i+1})$ is

$$(g'^2(\tau_i^{\,1}) + h'^2(\tau_i^{\,2}))^{1/2}.$$

But the sequence (φ_n) converges uniformly to the function φ:

$$x \to (g'^2(x) + h'^2(x))^{1/2}.$$

Indeed, for every $t \in [t_i, t_{i+1})$ we have, by the triangle inequality in $\mathbf{R}^2$,

$$|\varphi_n(t) - \varphi(t)| \leqslant [(g'(\tau_i^{\,1}) - g'(t))^2 + (h'(\tau_i^{\,2}) - h'(t))^2]^{1/2}.$$

Since

$$|\tau_i^{\,1} - t|, \quad |\tau_i^{\,2} - t| \leqslant (b - a)/n$$

and since g' and h' are uniformly continuous, the right side of the above inequality tends to 0 as $n \to \infty$.

Therefore the integral V_{σ_n} of φ_n converges to that of φ; but the length of the curve is equal to the limit of the V_{σ_n}, from which the assertion follows.

Parametrized curves in a product space

Let E_i be a finite family of metric spaces; let d_i be the metric on E_i, and let d be any one of the usual metrics on the product E of the E_i.

Let $f = (f_i)$ be a mapping of $[a, b]$ into E, and let V (V_i) be the total variation of $f\,(f_i)$.

The inequality

$$d_i(x_i, y_i) \leqslant d(x, y) \leqslant \sum d_i(x_i, y_i)$$

implies a similar inequality for the variations on every finite subset σ of $[a, b]$, from which we readily obtain

$$V_i \leqslant V \leqslant \sum V_i.$$

In particular we can state:

24.7. Proposition. *To say that a parametrized curve in a finite product of metric spaces is rectifiable is equivalent to saying that each of its projections on the coordinate spaces is rectifiable.*

EXAMPLE 1. Let Γ be a curve in the Euclidean space $\mathbf{R}^n$ defined by a continuous mapping $f = (f_i)$ of $[a, b]$ into $\mathbf{R}^n$; to say that Γ is rectifiable is equivalent to saying that each of the f_i is of bounded variation.

EXAMPLE 2.   Let Γ be the graph in $\mathbf{R}^2$ of a continuous mapping f of $[a, b]$ into $\mathbf{R}$; here the graph Γ can be identified with the curve $x \rightarrow (x, f(x))$. Therefore this graph has finite length when f has bounded variation.

Z It is essential to note that the total variation V of f (or the length of the path in $\mathbf{R}$ which f traverses) is never equal to the length of the graph of f; the latter belongs to the interval $(V, V + b - a]$.

Numerical functions of bounded variation

The preceding examples show the importance of numerical functions of bounded variation; thus, we shall undertake a short study of such functions. More precisely, we shall study the structure of the family $\mathscr{V}$ of finite numerical functions of bounded variation on $[a, b]$.

For every $f \in \mathscr{V}$, we denote by $V(f)$ the total variation of f on $[a, b]$.

24.8. Proposition.   1. $\mathscr{V}$ *is a vector space, and* V *is a semi-norm on* $\mathscr{V}$ *in the sense that*:

$$V \geqslant 0; \qquad V(\lambda f) = |\lambda| (V(f); \qquad V(f_1 + f_2) \leqslant V(f_1) + V(f_2).$$

2. $\mathscr{V}$ *contains the convex cone* $\mathscr{V}_0$ *of increasing functions, and every element of* $\mathscr{V}$ *is the difference of two elements of* $\mathscr{V}_0$.

PROOF.   1.   Let f and g be arbitrary numerical functions on $[a, b]$, and put $h = f + g$. For all $u, v \in [a, b]$ we have

$$|h(u) - h(v)| = |(f(v) - f(u)) + (g(v) - g(u))| \leqslant |f(v) - f(u)| + |g(v) - g(u)|.$$

Therefore for every finite subset σ of $[a, b]$ we have

$$V_\sigma(h) \leqslant V_\sigma(f) + V_\sigma(g) \leqslant V_f + V_g,$$

hence

$$V(f + g) = V(h) \leqslant V(f) + V(g).$$

Therefore if f and $g \in \mathscr{V}$, then also $f + g \in \mathscr{V}$.

On the other hand, it is evident that $V(\lambda f) = |\lambda| V(f)$ for every $f \in \mathscr{V}$. Therefore $\mathscr{V}$ is indeed a vector space and V is a semi-norm on $\mathscr{V}$.

2.   We already know that if f is increasing, $V(f) = f(b) - f(a)$; therefore $\mathscr{V}_0 \subset \mathscr{V}$. Since $\mathscr{V}$ is a vector space, $f, g \in \mathscr{V}_0$ implies $f - g \in \mathscr{V}$.

To prove the second part of 2, suppose $f \in \mathscr{V}$. For every $t \in [a, b]$ let $\varphi(t)$ denote the total variation of f on $[a, t]$, and put

$$\psi(t) = \varphi(t) + f(t).$$

For all $u, v \in [a, b]$ such that $u < v$ we have

$$\psi(v) - \psi(u) = (\varphi(v) - \varphi(u)) + (f(v) - f(u)).$$

But it follows from the additivity of the total variation that $\varphi(v) - \varphi(u)$ is the total variation of f on $[u, v]$; therefore

$$\varphi(v) - \varphi(u) \geqslant |f(v) - f(u)|, \quad \text{whence} \quad \psi(v) - \psi(u) \geqslant 0.$$

Thus $\varphi, \psi \in \mathscr{V}_0$; since $f = \psi - \varphi$, the desired property is established.

24.9. Corollary. *Every numerical function of bounded variation on $[a, b]$ has a limit from the right and from the left at every point (with the obvious exceptions at a and b).*

Indeed, the increasing functions have this property, and this property is preserved by the subtraction of functions.

Case of continuous functions

With the above notation, if f is continuous and of bounded variation, the function φ is continuous (Corollary 1 of Theorem 24.6); therefore ψ is also continuous.

Thus, *every continuous numerical function of bounded variation is equal to the difference of two continuous increasing functions.*

Examples of numerical functions of bounded variation

1. Every function f on a finite interval I of **R** which is bounded and piecewise monotone, that is, for which there exists a finite partition of I into intervals, some of which may consist of one point, in each of which f is monotone (ignoring the one-point intervals). When f is moreover continuous, the total variation of f on I is the sum of its variations on each of these subintervals.

All the elementary functions are of this nature.

2. If f is of Lipschitz class with ratio k on $[a, b]$, then

$$V(f) \leqslant k(b - a).$$

This is the case, in particular, for functions f which are differentiable and whose derivative f' is bounded; in fact, if $|f'| \leqslant k$, then f is of Lipschitz class with ratio k.

More precisely if f' is continuous, then

$$V(f) = \int_a^b |f'(t)| \, dt.$$

This is a particular case of the relation established in Corollary 2 of Theorem 24.6 (for $n = 1$).

3. On the other hand, here is a simple example of a continuous function which is differentiable everywhere on $[a, b]$ and has infinite total variation on $[a, b]$:

The function f in question is defined on $[-1, 1]$ by

$$f(0) = 0; \qquad f(x) = x^2 \cos^2(\pi/x^2) \qquad \text{for all} \quad x \neq 0.$$

Indeed, for every integer $n > 1$, the total variation of f on $[n^{-1/2}, 1]$ is equal to $(1 + 1/2 + \cdots + 1/n)$, and this sum tends to $+\infty$ with n.

PROBLEMS

Note: The rather difficult problems are marked with an asterisk.

THE LINE **R** AND THE SPACE **R**^{n}

1. Let f be a strictly increasing surjection of an interval $[\alpha, \beta]$ to an interval $[a, b]$. Show that f is continuous and that the inverse function f^{-1} is defined and continuous on $[a, b]$ (in other words, that f is a homeomorphism).

*__2.__ Let A and B be countable everywhere dense subsets of $(0, 1)$.

(a) Show that there exists an infinity of increasing bijections of A to B.

(b) Show that such a bijection extends in a unique way to a homeomorphism of $[0, 1]$ with itself.

3. Show that there does not exist any countable partition of the interval $[0, 1]$ into nonempty closed subsets.

4. Let $0.a_1 a_2 \cdots a_n \cdots$ denote the reduced decimal expansion of an $x \in [0, 1)$; put $S_n(x) = a_1 + a_2 + \cdots + a_n$, and let $\lambda \in [0, 9)$. Show that the set of x such that $S_n \leqslant \lambda n$ for every n is compact, has no isolated points, and does not contain any interval.

5. Show that every isometry of **R** into **R** is of the form $x \to a + x$ or $x \to a - x$.

6. Show that in $\mathbf{R}^n$ ($n \geqslant 2$) the complement of every compact interval is connected.

7. Let D be a domain of $\mathbf{R}^n$ ($n \geqslant 2$).

(a) Show that for any distinct points a, b, c of D, there exists a polygonal line in D containing a and b but not c.

(b) Deduce from this that D is not homeomorphic to any subset of $\mathbf{R}$.

8. Show that every simple arc of $\mathbf{R}^n$ is nondense on $\mathbf{R}^n$ (use Problem 7).

9. Show that in $\mathbf{R}^n$ the set A obtained from the sphere $\Sigma\, x_i{}^2 = 1$ by removing the point $(0, ..., 0, 1)$ is homeomorphic to $\mathbf{R}^{n-1}$. (Start with $n = 2$ or 3 by using a stereographic projection and generalize this procedure.)

10. Show that every open ball of $\mathbf{R}^n$ is homeomorphic to $\mathbf{R}^n$.

11. Show that every compact convex subset of $\mathbf{R}^2$ is either a segment, or is homeomorphic to a closed disk. State and prove a similar result for $\mathbf{R}^n$.

12. Let ω be an open set in $\mathbf{R}^n$ containing O. Let E be the set of $x \in \omega$ such that $[O, x] \subset \omega$ (the *star* of O in ω); show that E is open and intersects every halfline δ from the origin in an interval.

For every δ, put $\varphi(\delta) = $ length of $\delta \cap$ E. Show that φ is a lower semicontinuous function of δ (see Chapter II).

13. Let f be an isometric surjection of $\mathbf{R}^n$ to a subset A of $\mathbf{R}^n$.

(a) Show that the image $f(\varDelta)$ of every line $\varDelta$ in $\mathbf{R}^n$ is a line.

(b) Deduce from this that f is an affine transformation, and that $A = \mathbf{R}^n$.

TOPOLOGICAL SPACES

14. Let E be a topological space containing a countable everywhere dense subset. Show that every family of nonempty open and disjoint subsets of E is finite or countable.

*15. Consider the family $\mathcal{O}$ of subsets of $\mathbf{R}$ of the form:

$$X = (\text{open set of } \mathbf{R}) - (\text{finite or countable set of points}).$$

Show that $\mathcal{O}$ is the family of open sets for a topology $\mathscr{T}$ on $\mathbf{R}$, and study this topology. In particular, determine the compact sets of $\mathscr{T}$.

16. Let A be a closed subset of $\mathbf{R}^2$; let S be the set of points x of A which have in A a neighborhood contained in an angle $< \pi$ and with vertex x. Show that S is finite or countable.

17. Let X^* denote the boundary of a subset X of a topological space E; show that

$$X^* = (X \cap (\overline{\complement X})) \cup (\overline{X} \div X).$$

*18. Let E be a topological space, and let X be a subset of E. The *sequential adherence* of X is defined as the set of points of E which are limits of a sequence of points of X; X is said to be *sequentially closed* if it is identical with its sequential adherence. Show by examples that the sequential adherence of A is not always sequentially closed (use Problem 107).

What might one call the *sequential closure* of X? Does it always exist?

19. Let E be a topological space, and X a closed subset of E. The set $X^{(1)}$ of accumulation points of X is called the *derived set* of X; the successive derived sets $X^{(n)}$ are defined by the condition that $X^{(n+1)}$ is the derived set of $X^{(n)}$. We then set

$$X^\omega = \bigcap X^{(n)}.$$

Construct a closed set A in $\mathbf{R}$ such that $A^{(n)}$ (respectively, A^ω) consists of a single point.

20. Let f be a mapping of a topological space E into $\mathbf{R}$; show that if for every $\lambda \in \mathbf{R}$, $\{x : f(x) < \lambda\}$ and $\{x : f(x) > \lambda\}$ are open, then f is continuous. More generally, let f be a mapping of E into a topological space F, and let (ω_i) be a family of open sets in F such that every open set in F is the union of finite intersections of the open sets ω_i (the family (ω_i) is said to *generate* the topology of F). How can one characterize the continuous mappings f in terms of the open sets ω_i?

21. A mapping f of a topological space E into a topological space F is said to be *open* if $f(\omega)$ is an open set in F for every open set ω in E.

(a) Show that the projection of a product space on each of the factor spaces is an open mapping.

(b) Characterize the continuous mappings of $\mathbf{R}$ (respectively, $\mathbf{R}^n$) into $\mathbf{R}$ which are open.

(c) Show that every holomorphic mapping of $\mathbf{C}$ into $\mathbf{C}$ which is not constant, is open.

22. Let f be a continuous mapping of a topological space E into $\mathbf{R}$. Show that for every open set ω in $\mathbf{R}$, $f^{-1}(\omega)$ is an open F_σ set (see Problem 73).

23. Let E be a topological space with a *countable base* (see Problem 88), and let f be a numerical function on E. Show that if M denotes the set of $x \in$ E at which f has a local maximum, then $f(M)$ is finite or countable.

24. Let E be a separated topological space with a countable base; show that the set P of points of E which do not have any countable neighborhood is perfect (i.e., closed and without isolated points). Show that E $\div$ P is at most countable.

25. Show that the family of open (and of closed) sets in **R** has the cardinality of the continuum; same problem for **R**^{n}. Deduce from this the cardinality of the family of continuous mappings of **R**^{n} into **R**^{p}.

26. We say that a quadratic form $\sum a_{ij}x_ix_j$ with real coefficients and in n variables is positive definite if it is > 0 for every $(x_i) \neq 0$. Show that the set of points $a = (a_{ij})$ in **R**^{N}, where $N = n(n - 1)/2$, representing these forms is open.

27. Does there exist a continuous numerical function on $[0, 1]$ such that $f(x)$ is rational for x irrational, and irrational for x rational?

28. Find two subsets X, Y of **R**, each of which is the image of the other under a continuous bijection, without being homeomorphic.

29. Let X be a subset of a topological space E. Under what conditions is the characteristic function of X continuous?

30. Let X, Y be subsets of a separated topological space E, such that E $=$ X $\cup$ Y. When the restrictions of f to X and Y are continuous, is f continuous? Examine the case where X and Y are closed (or open).

31. Show that for every topological space E the diagonal Δ of E $\times$ E is homeomorphic to E.

32. Let f be a continuous mapping of a topological space E into a topological space F, and let Γ be the graph of f in E $\times$ F. Show that E and Γ are homeomorphic.

33. Let E be a separated topological space, and let f be a continuous mapping of E into itself. Show that the set I of points $x \in$ E such that $f(x) = x$ is closed.

Give various examples for which I is empty and E is compact. Show that then $d(x, f(x))$ is always greater than some constant $k > 0$.

Show that I is nonempty if E is a finite union of segments of **R**^{2} containing O.

34. Show that in order for a space E to be separated, it is necessary and sufficient that the diagonal of E^2 be closed in E^2.

35. Let f and g be continuous mappings of a space X into a *separated* space Y. Show that the set of points $x \in E$ such that $f(x) = g(x)$ is closed.

36. Let f and g be continuous mappings of a topological space E into a separated topological space F. If the restrictions of f and g to an everywhere dense subset of E coincide, show that $f = g$.

37. Let $(a_{m.n})$ be a mapping of $\mathbf{N}^2$ into a separated topological space. Show that if

$$\lim_{m\to\infty,n\to\infty} a_{m,n} = a \quad \text{and} \quad \lim_{m\to\infty} a_{m,n} = b_n, \quad \text{then} \quad \lim_{n\to\infty} b_n = a.$$

38. Let E be a separated topological space, and let (a_n) be a sequence of points of E which converges to a. Show that the set $\{a, a_1, a_2, \ldots\}$ is compact.

39. Construct a mapping $(x, y) \to f(x, y)$ of $\mathbf{R}^2$ into $\mathbf{R}$ such that:

(1) The partial mappings $x \to f(x, y)$ and $y \to f(x, y)$ are continuous.

(2) The set of points of discontinuity of f is everywhere dense on $\mathbf{R}^2$.

40. Let E be a topological space, and (ω_i) a base of open sets for E (see Problem 88). Show that if every covering of E by sets ω_i contains a finite subcovering, then E is compact.

41. Let (K_n) be a decreasing sequence of nonempty compact sets in a separated space E. Show that $K = \bigcap K_n$ is nonempty, and that for every open set ω containing K, there exists a K_n contained in ω.

42. Let E be an infinite compact space; we denote by Δ the diagonal of $E \times E$. Show that there exists a countable subset A of $E \times E$ such that

$$A \cap \Delta = \varnothing \quad \text{and} \quad \bar{A} \cap \Delta \neq \varnothing.$$

43. We denote by $\prec$ the order relation on the set $E = [0, 1]^2$ defined by

$$(x, y) \prec (x', y') \qquad \text{when either} \qquad x < x', \qquad \text{or} \qquad x = x' \quad \text{and} \quad y \leqslant y'.$$

(a) Show that this is a total ordering (the lexicographic order).

(b) Show that E, taken with the topology associated with this order, is compact.

44. Let (A_n) be a decreasing sequence of subsets of $\mathbf{R}$, each of which is a finite union of pairwise disjoint closed intervals. We assume that each of the intervals making up A_n contains exactly two of the intervals which make up A_{n+1}, and that the diameter of these intervals tends to 0 with $1/n$. Show that the set $A = \bigcap A_n$ is compact and without isolated points; show also that any two such sets A are homeomorphic.

45. Show that in every separated space X, if two compact subsets A and B are disjoint, then they have disjoint neighborhoods. (Start by treating the case where B consists of a single point.)

46. Let X be a compact space, and Y an arbitrary topological space. Show that if A is closed in X $\times$ Y, its projection on Y is closed.

47. Let f be a mapping of a space X into a *separated* space Y.

    (a) Show that if f is continuous, the graph of f is closed in X $\times$ Y. Show by an example (where X = Y = **R**) that the converse is false.

    (b) Show, on the other hand, that if Y is compact, these two assertions are equivalent.

48. Let L and X be compact spaces, and let f be a continuous mapping of L $\times$ X into a separated space Y such that, for every $\lambda \in L$, the mapping $x \rightarrow f(\lambda, x)$ of X into Y is injective. Let $y_0 \in Y$.

    (1) Show that the set L_0 of $\lambda \in L$ such that the equation $y_0 = f(\lambda, x)$ has a solution is closed in L.

    (2) Show that the solution $x = \varphi(\lambda)$ of this equation is a continuous function of λ on L_0.

49. Let C_1 and C_2 be circles in **R**³. Show, making use of the properties of the maximum of the distance between a point of C_1 and a point of C_2, that there exists at least one line which meets C_1, C_2 and their axes.

50. In the plane **R**² referred to two arbitrary axes, a line is defined by its equation $ax + by + c = 0$, where a and b are not both zero. Using this form, establish a correspondence between the set D of these lines and a set of lines in **R**³ passing through the origin. What natural topology on D can one deduce from this; does this topology depend on the axes chosen?

    What element can be added to D to make it compact? Indicate other spaces homeomorphic to this compact set.

    Will this procedure work for the lines in **R**³?

51. Show that if the product X $\times$ Y is compact, then X and Y are compact. What is the analogous statement when X $\times$ Y is locally compact?

52. Let Δ_1, Δ_2, Δ_3 be lines in $\mathbf{R}^3$, no two of which are parallel or perpendicular to each other. Show that among the triangles (x_1, x_2, x_3) where $x_i \in \Delta_i$ $(i = 1, 2, 3)$, there is one whose area (respectively, perimeter) is minimum.

53. Show that the set of points in $\mathbf{R}^2$ which have at least one irrational coordinate is connected.

54. Let (C_n) be a decreasing sequence of continua in a topological space E. Show that their intersection $C = \cap\, C_n$ is also a continuum.

55. Show that the graph of the function $y = \sin 1/x$ $(x \in (0, 1])$ is connected. Determine its closure and show that it is a continuum which is not a simple arc.

56. Let G be an open set in $\mathbf{R}^n$.

(a) Show that each of the connected components of G is open (therefore also a domain).

(b) Show that the family of these connected components is at most countable.

57. Let A be a totally ordered set, taken with the topology associated with this order. Show that if A is connected, every subset of A which is bounded from above has a supremum, and that no point of A has a successor (y is the successor of x if $x < y$ and $(x, y) = \emptyset$). Is the converse true?

*58. Let f be a homeomorphism of $[0, 1]$ with itself. (1) Show that f either leaves the endpoints fixed, or interchanges them. (2) If $f^2 =$ the identity, show that f is either the identity, or, in a sense to be made precise, equivalent to a central symmetry.

59. Let f be a continuous mapping of $[0, 1]$ into itself; show that f has at least one fixed point.

60. Let A be a closed subset of $[0, 1] \times [0, 1]$ such that, for every $x \in [0, 1]$, the set of y for which $(x, y) \in A$ is a closed interval l_x. Show that there exists an x such that $x \in l_x$.

61. Let E be a topological space and let A be a subset of E. Show that every connected subset of E which meets $\mathring{A}$ and $\complement A$ also meets the boundary of A.

METRIC SPACES

62. Let E be the metric space obtained by taking the sphere $x^2 + y^2 + z^2 = 1$ of $\mathbf{R}^3$ with the geodesic distance. For every $m \in E$

and every number $\rho > 0$, calculate the diameter $\delta(\rho)$ in E of the "circle" with center m and radius ρ. Show that $\delta(\rho)$ is not an increasing function of ρ.

*63. We use the notation of the problem of Chapter I (Volume 1) concerning the Cantor-Bernstein theorem.

We now assume that A and E are topological spaces (respectively, metric spaces) and that φ, ψ are homeomorphisms (respectively, isometries). To what assertions does the proof suggested in that problem lead?

64. Let (a_n) be a sequence of points of a metric space. Show that the set of adherent points of this sequence is identical with the set of limits of convergent subsequences of (a_n).

65. Let f be a mapping of a metric space E into a topological space F. Show the equivalence of the continuity of f at a point $a \in$ E with the following property:

For every sequence (a_n) in E such that $\lim a_n = a$, we have $\lim f(a_n) = f(a)$.

66. Let f be a mapping of a topological space X into a metric space Y. For every $x_0 \in$ X the *oscillation* of f at x_0 is the positive number $\omega(f, x_0) = $ infimum of diameter of $f(V)$, where V runs through the family of neighborhoods of x_0.

   (a) Show that the continuity of f at x_0 is equivalent to $\omega(f, x_0) = 0$.

   (b) Show that for every $\epsilon > 0$, the set of points x of E at which $\omega(f, x) \geqslant \epsilon$ is closed.

67. Let E be a metric space, and let $(m, n) \to a_{mn}$ be a mapping of $\mathbf{N}^2$ into E. Assume that

$$\lim_{n \to \infty} a_{mn} = a_m \qquad \text{and} \qquad \lim_{m \to \infty} a_m = a.$$

Show that there exists a subsequence $n \to p_n$ of $\mathbf{N}$ such that

$$\lim_{n \to \infty} a_{n, p_n} = a.$$

Does this result extend to the case of any topological space E?

68.   Let X be a metric space and A a subset of X. For every number $\rho > 0$, we denote by $B(A, \rho)$ the set of $x \in$ X such that $d(x, A) < \rho$.

   (a) Show that $B(A, \rho) = \bigcup_{x \in A} B(x, \rho)$.

   (b) Show that $\bar{A} = \bigcap_{\rho} B(A, \rho)$.

69. Let X be a metric space and A, B *closed* subsets of X. We denote by D_A, D_B, I, respectively, the set of points x such that

$$d(x, A) < d(x, B); \qquad d(x, A) > d(x, B); \qquad d(x, A) = d(x, B).$$

(a) Show that D_A and D_B are open. Deduce from this that A and B have disjoint open neighborhoods.

(b) Show that I is closed, and determine this set when X is a plane and when A, B denote lines, circles, or closed disks in X.

70. Show that every metric space is homeomorphic to a bounded metric space. Is there an analogous statement for the uniform structure?

71. Construct examples of continuous (and even uniformly continuous) bijections of one metric space E to another one F, which are not homeomorphisms.

***72.** Let f be a mapping of an everywhere dense subset A of a topological space E into a metric space F such that $\lim_{x \in A, x \to a} f(x)$ exists for every $a \in E$. Show that there exists a unique extension of f to all of E which is a continuous mapping of E into F.

73. We shall say that a subset X of a topological space is an F_σ (respectively, G_δ) set if X is a countable union of closed sets (respectively, a countable intersection of open sets).

(a) Show that the class of F_σ (respectively, G_δ) sets is closed under countable union (respectively, countable intersection).

(b) Show that the complement of an F_σ set is a G_δ set, and vice versa.

(c) Give examples of subsets of **R** which are F_σ sets and which are neither open nor closed.

(d) Show that in a metric space, every open set is an F_σ, and every closed set a G_δ.

74. Let E be a set with an ecart d and with the topology associated with this ecart. Show that for every $X \subset E$, the mapping $x \to d(x, X)$ is continuous.

Show that

$$\bar{X} = \{x : d(x, X) = 0\}.$$

75. If a numerical function f is uniformly continuous in $\mathbf{R}^n$, show that $|f(x)| \leqslant a|x| + b$, where a and b are positive constants and $|x|$ is the distance from x to the origin.

76. For every metric space E, show that the metric $d(x, y)$ is uniformly continuous on E^2.

77. Construct an example of a numerical function on $[0, 1]$ which has a finite derivative everywhere, and yet which is not of Lipschitz class.

78. Let E, F be metric spaces, and Φ a family of mappings of E into F. We assume that for every $x \in E$, every $f \in \Phi$, and every $\epsilon > 0$ there exists $\eta(x, f, \epsilon) > 0$ such that

$$(d(x, y) < \eta(x, f, \epsilon)) \Rightarrow (d(f(x), f(y)) < \epsilon).$$

Interpret the meaning of the assertion that η does not depend on ϵ, or does not depend on x, or does not depend on f, or does not depend on either f or x.

79. Let E be a metric space, and $A \subset E$. Show that the compactness of $\bar{A}$ is equivalent to each of the following conditions:

(a) Every sequence of points of A contains a subsequence which converges in E.

(b) Every infinite subset of A has at least one accumulation point in E.

80. Let (F_i) be a finite family of closed sets in a compact metric space whose intersection is empty. Show that there exists an $\epsilon > 0$ such that every set which meets all the F_i has diameter at least equal to ϵ.

*__81.__ Let K be a compact set in a metric space E; we denote by $B(\epsilon)$ the set of $x \in E$ such that $d(x, K) < \epsilon$. Show that the $B(\epsilon)$ form a base of neighborhoods of K. Does this conclusion extend to noncompact sets K?

82. Let E be a compact metric space. Show that every metric subspace A of E which is isometric to E is identical with E. Show by a simple example that this is not always true when E is not compact.

83. Let X and Y be compact metric spaces, f a mapping of X into Y, and g a mapping of Y into X. Show that if f and g are isometries, then $f(X) = Y$ and $g(Y) = X$.

84. Let E be an incomplete metric space. Show that one can define continuous functions f of each of the following types on E:

(a) f is continuous and unbounded.

(b) f is continuous and bounded, but not uniformly continuous.

Then study the same questions when E is only noncompact.

85. We have emphasized in this chapter that the pointwise convergence of a sequence of functions does not in general imply its uniform convergence. Prove, however, that this implication is true in each of the following circumstances:

    (a) X is a compact space and (f_n) is an *increasing* sequence of lower semicontinuous mappings of X into **R** (that is, $f_p(x) \leqslant f_q(x)$ for every $x \in X$ if $p \leqslant q$) which converges pointwise to a *continuous* function f (this result extends Dini's theorem).

    (b) $X = [0, 1]$ and (f_n) is a sequence of increasing mappings of X into **R** (not necessarily continuous) which converges pointwise to a continuous function f.

86. Let X and Y be metric spaces, with X compact. Let f and f_n $(n \in \mathbf{N})$ be continuous mappings of X into Y. Show that if, for every $x \in X$, $d(f(x), f_n(x))$ *decreases* to 0, then (f_n) converges uniformly to f.

More generally, show that if there exists a constant $k > 0$ such that for all integers p, q and for every x,

$$d(f(x), f_{p+q}(x)) \leqslant k \, d(f(x), f_p(x)),$$

then the pointwise convergence of (f_n) to f implies uniform convergence. This result extends Dini's theorem in two directions.

87. Show that every compact metric space is finite or countable, or else has the cardinality of the continuum.

88. A *base* of a topological space E is a family of open sets in E such that every open set in E is the union of a subfamily of the base. Show that:

    (a) If E has a countable base, then every open covering of E has a countable subcovering.

    (b) If E has a countable base, so does every subspace of E.

    (c) If the spaces E_1 and E_2 have countable bases, so does their product $E_1 \times E_2$.

    (d) If E has a countable base, there exists a countable everywhere dense subset D of E.

    (e) Every compact metric space has a countable base.

    (f) $\mathbf{R}^n$ has a countable base.

89. Put a natural topology on the collection of halflines from the origin O in $\mathbf{R}^n$; same problem for the lines containing O. Show that the spaces obtained are compact and metrizable.

90. We denote by E (respectively E') the collection of circles in the Euclidean plane $\mathbf{R}^2$ of radius $\geqslant 0$ (respectively, > 0). (Every circle in the plane is thus represented by a point of E).

(a) One can show, for a natural topology which it is required to specify, that E is homeomorphic to a closed halfspace of $\mathbf{R}^3$; what does E′ become under this homeomorphism?

(b) Let f be the mapping of E into $\mathbf{R}^2$ which associates, with every circle C, its center $f(C)$. Show that f is continuous. Let A be a closed subset of $\mathbf{R}^2$. What can be said of the set of elements of E whose centers belong to A, and of the set of elements of E such that the corresponding circumference meets A?

(c) Show that the set of elements of E for which the circumference is contained in a compact set K in $\mathbf{R}^2$ is compact; show that among these elements there exists one whose radius is maximum.

91. Show that for every Cauchy sequence (a_n) in a metric space, the set $\{a_1, a_2, \ldots\}$ is bounded. Show by an example that the converse is false, and that there can even exist bounded sequences none of whose subsequences is a Cauchy sequence.

92. Let E be a metric space, (a_n) a Cauchy sequence in E, and (b_n) a sequence of numbers > 0. Show that there exists a subsequence (a_{n_p}) of the given sequence such that $d(a_{n_p}, a_{n_{p+1}}) < b_p$ for all p.

93. Let E and F be metric spaces, and let f be a bijection of E to F. Show that if F is complete, if f is uniformly continuous, and if f^{-1} is continuous, then E is also complete.

94. Show that every metric space in which every closed ball is compact, is complete; show that its compact subsets are closed bounded sets.

95. Let E be a complete metric space; show that one criterion for the compactness of E is that for every $\epsilon > 0$ there exists a finite covering of E by sets of diameter $< \epsilon$.

96. Let f be a continuous mapping of a metric space E into a metric space F which is uniformly continuous on every bounded subset of E.

(a) Show that for every Cauchy sequence (a_n) in E, $(f(a_n))$ is a Cauchy sequence in F.

(b) If $E \subset E'$ with E everywhere dense on E′, and if F is complete, show that f can be extended in a unique way to a continuous mapping of E′ into F.

97. Show that if the product $X \times Y$ of two metric spaces is complete, then X and Y are complete.

98. If E is an arbitrary set and F is a metric space, show that the subset $\mathscr{B}(E, F)$ of $\mathscr{F}(E, F)$ consisting of the bounded mappings of E into F is both open and closed in $\mathscr{F}(E, F)$.

99. Show that the subspace F' of $\mathscr{F}(E, F)$ consisting of the constant mappings of E into F is closed in $\mathscr{F}(E, F)$ and isometric to F.

100. Show that for every set E, the mapping $u \rightarrow \sup u(x)$ of $\mathscr{B}(E, \mathbf{R})$ into $\bar{\mathbf{R}}$ is continuous.

101. Let E be a compact metric space, and F a metric space with a countable base. Show that $\mathscr{C}(E, F)$ is a space with a countable base.

The following three problems lead to the basic results
of the theory of *category*.

*__102.__ Let E be a complete metric space, and let (G_n) be a sequence of open sets in E, each of which is everywhere dense on E $(\overline{G_n} = E)$.

  (a) Show that the set $G = \bigcap G_n$ is also the intersection of a *decreasing* sequence of open everywhere dense subsets of E.

  (b) Deduce from this that G is nonempty, and more precisely that G is everywhere dense on E.

103. Let E be a complete metric space. Deduce from Problem 102 that it is not possible to have

$$E = \bigcup_n A_n , \quad \text{where each } A_n \text{ is nondense on E.}$$

104. Let E be a complete metric space. Deduce from Problem 103 that if

$$E = \bigcup_n A_n ,$$

where each A_n is closed, then there exists at least one A_n whose interior $\overset{\circ}{A}_n$ is nonempty, and more precisely that the open set $G = \bigcup \overset{\circ}{A}_n$ is everywhere dense on E.

105. For every rational number $x \in [0, 1)$, we put $x = p/q$, where p and q are mutually prime integers. Let n be an integer $\geqslant 3$ and let $i(x)$ be the open interval of $\mathbf{R}$ with center x and halflength $1/q^n$. Set

$$G_n = \bigcup_x i(x).$$

  (a) Show that for every n, the sum l_n of the lengths of the $i(x)$ is finite and $l_n \rightarrow 0$.

  (b) Show that $G = \bigcap G_n$ contains other points beside the rationals. Give an example of such a point.

106. Let E be a countable set whose points are a_1, a_2, ... Put

$$d(a_p, a_p) = 0; \qquad d(a_p, a_q) = 10 + 1/p + 1/q \qquad \text{if } p \neq q.$$

(a) Show that d is a metric, and that E is complete in this metric.

(b) Let f be the mapping of E into E such that $f(a_p) = a_{p+1}$. Show that f is strictly distance decreasing and that yet f has no fixed point.

(c) By slightly modifying this example, construct a complete metric space F and a mapping f of F into itself which is strictly distance decreasing, and which has a fixed point a, and such that nevertheless $(f^{(n)}(x))$ does not tend to a for any $x \neq a$.

*107. Let E be the collection of arbitrary mappings of $[0, 1]$ into itself. For every $f_0 \in$ E, integer $n > 0$, points x_1, ..., x_n of $[0, 1]$ and $\epsilon > 0$, the set $V(f_0, \epsilon; x_1, ..., x_n)$ consisting of all f such that $|f(x_i) - f_0(x_i)| < \epsilon$ $(i = 1, ..., n)$ is called an *elementary set* with center f_0. Every union of elementary sets is called an "open" set in E.

(a) Verify that these "open" sets satisfy axioms O_1, O_2, O_3, O_4 and therefore define a topology on E.

(b) If we call every function f which is everywhere zero on $[0, 1]$ except at a finite number of points a *simple* function, show that the set of simple functions is everywhere dense on E.

(c) Show that a function which is nonzero for an uncountable infinity of values of x cannot be the limit in E of a *sequence* of simple functions.

(d) Deduce from this that one cannot define a metric on E for which the associated topology is that of E; in other words, E is not metrizable.

(e) Show that every simple function is the limit of a sequence of continuous functions; that the function g which equals 1 on the rationals and 0 everywhere else is the limit of a sequence of simple functions; that g, however, is not the limit of a sequence of continuous functions.

108. Let $\mathscr{F}$ be an equicontinuous family of (continuous) numerical functions on a metric space E, and let f be the upper envelope of the element of $\mathscr{F}$.

Show that if E is connected, then f is everywhere finite or everywhere $+\infty$; show that if f is finite, it is uniformly continuous.

109. Let f be a uniformly continuous numerical function on **R**. Put

$$f_a(x) = f(x - a).$$

Show that the set of functions f_a is equicontinuous on **R**. Deduce from this that on every compact set K in **R**, the set of oscillations of the f_a is bounded from above.

110. Let A be a nonempty subset of a metric space E and let f be a mapping of A into **R** which is of Lipschitz class with ratio k. For every $x \in$ E and every $y \in$ A we put

$$f_y(x) = f(y) + k\, d(x, y).$$

Show that g, defined by

$$g(x) = \inf_{y \in A} f_y(x),$$

is finite for every x, and of Lipschitz class with ratio k, and that its restriction to A is identical with f.

111. Let E be a compact metric space, and let J be a compact subset of the space $\mathscr{C}$ of continuous numerical functions on E, taken with the metric of uniform convergence. Show that for every $\epsilon > 0$ there exists a constant $k > 0$ with the following properties:

For every $\alpha \in$ J, there exists $\beta \in \mathscr{C}$ such that $\| \alpha - \beta \| \leqslant \epsilon$, with β of Lipschitz class with ratio k. (Apply the preceding problem, taking for A a suitable finite subset of E.)

*112. Let f be a continuous numerical function of bounded variation on $[0, 1]$ and let $g(x)$ be the total variation of f on $[0, x]$.

Show that the graphs of f and g (in Cartesian coordinates) have the same length.

Show that the surfaces of revolution about the y axis generated by these graphs have the same area, and more precisely are "isometric" (by a homeomorphism preserving the lengths of curves).

113. Let

$$f(x) = \sum_n 2^{-n} \sin(10^n x);$$

show that the total variation of f on every interval of **R** is infinite.

DEFINITIONS AND AXIOMS

Axioms of topological spaces

O_1 : The empty set and the entire space are open sets.
O_2 : Every *finite* intersection of open sets is an open set.
O_3 : Every union of open sets is an open set.

The complement of an open set is called a *closed* set.

Properties of closed sets

F_1 : The entire space and the empty set are closed sets.
F_2 : Every *finite* union of closed sets is a closed set.
F_3 : Every intersection of closed sets is a closed set.

Every subset of a space E which contains an open set containing a given point x is called a *neighborhood* of x.

Separated space. A space E is said to be *separated* if it satisfies the following axiom:

O_4 : Any two distinct points of E have disjoint neighborhoods.

Product of spaces. If E_1, E_2 are topological spaces, the topological product space $E = E_1 \times E_2$ is the space obtained by taking, as the open subsets of the set $E_1 \times E_2$, all unions of elementary sets $\omega_1 \times \omega_2$, where ω_i is an open set in E_i ($i = 1, 2$).

Compact space. A space E is said to be *compact* if it is separated and moreover satisfies the axiom for open coverings:

O_5 : Every open covering of E has a finite subcovering.

Connected space. A space E is said to be connected if E and Ø are the only subsets which are both open and closed sets in E.

Topological group, ring and field. A *topological group* is a group with a topology for which the functions (x^{-1}) and (xy) are continuous.

A *topological ring* is a ring with a topology for which the functions $(-x)$, $(x + y)$, (xy) are continuous.

A *topological field*: Same conditions as for rings, with in addition the continuity of x^{-1} for all $x \neq 0$.

METRIC SPACES.   A *metric* space is a set E with which there is associated a *metric* $(d(x, y))$, that is, a numerical function defined on E^2 such that:

M_1 : $d(x, y) > 0$ if $x \neq y$; $d(x, x) = 0$.
M_2 : $d(x, y) = d(y, x)$ (symmetry).
M_3 : $d(x, y) \leqslant d(x, z) + d(z, y)$ (triangle inequality).

A metric space E is said to be *complete* if every Cauchy sequence in E is convergent.

TRACE, INJECTION, SURJECTION, BIJECTION.   The *trace* of a subset A (a family $\mathscr{F}$ of subsets) of a space E on a subset B of E is the set $A \cap B$ (the family of sets $F \cap B$, $F \in \mathscr{F}$).

A mapping $f : X \to Y$ is called an *injection* if x_1 , $x_2 \in X$, $x_1 \neq x_2$, implies $f(x_1) \neq f(x_2)$, a *surjection* if $f(X) = Y$, and a *bijection* if it is both an injection and a surjection.

REVIEW OF SOME CLASSICAL NOTATION

The symbols **N**, **Z**, **Q**, **R**, **C** denote,respectively, the set $\{0, 1, 2, ...\}$ of natural integers, the set of integers of arbitrary sign, the set of rational numbers, the set of real numbers, the set of complex numbers.

The symbols **Q**$_+$, **R**$_+$ denote the set of element $\geqslant 0$ of **Q** and **R**, respectively.

The symbols **N***, **Z***, **Q***, **R***, **C*** denote, respectively, **N**, **Z**, **Q**, **R**, **C** with their element 0 deleted.

Finally, **R̄** denotes the set $[-\infty, +\infty]$ obtained from **R** by adjoining two points at infinity.

BIBLIOGRAPHY

BOURBAKI, N., *Topologie générale*, Chapters I, III, IV, IX (Actualités scientifiques et industrielles). Hermann, Paris.

DIEUDONNÉ, J. *Foundations of Modern Analysis*. Academic Press, New York, 1960.

FRANKLIN, P., *A Treatise on Advanced Calculus*. Wiley, New York, 1940.

GAAL, S. A., *Point Set Topology*, Academic Press, New York, 1964.

KELLEY, J. L., *General Topology*. Van Nostrand, Princeton, New Jersey, 1955.

KURATOWSKI, C., *Topologie*, Vol. I, 4th ed. 1958; Vol. II, 2nd ed., 1952, Warsaw.

NEWMAN, M. H. A., *Elements of Topology of Plane Sets of Points*. Cambridge Univ. Press, London and New York, 1939.

SIERPINSKI, W., *General Topology*. Univ. of Toronto Press, Toronto, 1952.

WHYBURN, G. T., *Analytic Topology*. A.M.S. Colloquium Publ. 28, New York, 1942.

CHAPTER II

Numerical Functions

By a *numerical* function on a set E we shall mean a mapping of E into the extended line $\bar{\mathbf{R}} = [-\infty, +\infty]$; the mappings into $\mathbf{R}$ will be called *finite* numerical functions, or simply numerical functions when it is clear from the context that they are finite.

In this chapter we shall study the special properties of numerical functions which result from the fact that $\mathbf{R}$ is a field and an ordered set; in particular we shall study certain classes of mappings of an interval of $\mathbf{R}$ into $\mathbf{R}$.

I. NUMERICAL FUNCTIONS DEFINED ON AN ARBITRARY SET

1. ORDER RELATION ON $\mathscr{F}(E, \mathbf{R})$ AND ON $\mathscr{F}(E, \bar{\mathbf{R}})$

We shall denote by $\mathscr{F}(E, \bar{\mathbf{R}})$ (respectively, $\mathscr{F}(E, \mathbf{R})$) the set of numerical (respectively, finite numerical) functions on E.

The set $\mathscr{F}(E, \mathbf{R})$ can evidently be given an algebraic structure. It possesses an order structure as well which is compatible with its algebraic structure:

For every $f \in \mathscr{F}(E, \mathbf{R})$ we shall say that f is *positive*, and write $f \geqslant 0$, if $f(x) \geqslant 0$ for every $x \in E$.

It is immediate that if $f \geqslant 0$, $g \geqslant 0$, and if $\lambda \in \mathbf{R}_+$, then

$$f + g \geqslant 0, \qquad fg \geqslant 0, \qquad \text{and} \qquad \lambda f \geqslant 0.$$

More generally, for all $f, g \in \mathscr{F}(E, \mathbf{R})$ we put

$$f \leqslant g \qquad \text{if} \qquad g - f \geqslant 0$$

(which is equivalent to $f(x) \leqslant g(x)$ for every $x \in E$). It is immediate that the relation $\leqslant$ is an order relation on $\mathscr{F}(E, \mathbf{R})$ (a nontotal order if E contains more than one point); and one can verify that for all $f, g, h \in \mathscr{F}(E, \mathbf{R})$ and for every $\lambda \in \mathbf{R}_+$, the relation $f \leqslant g$ implies

$$f + h \leqslant g + h; \qquad \lambda f \leqslant \lambda g; \qquad fh \leqslant gh \qquad \text{if} \qquad h \geqslant 0.$$

Similarly, one can verify that the relation defined on $\mathscr{F}(E, \bar{\mathbf{R}})$ by

$$f \leqslant g \quad \text{if} \quad f(x) \leqslant g(x) \quad \text{for every} \quad x \in E$$

is an order relation. It is, however, well to note that the operations in $\mathscr{F}(E, \mathbf{R})$ do not extend to $\mathscr{F}(E, \bar{\mathbf{R}})$; in particular, this last set is not a vector space.

For every $f \in \mathscr{F}(E, \bar{\mathbf{R}})$ we denote by $|f|$ the function such that $|f|(x) = |f(x)|$ for every $x \in E$.

We evidently have the relation

$$-|f| \leqslant f \leqslant |f|.$$

REMARK. It should be noted that the relation $f \geqslant 0$ does not imply that either $f(x) = 0$ for every x, or $f(x) > 0$ for every x.

2. BOUNDS OF A NUMERICAL FUNCTION

We recall that $\bar{\mathbf{R}}$ is isomorphic (for the order relations) to $[0, 1]$; it follows that every nonempty subset of $\bar{\mathbf{R}}$ has a supremum and an infimum; we can therefore give the following definition:

2.1. Definition. FOR EVERY $f \in \mathscr{F}(E, \bar{\mathbf{R}})$ AND EVERY NONEMPTY SUBSET X OF E, THE *SUPREMUM* (*INFIMUM*) OF f ON X IS DEFINED AS THE SUPREMUM (INFIMUM) OF $f(X)$ IN $\bar{\mathbf{R}}$.

THESE ARE DENOTED BY $\sup_{x \in X} f(x)$ AND $\inf_{x \in X} f(x)$.

The properties of the supremum and infimum of a subset of $\bar{\mathbf{R}}$ imply, for example, that the number $a = \sup_{x \in X} f(x)$ is characterized by the following properties:

1.   For every $x \in X$ we have $f(x) \leqslant a$;

2.   For every $b < a$, there exists $x \in X$ such that $b < f(x)$.

When f is everywhere finite on X, the oscillation of f on X (see Chapter I, Section 15) is equal to

$$(\sup_{x \in X} f(x) - \inf_{x \in X} f(x)).$$

When f is not everywhere finite on X, this difference will by definition be the oscillation of f on X, at least when this difference is meaningful, that is, when $f(X)$ does not consist of the single point $+\infty$ or $-\infty$.

2.2. Definition. WE SHALL SAY THAT f IS *BOUNDED FROM ABOVE* (*BELOW*) ON X WHEN ITS SUPREMUM (INFIMUM) ON X IS $< +\infty$ ($> -\infty$).

WE SHALL SAY THAT f IS *BOUNDED* ON X IF IT IS BOUNDED FROM ABOVE AND FROM BELOW.

It is immediate that $\inf_{x\in X} f(x) = -\sup_{x\in X} (-f(x))$; this relation often makes it possible to restrict oneself to the study of the supremum.

Z To say that f is bounded on X is equivalent to saying that there exist a, $b \in \mathbf{R}$ such that $a \leqslant f(x) \leqslant b$ for every $x \in X$. Thus if f is bounded on X, it is finite on X; on the other hand, f can be finite on X without being bounded:

This is the case for the mapping $x \to x^2$ of $\mathbf{R}$ into $\mathbf{R}$.

2.3. Proposition.   *Let* (f_i) *be a finite family of elements of* $\mathscr{F}(E, \mathbf{R})$; *then*

$$\sup_{x\in X} \sum_i f_i(x) \leqslant \sum_i \sup_{x\in X} f_i(x),$$

and if the f_i *are* $\geqslant 0$, *then*

$$\sup_{x\in X} \prod_i f_i(x) \leqslant \prod_i \sup_{x\in X} f_i(x).$$

We shall, for example, prove the first relation; we have

$$f_i(x) \leqslant \sup_{x\in X} f_i(x), \qquad \text{whence} \qquad \sum_i f_i(x) \leqslant \sum_i \sup_{x\in X} f_i(x),$$

which gives the desired relation.

3. UPPER AND LOWER ENVELOPES OF A FAMILY OF FUNCTIONS

Let $(f_i)_{i\in I}$ be a family of numerical functions on a set E. In order that a numerical function g be an upper bound for this family, it is necessary and sufficient that $f_i(x) \leqslant g(x)$ for every $x \in E$ and every $i \in I$. Among these functions g there thus exists one which is smaller than all the others, namely the function f defined by $f(x) = \sup_{i\in I} f_i(x)$; in other words, the ordered set $\mathscr{F}(E, \bar{\mathbf{R}})$ is a complete lattice.

3.1. Definition.   THE *UPPER ENVELOPE* OF THE FAMILY OF FUNCTIONS $(f_i)_{i\in I}$, WHICH IS DENOTED BY $\sup_{i\in I} f_i$, IS DEFINED AS THE FUNCTION f SUCH THAT
$$f(x) = \sup_{i\in I} f_i(x) \qquad \text{for every} \quad x \in E.$$

THE LOWER ENVELOPE $\inf_{i\in I} f_i$ IS DEFINED SIMILARLY.

REMARK. One should note the similarity of the notations for the supremum of a function and the upper envelope of a family of functions; this similarity is in no way fortuitous, for the two formulas represent the supremum of a subset of a complete lattice, namely $\bar{\mathbf{R}}$ in the first case, and $\mathscr{F}(\mathrm{E}, \bar{\mathbf{R}})$ in the second.

EXAMPLE 1. Let f_n be the mapping $x \to \sin 2\pi n x$ of $\mathbf{R}$ into $\mathbf{R}$; the upper envelope of the family $(f_n)_{n \in \mathbf{Z}}$ is a function f such that $f(x) = 1$ if x is irrational or equal to an irreducible fraction of the form $p/4q$, and $f(x) \neq 1$ everywhere else.

EXAMPLE 2. Let φ_A be the characteristic function of a closed set $\mathrm{A} \subset \mathbf{R}$. This function is the lower envelope of the continuous functions which are everywhere $\geqslant \varphi_\mathrm{A}$.

3.2. GEOMETRIC INTERPRETATION. For every $f \in \mathscr{F}(\mathrm{E}, \bar{\mathbf{R}})$, let $\mathrm{A}(f)$ be the set of points of the product space $\mathrm{E} \times \bar{\mathbf{R}}$ which lie on or above the graph of f, in other words, the points (x, y) such that $y \geqslant f(x)$.

Specifying $\mathrm{A}(f)$ is equivalent to specifying f. It is immediate that for every family $(f_i)_{i \in \mathrm{I}}$ we have

$$\mathrm{A}(\sup_{i \in \mathrm{I}} f_i) = \bigcap_i \mathrm{A}(f_i).$$

Similarly, when I is finite,

$$\mathrm{A}(\inf_{i \in \mathrm{I}} f_i) = \bigcup_i \mathrm{A}(f_i).$$

When I is infinite, the left side of the last relation still contains the right side, but is not necessarily identical with it.

UPPER ENVELOPE IN $\mathscr{F}(\mathrm{E}, \mathbf{R})$. UNIFORMLY BOUNDED FAMILIES. (a) If $(f_i)_{i \in \mathrm{I}}$ is a finite family of finite numerical functions, its upper envelope is again finite; but if I is infinite, its upper envelope need not be finite; in order that it be finite, it is necessary and sufficient that for every x the family of numbers $(f_i(x))_{i \in \mathrm{I}}$ be bounded from above.

(b) If $(f_i)_{i \in \mathrm{I}}$ is a family of numerical functions, each of which is bounded from above, this does not imply that $\sup_{i \in \mathrm{I}} f_i$ is bounded from above.

For example, the family (f_n) of constant mappings $x \to n$ of an arbitrary E into $\mathbf{R}$ consists of bounded functions, but its upper envelope is not bounded from above.

When $\sup_{i \in \mathrm{I}} f_i$ is bounded from above, one says that the family $(f_i)_{i \in \mathrm{I}}$

is *uniformly bounded from above*; this amounts to saying that there exists a finite number λ such $f_i(x) \leqslant \lambda$ for every $i \in I$ and every $x \in E$.

Families *uniformly bounded from below* are defined similarly. A family which is uniformly bounded from above and from below is said to be *uniformly bounded*.

DEFINITION OF f^+ AND f^-. For every numerical function f, we put $f^+ = \sup(f, 0)$. In other words, f^+ is defined by the relation

$$f^+(x) = (f(x))^+ \qquad \text{for every} \quad x \in E.$$

Similarly, we put

$$f^- = \sup(-f, 0) = (-f)^+.$$

It should be observed that we always have $f^+ \geqslant 0$ and $f^- \geqslant 0$.

It follows from the relations for real numbers

$$a = a^+ - a^-; \qquad |a| = a^+ + a^-,$$

that

$$f = f^+ - f^-; \qquad |f| = f^+ + f^-.$$

Hence

$$f^+ = \tfrac{1}{2}(|f| + f); \qquad f^- = \tfrac{1}{2}(|f| - f).$$

More generally, we have

$$\sup(f, g) = \tfrac{1}{2}[(f + g) + |f - g|]; \qquad \inf(f, g) = \tfrac{1}{2}[(f + g) - |f - g|].$$

It follows at once that

$$\sup(f, g) + \inf(f, g) = f + g.$$

II. LIMIT NOTIONS ASSOCIATED WITH NUMERICAL FUNCTIONS

With every $f \in \mathscr{F}(E, \bar{\mathbf{R}})$ and with every $x \in E$ there is associated the element $f(x)$ of $\bar{\mathbf{R}}$. Since $\bar{\mathbf{R}}$ is a topological space, with every sequence of elements of E or of $\mathscr{F}(E, \bar{\mathbf{R}})$ or, more generally, with every filter base on E or on $\mathscr{F}(E, \bar{\mathbf{R}})$ we shall therefore be able to associate limit elements.

We will first examine the notions associated with a filter base on E, and then those associated with a filter base on $\mathscr{F}(E, \bar{\mathbf{R}})$.

4. LIMITS SUPERIOR AND INFERIOR OF A FUNCTION ALONG A FILTER BASE ON E

Let f be a numerical function on E, and let $\mathscr{B}$ be a filter base on E. We have defined (in Chapter I, Section 8) the adherence of f along $\mathscr{B}$ as the set

$$\tilde{f}(\mathscr{B}) = \bigcap_{B \in \mathscr{B}} \overline{f(B)}.$$

Since the family of sets $\overline{f(B)}$ has the finite intersection property (Chapter I, Section 11), and since $\mathbf{\bar{R}}$ is compact, $\tilde{f}(\mathscr{B})$ is nonempty. Since, besides, every nonempty subset of $\mathbf{\bar{R}}$ has a supremum, we can establish the following definition:

4.1. Definition. THE *LIMIT SUPERIOR* OF f ALONG THE FILTER BASE $\mathscr{B}$ IS DEFINED AS THE SUPREMUM OF THE SET $\tilde{f}(\mathscr{B})$. IT IS DENOTED BY

$$\varlimsup_{\mathscr{B}} f \qquad \text{or} \qquad \lim_{\mathscr{B}} \sup f.$$

THE LIMIT INFERIOR IS DEFINED SIMILARLY.

SPECIAL CASES. 1. Let (x_n) be a sequence of points of E; the sets $B_n = \{x_i : i \geqslant n\}$ form a filter base $\mathscr{B}$ on E. The limit superior of f along $\mathscr{B}$ is also called the limit superior of the sequence $(f(x_n))$.

2. Suppose E has a topology; let A be a nonempty subset of E, and let $a \in \bar{A}$. Let $\mathscr{B}$ denote the collection of subsets of E of the form $A \cap V$, where V is a neighborhood of a; since $a \in \bar{A}$, it is clear that $\mathscr{B}$ is a filter base.

In this case, $\lim \sup_{\mathscr{B}} f$ is denoted by $\lim \sup_{x \to a, x \in A} f(x)$. For example, if $E = [\alpha, \beta] \subset \mathbf{R}$ and if $A = (a, \beta]$, then $\lim \sup_{\mathscr{B}} f$ is called the limit superior of f from the right at the point a.

3. Suppose that E is an ordered set which is directed in the increasing direction, that is, every finite subset of E has an upper bound, and suppose that f is an increasing mapping of E into $\mathbf{\bar{R}}$.

If $\mathscr{B}$ denotes the collection of subsets of E of the form $\{x : x \geqslant a\}_{a \in E}$, one can verify that $\mathscr{B}$ is a filter base and that

$$\varlimsup_{\mathscr{B}} f = \lim_{\mathscr{B}} \sup f = \sup_{x \in E} f(x).$$

IMMEDIATE PROPERTIES. 1. The limit superior of f along $\mathscr{B}$ belongs to the adherence of f along $\mathscr{B}$.

2. $\lim \inf_{\mathscr{B}} f = -\lim \sup_{\mathscr{B}} (-f)$.

4.2. Lemma.   *Let f be a mapping of a set* E *into a compact space* X; *let $\mathscr{B}$ be a filter base on* E, *and let $\tilde{f}(\mathscr{B})$ be the adherence of f along $\mathscr{B}$.*
   Then for every open set ω in X *such that $\tilde{f}(\mathscr{B}) \subset \omega$, there exists* $B \in \mathscr{B}$ *such that $\overline{f(B)} \subset \omega$.*

Indeed, the traces of the closed sets $\overline{f(B)}$ on the compact set $\complement\,\omega$ have intersection $\tilde{f}(\mathscr{B}) \cap \complement\,\omega = \varnothing$; therefore there exists a finite family $(\overline{f(B_i)})$ of these closed sets whose intersection does not meet $\complement\,\omega$. But there exists $B \in \mathscr{B}$ contained in $\bigcap B_i$; this is the desired B.

4.3. Proposition.   *If f is a numerical function on* E, *to say that f converges to a along a filter base $\mathscr{B}$ is equivalent to saying that*

$$a = \lim_{\mathscr{B}}\sup f = \lim_{\mathscr{B}}\inf f, \quad \text{or that} \quad \{a\} = \tilde{f}(\mathscr{B}).$$

Indeed, if $a = \lim_{\mathscr{B}} f$, then every closed neighborhood V of a in $\bar{\mathbf{R}}$ contains a set $f(B)$, therefore also $\overline{f(B)}$; hence $\tilde{f}(\mathscr{B}) \subset V$. It follows that $\tilde{f}(\mathscr{B}) = \{a\}$.
   Conversely, if $\{a\} = \tilde{f}(\mathscr{B})$, for every neighborhood V of a there exists by Lemma 4.2 a $B \in \mathscr{B}$ such that $\overline{f(B)} \subset V$; thus f converges to a along $\mathscr{B}$.

4.4. Definition.   LET f BE A MAPPING OF A TOPOLOGICAL SPACE E INTO $\mathbf{R}$. FOR EVERY $a \in$ E, THE *OSCILLATION* OF f AT THE POINT a IS DEFINED AS THE NUMBER

$$\omega(f, a) = \lim_{x \to a}\sup f(x) - \lim_{x \to a}\inf f(x).$$

This difference is always meaningful, since the set of adherent values of f at a always contains $f(a)$, which is finite.

4.5. Proposition.   *Let $f \in \mathscr{F}(E, \mathbf{R})$, where* E *is a topological space. To say that f is continuous at a is equivalent to saying that the oscillation of f at a is zero.*

This is an immediate consequence of Proposition 4.3.

4.6. Proposition.   *Let $f, g \in \mathscr{F}(E, \bar{\mathbf{R}})$ with $f \leqslant g$, and let $\mathscr{B}$ be a filter base on* E; *then*

$$\lim_{\mathscr{B}}\sup f \leqslant \lim_{\mathscr{B}}\sup g; \quad \lim_{\mathscr{B}}\inf f \leqslant \lim_{\mathscr{B}}\inf g.$$

Indeed, denote the members of the first inequality by α and β, respectively.

If $\beta = +\infty$, the first relation is satisfied. If $\beta < +\infty$, Lemma 4.2 shows that for every k such that $\beta < k$, there exists $\mathrm{B} \in \mathscr{B}$ such that $g(\mathrm{B}) < k$, hence $f(\mathrm{B}) < k$ and so $\overline{f(\mathrm{B})} \leqslant k$; therefore $\alpha \leqslant k$. Since this relation holds for all $k > \beta$, we have $\alpha \leqslant \beta$.

The second inequality is deduced from the first by replacing f by $-g$ and g by $-f$.

4.7. Corollary. *If $f \leqslant g$ and if f and g have the respective limits α and β along $\mathscr{B}$, then $\alpha \leqslant \beta$.*

Z The compactness of X is essential for the validity of Lemma 4.2; also, the consequences of this lemma which we have obtained for $\overline{\mathbf{R}}$ do not extend to $\mathbf{R}$.

For example, the finite numerical function g defined on $\mathbf{R}$ by

$$g(x) = 1/x \quad \text{if} \quad x > 0; \qquad g(x) = 0 \quad \text{if} \quad x \leqslant 0$$

has only the point 0 as an adherent value in $\mathbf{R}$ at $x = 0$, although it is not continuous at 0.

Similarly, if we denote by f the lower envelope of g and 1, then $f \leqslant g$, and yet the adherent values in $\mathbf{R}$ of f and g at the point $x = 0$ are, respectively, $\{0, 1\}$ and $\{0\}$.

5. LIMITS SUPERIOR AND INFERIOR OF A FAMILY OF FUNCTIONS

Let $(f_i))_{i \in \mathrm{I}}$ be a family of elements of $\mathscr{F}(\mathrm{E}, \overline{\mathbf{R}})$ and let $\mathscr{B}$ be a filter base on I.

For every $x \in \mathrm{E}$, the mapping $\varphi_x : i \to f_i(x)$ of I into $\overline{\mathbf{R}}$ has an adherence $\overline{\varphi_x}(\mathscr{B})$ along $\mathscr{B}$.

Every mapping f of E into $\overline{\mathbf{R}}$ such that $f(x) \in \overline{\varphi_x}(\mathscr{B})$ for every $x \in \mathrm{E}$ is called an adherent point of the family (f_i) along $\mathscr{B}$.

The set of these adherent points contains its infimum and supremum, which are simply the mappings

$$x \to \lim_{\mathscr{B}} \inf f_i(x) \qquad \text{and} \qquad x \to \lim_{\mathscr{B}} \sup f_i(x).$$

We will denote them by

$$\lim_{\mathscr{B}} \inf(f_i) \qquad \text{and} \qquad \lim_{\mathscr{B}} \sup(f_i).$$

5.1. Proposition. *Let $(f_i)_{i \in \mathrm{I}}$ and $(g_i)_{i \in \mathrm{I}}$ be two families of elements of $\mathscr{F}(\mathrm{E}, \overline{\mathbf{R}})$, and let $\mathscr{B}$ be a filter base on I.*

If $f_i \leqslant g_i$ for every $i \in I$, then we also have

$$\lim_{\mathscr{B}} \sup(f_i) \leqslant \lim_{\mathscr{B}} \sup(g_i); \qquad \lim_{\mathscr{B}} \inf(f_i) \leqslant \lim_{\mathscr{B}} \inf(g_i).$$

Indeed, for every $x \in E$, Proposition 4.6 applied to φ_x shows, for example, that

$$\lim_{\mathscr{B}} \sup f_i(x) \leqslant \lim_{\mathscr{B}} \sup g_i(x).$$

Z If $f_i < g_i$ for every i, that is, $f_i(x) < g_i(x)$ for every i and every x, the strict inequality does not pass to the limit, that is, one does not in general have

$$\lim_{\mathscr{B}} \sup(f_i) < \lim_{\mathscr{B}} \sup(g_i).$$

6. OPERATIONS ON CONTINUOUS FUNCTIONS

6.1. Proposition. *Let* E *be a topological space and let* $a \in E$. *The subset* A *of* $\mathscr{F}(E, \mathbf{R})$ *consisting of the functions which are continuous at* a *is a subalgebra of* $\mathscr{F}(E, \mathbf{R})$ *which is a lattice.*

Indeed, the continuity of addition and multiplication on $\mathbf{R}$ implies that if f and g are continuous at a, the same is true of $f + g$, fg, and of λf for every scalar λ. On the other hand, the mapping $\varphi : u \to |u|$ of $\mathbf{R}$ into $\mathbf{R}$ is continuous; thus $|f| = \varphi \circ f$ is in A for every $f \in A$. More generally, then, the relation

$$\sup(f, g) = \tfrac{1}{2}[(f + g) + |f - g|]$$

shows that if $f, g \in A$, then $\sup(f, g) \in A$. This conclusion evidently extends to the upper and lower envelopes of every finite family of elements of A.

6.2. Proposition. *Let* E *be a metric space, and let* U *(respectively,* L*) be the subset of* $\mathscr{F}(E, \mathbf{R})$ *consisting of the functions which are uniformly continuous (respectively, of Lipschitz class) on* E.
Then U *and* L *are lattices and vector subspaces of* $\mathscr{F}(E, \mathbf{R})$.

The proof goes through like that of the preceding proposition, upon observing that the mappings $(u, v) \to u + v$ of $\mathbf{R}^2$ into $\mathbf{R}$ and $u \to |u|$ of $\mathbf{R}$ into $\mathbf{R}$ are of Lipschitz class and therefore uniformly continuous.

Z It is not true that U and L are closed under multiplication. For example, the numerical function $x \to x$ belongs to U and L, but its square $x \to x^2$ belongs to neither one.

6.3. Proposition. *Let* $(f_i)_{i \in I}$ *be an arbitrary family of elements of* $\mathscr{F}(E, \mathbf{R})$ *and let f be its upper envelope.*

If each f_i *is of Lipschitz class with ratio k, and if f is finite at one point at least, then f is everywhere finite, and is of Lipschitz class with ratio k.*

Indeed, for all $x, y \in E$ we have by hypothesis

$$f_i(y) \leqslant k\, d(x, y) + f_i(x),$$

hence

$$f(y) \leqslant k\, d(x, y) + f(x).$$

Therefore if $f(x) < \infty$, then also $f(y) < \infty$, hence $f(y)$ is finite. We can therefore write, for all $x, y \in E$,

$$f(y) - f(x) \leqslant k\, d(x, y) \quad \text{and similarly} \quad f(x) - f(y) \leqslant k\, d(x)\, y).$$

Therefore f is of Lipschitz class with ratio k.

Clearly a similar assertion holds for the lower envelope.

EXAMPLE. Let E be a metric space, and let $A \subset E$.

For every $x \in E$ we put

$$f(x) = \sup_{a \in A} d(x, a); \qquad g(x) = \inf_{a \in A} d(x, a).$$

Each of the functions $x \to d(x, a)$ is of Lipschitz class with ratio 1; therefore g is of Lipschitz class with ratio 1, and if f is finite at one point (which is equivalent to saying that A is bounded), then f is finite everywhere, and is of Lipschitz class with ratio 1.

Z It is false that an upper or lower envelope of uniformly continuous functions is uniformly continuous. It need not be even continuous; for example, the family of functions $1/(1 + x^2)^n$ on $[0, 1]$ has a discontinuous lower envelope. To obtain an assertion of this kind, it would be necessary to assume that the family (f_i) have an additional property, for example, that it be equicontinuous.

We shall see in the following section that the upper or lower envelopes of families of continuous functions, while not being necessarily continuous, still have striking properties.

III. SEMICONTINUOUS NUMERICAL FUNCTIONS

Let f be a numerical function defined on a topological space E. To say that f is continuous at $x_0 \in E$ is equivalent to saying that each of the following conditions holds:

1. For every $\lambda < f(x_0)$ there exists a neighborhood V of x_0 such that $\lambda < f(V)$.

2. For every $\lambda > f(x_0)$ there exists a neighborhood V of x_0 such that $\lambda > f(V)$.

When only one of these conditions is retained, one is led to the notion of semicontinuity.

7. SEMICONTINUITY AT A POINT

7.1. Definition. LET E BE A TOPOLOGICAL SPACE, AND LET $f \in \mathscr{F}(E, \bar{\mathbf{R}})$. WE SHALL SAY THAT f IS *LOWER* SEMICONTINUOUS AT THE POINT $a \in E$ IF, FOR EVERY $\lambda < f(a)$, THERE EXISTS A NEIGHBORHOOD V OF a SUCH THAT $\lambda < f(V)$.

WHEN THIS CONDITION HOLDS AT EVERY POINT $a \in E$, THEN f IS SAID TO BE LOWER SEMICONTINUOUS ON E.

THE DEFINITION OF UPPER SEMICONTINUITY IS OBTAINED BY REVERSING THE DIRECTION OF THE INEQUALITIES.

It is immediate that the lower semicontinuity of f at a is equivalent to the upper semicontinuity of $-f$ at the same point. This remark will permit us to formulate most of our results for lower semicontinuous functions only.

EXAMPLE 1. Let f_n be the mapping of **R** into **R** such that $f(0) = 0$ and $f(x) = x^{-n}$ for $x \neq 0$.

For every even integer n, f_n is lower semicontinuous at the point 0.

For every odd integer n, f_n is neither lower nor upper semicontinuous at the point 0.

EXAMPLE 2. Let f be the mapping of **R** into **R** such that $f(x) = 0$ if x is rational, and $f(x) = 1$ if x is irrational.

The function f is lower semicontinuous at every rational point, and upper semicontinuous at every irrational point.

7.2. Proposition. *To say that f is lower semicontinuous at a is equivalent to saying that*

$$f(a) = \liminf_{x \to a} f(x).$$

PROOF. (a) Suppose that f is lower semicontinuous at a, and let $\lambda < f(a)$. Then there exists a neighborhood V of a such that $\lambda < f(V)$; therefore

$$\lambda \leqslant \overline{f(V)}, \qquad \text{from which} \qquad \lambda \leqslant \liminf_{x \to a} f(x).$$

Since this relation holds for all $\lambda < f(a)$, we also have

$$f(a) \leqslant \lim_{x \to a} \inf f(x).$$

But the reverse inequality is true, since $f(a) \in f(V)$ for every V, which implies the desired equality.

(b)   Conversely, suppose $f(a) = \lim \inf_{x \to a} f(x)$. For every $\lambda < f(a)$ there exists, by Lemma 4.2, a neighborhood V of a such that $\lambda < f(V)$; that is, f is lower semicontinuous at a.

7.3. Proposition.   *The set $\mathscr{I}(a)$ of functions which are lower semicontinuous at a and $> -\infty$ is closed under addition.*

Indeed, let $f, g \in \mathscr{I}(a)$, and let $\lambda < f(a) + g(a)$. We can write $\lambda = \alpha + \beta$, where $\alpha < f(a)$ and $\beta < g(a)$. Then there exists a neighborhood U of a such that $\alpha < f(U)$, and a neighborhood V of a such that $\beta < g(V)$. Therefore

$$\lambda = \alpha + \beta < (f + g)(x) \qquad \text{for all} \qquad x \in U \cap V.$$

This proves that $f + g \in \mathscr{I}(a)$.

7.4. Corollary.   *The subset of $\mathscr{F}(E, \mathbf{R})$ consisting of the functions which are lower semicontinuous at a is a convex cone.*

We are going to break off the study of semicontinuity at a point in order to study the much more interesting case of semicontinuity on the entire space.

8. FUNCTIONS, LOWER SEMICONTINUOUS ON THE ENTIRE SPACE

In order that a mapping f of a space E into a space F be continuous in E, it is necessary and sufficient that the inverse image of every closed set in F be a closed set in E. We shall see that there exists a similar characterization of semicontinuous functions.

8.1. Proposition.   *To say that a mapping f of a space E into $\overline{\mathbf{R}}$ is lower semicontinuous on E is equivalent to saying that for every $\lambda \in \overline{\mathbf{R}}$, the set of x such that $f(x) \leqslant \lambda$ is closed (or, what amounts to the same, that the set of x for which $\lambda < f(x)$ is open).*

Indeed, the lower semicontinuity of f at a point a is equivalent to the statement that, for every $\lambda < f(a)$, the set of x such that $\lambda < f(x)$ is a neighborhood of a; in other words, that for every λ the set of x such that $\lambda < f(x)$ is a neighborhood of each of its points, hence an open set.

8.2. Corollary.   *Let φ_A be the characteristic function of a subset A of E. Then the lower semicontinuity of φ_A is equivalent to the assertion that A is open.*

Indeed, the set of x such that $\lambda < \varphi_A(x)$ is either $\emptyset$, if $\lambda \geqslant 1$, or A if $\lambda < 1$.

Similarly, the upper semicontinuity of φ_A is equivalent to the assertion that A *is closed.*

Geometric interpretation of lower semicontinuity

In Section 3.2 we associated with every mapping f of a set E into $\bar{\mathbf{R}}$ a subset A(f) of the product space E $\times$ $\breve{\mathbf{R}}$.

We shall give a simple interpretation of lower semicontinuity by means of A(f) (see Fig. 6).

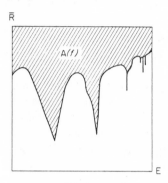

Fig. 6.

8.3. Proposition.   *To say that a mapping f of a topological space* E *into* $\bar{\mathbf{R}}$ *is lower semicontinuous is equivalent to saying that* A(f) *is closed in* E $\times$ $\bar{\mathbf{R}}$.

Proof.   The assertion that A(f) is closed is equivalent to the assertion that its complement is open, or again that the complement $\complement$A(f) is a neighborhood of each of its points.

To say that f is lower semicontinuous in E is equivalent to saying that for every pair (a, λ) such that $\lambda < f(a)$ (that is, for every $(a, \lambda) \in \complement$A($f$)) and for every μ satisfying $\lambda < \mu < f(a)$, we have $\mu < f(x)$ for every x in some neighborhood V of a. In other words, this is equivalent to saying that there exists a neighborhood of (a, λ) (namely V $\times [-\infty, \mu)$) contained in $\complement$A(f).

This proves the stated equivalence.

Operations on lower semicontinuous functions

Proposition 7.3 shows us that the class of lower semicontinuous functions is closed under addition; we are going to see that it is closed under other operations as well.

8.4. Proposition. *Let f be a lower semicontinuous mapping of a space* E *into an interval* $[\alpha, \beta]$ *of* $\bar{\mathbf{R}}$, *and let φ be an increasing and continuous mapping of* $[\alpha, \beta]$ *into* $\bar{\mathbf{R}}$. *Then the composition* $g = \varphi \circ f$ *is lower semicontinuous.*

This is a direct consequence of Proposition 8.1; indeed, for every λ, $\varphi^{-1}([-\infty, \lambda])$ is of the form $[\alpha, \mu]$, and $f^{-1}([\alpha, \mu])$ is closed since it is identical with $f^{-1}([-\infty, \mu])$. But this last set is simply $g^{-1}([-\infty, \lambda])$, which proves the proposition.

8.5. Corollary. *If f and g are > 0 and lower semicontinuous on* E, *so is fg.*

We apply Proposition 8.4, taking for φ successively a logarithm and an exponential:

Indeed, $\log f$ and $\log g$ are $> -\infty$ and lower semicontinuous; therefore $\log fg = \log f + \log g$ is lower semicontinuous, hence fg is also.

8.6. Theorem. *The upper envelope of every family* $(f_i)_{i \in I}$ *of numerical lower semicontinuous functions is lower semicontinuous.*

The lower envelope of every **finite** *family of numerical lower semicontinuous functions is lower semicontinuous.*

This is an immediate consequence of Proposition 8.3 and the formulas of Section 3.2.

Indeed, if each $A(f_i)$ is closed, then $\bigcap A(f_i)$ is closed, and therefore $\sup(f_i)$ is lower semicontinuous. Similarly if I is finite, $\bigcup A(f_i)$ is closed; therefore $\inf_i (f_i)$ is lower semicontinuous.

SPECIAL CASE. The upper envelope of every family of *continuous* functions is lower semicontinuous.

More particularly, if (f_n) is an increasing sequence of continuous numerical functions, its limit is identical with $\sup(f_n)$; therefore f is lower semicontinuous. The converse of this proposition is studied in Problems 9 and 10.

Similar results are obtained for upper semicontinuity by replacing the upper envelope by the lower envelope and vice versa.

Z Theorem 8.6 does not extend to the lower envelope of every infinite family of lower semicontinuous functions.

Indeed, let f be an *arbitrary* numerical function on E. Then f is the lower envelope of the functions f_a defined by

$$f_a(x) = +\infty \quad \text{for} \quad x \neq a; \qquad f_a(a) = f(a),$$

and it is immediate that each of the functions f_a is lower semicontinuous.

9. CONSTRUCTION OF LOWER SEMICONTINUOUS FUNCTIONS

Semicontinuous functions are at least as close to ordinary experience as continuous functions. An example will explain this. When we look at an opaque object, we see only one point of this object along every halfline issuing from the eye; the distance from this point to the eye is a function of the direction of the halfline; this function is not continuous, but lower semicontinuous, if we take the object under consideration to be a closed set.

This example, suitably generalized, is incidentally capable of giving the most general semicontinuous functions.

Indeed, with E a topological space, let A be a closed subset of the product space $E \times \bar{\mathbf{R}}$. For every $x \in E$ let $f_A(x)$ be the infimum of the ordinates of the points of A having abscissa x (or $+\infty$ if there is no such point).

It is easily shown that the function f_A thus defined is lower semicontinuous. Conversely, by Proposition 8.3 every lower semicontinuous function on E can be obtained in this way.

EXAMPLE.   Let g be an arbitrary mapping of a topological space E into $\bar{\mathbf{R}}$, and let Γ be the graph of g. The set $\bar{\Gamma}$ is a closed subset of $E \times \bar{\mathbf{R}}$. The function f_Γ associated with $\bar{\Gamma}$ by the above procedure is lower semicontinuous; one can easily verify that

$$f_\Gamma(x) = \lim_{t \to x} \inf g(t)$$

for every $x \in E$. Similarly, the function $\lim \sup_{t \to x} g(t)$ is upper semicontinuous. Their difference $\omega(f; x)$ is therefore upper semicontinuous.

10. SEMICONTINUOUS FUNCTIONS ON A COMPACT SPACE

10.1. Theorem.   *For every lower semicontinuous mapping f of a compact space E into $\bar{\mathbf{R}}$, there exists at least one point a of E such that*

$$f(a) = \inf_{x \in E} f(x).$$

Indeed, let us put $m = \inf_{x \in E} f(x)$.

For every $\lambda > m$ the set E_λ of x such that $f(x) \leqslant \lambda$ is closed and nonempty. On the other hand, the family of sets E_λ is totally ordered by inclusion, as E_λ is an increasing function of λ; therefore (Chapter I, Proposition 11.4) the intersection of the E_λ is nonempty. At every point a of this intersection we have $f(a) \leqslant \lambda$ for every $\lambda > m$; hence $f(a) \leqslant m$.

Since on the other hand $f \geqslant m$ by the definition of m, we have $f(a) = m$.

10.2. **Corollary.** *Every lower semicontinuous mapping f of a compact space* E *into* $(-\infty, +\infty]$ *is bounded from below on* E.

Indeed, we then have $m = f(a) > -\infty$, and therefore $f \geqslant f(a) > -\infty$. Analogous results hold for upper semicontinuous functions.

If we apply these results to a continuous function, we obtain an earlier result stating that a continuous function on a compact space attains its infimum and supremum on the space.

We are now going to study an important application of these results to the calculus of variations.

11. SEMICONTINUITY OF LENGTH

The length of a curve is a function of the curve; when the curve varies continuously, in a sense which we shall make precise, one might expect that its length also varies continuously. This is not so, as the following elementary example shows:

Let C_n be the plane curve with equation $y = n^{-1} \sin nx$, where $0 \leqslant x \leqslant \pi$ and $n \in \mathbf{N}^*$ (in Cartesian coordinates).

It is immediate that all these curves have the same length and that this length is a number $l > \pi$. But as $n \to +\infty$, these curves converge uniformly to the segment $[0, \pi]$. Therefore uniform convergence does not imply the convergence of the lengths.

This example can be modified to go through with any number $l \geqslant \pi$. But it is noteworthy that one cannot take $l < \pi$.

In other words, the limit inferior of the lengths of the curves which converge to the segment $[0, \pi]$ is equal to π. This is nothing more than lower semicontinuity, which we shall now make precise.

The space of parametrized curves

Let T be a compact interval of **R** and let E be a metric space. By an earlier definition (Chapter I, Section 24) every continuous mapping f of T into E defines a parametrized curve. Therefore the set $\mathscr{C}(T, E)$ of continuous mappings of T into E can be regarded as the set of parametrized curves in E defined on T.

We shall take as the topology on $\mathscr{C}(T, E)$ the topology associated with the metric of uniform convergence, defined by

$$d(f, g) = \sup_{t \in T} d(f(t), g(t)).$$

For every $f \in \mathscr{C}(\mathrm{T}, \mathrm{E})$ we denote by $\mathrm{L}(f)$ the length of the curve defined by f. We thus have a numerical function defined on the topological space $\mathscr{C}(\mathrm{T}, \mathrm{E})$.

11.1. Theorem.   *The length* $\mathrm{L}(f)$ *is a lower semicontinuous function of* f *in* $\mathscr{C}(\mathrm{T}, \mathrm{E})$.

PROOF.   For every finite subset $\sigma = \{t_1, t_2, ..., t_n\}$ of T, where $t_1 < t_2 < \cdots < t_n$, and for every $f \in \mathscr{C}(\mathrm{T}, \mathrm{E})$, we put

$$\mathrm{V}_\sigma(f) = \sum_i d(f(t_i), f(t_{i+1})).$$

For every $a \in \mathrm{T}$, the mapping $f \to f(a)$ of $\mathscr{C}(\mathrm{T}, \mathrm{E})$ into E is continuous; therefore the mapping $f \to \mathrm{V}_\sigma(f)$ is continuous for every σ.

But $\mathrm{L}(f) = \sup_\sigma \mathrm{V}_\sigma(f)$ (see Chapter I, Section 24); hence L is the upper envelope of the continuous functions $\mathrm{V}_\sigma(f)$. Therefore it is lower semicontinuous by Theorem 8.6.

11.2. Corollary.   *The mapping* $f \to$ *(total variation of* f) *of* $\mathscr{C}(\mathrm{T}, \mathbf{R})$ *into* $\bar{\mathbf{R}}$ *is lower semicontinuous.*

Application to the calculus of variations

One of the problems of the calculus of variations in one variable consists in finding, among a given set of curves, one whose length is the smallest possible.

The solution of this problem is furnished by the following lemma, which is a consequence of Theorems 10.1 and 11.1 taken together.

11.3. Lemma.   *For every compact subset* K *of* $\mathscr{C}(\mathrm{T}, \mathrm{E})$, *there exists an element* f_0 *of* K *such that*

$$\mathrm{L}(f_0) = \inf_{f \in \mathrm{K}} \mathrm{L}(f).$$

We are therefore led to investigate the compact subsets of $\mathscr{C}(\mathrm{T}, \mathrm{E})$.

11.4. Lemma.   *Let* T *be an interval* $[a, b]$, *where* $a < b$. *For every* $f \in \mathscr{C}(\mathrm{T}, \mathrm{E})$ *such that* $\mathrm{L}(f) < l$, *there exists an increasing homeomorphism* α *of* $[0, 1]$ *with* $[a, b]$ *such that* $f \circ \alpha$ *is of Lipschitz class with ratio* l.

PROOF.   For every $x \in [a, b]$, let $\mathrm{V}(x)$ be the total variation of f on $[a, x]$; we then put

$$\beta(x) = k_1 \mathrm{V}(x) + k_2(x - a).$$

One can verify that if $k_1 = l^{-1}$ and $k_2 = (l - \mathrm{L}(f))/(b - a)l$, the mapping β is an increasing homeomorphism of $[a, b]$ with $[0, 1]$. We denote the inverse mapping β^{-1} by α.

Since an increasing change of variable does not change the total variation (Chapter I, Proposition 24.5), for every $x, y \in [0, 1]$ such that $x < y$ we have

$$|f \circ \alpha(y) - f \circ \alpha(x)| \leqslant \text{total variation of } f \circ \alpha \text{ on } [x, y]$$

$$= \text{total variation of } f \text{ on } [\alpha(x), \alpha(y)]$$

$$= V(\alpha(y)) - V(\alpha(x)) \leqslant l(\beta(\alpha(y)) - \beta(\alpha(x))) = l(y - x).$$

The inequality $|f \circ \alpha(y) - f \circ \alpha(x)| \leqslant l(y - x)$ establishes the stated property.

11.5. Corollary. *For every family $(C_i)_{i \in I}$ of parametrized curves in* E *of length $< l$, there exists a family $(C_i')_{i \in I}$ of parametrized curves belonging to* $\mathscr{C}([0, 1], E)$ *such that, for every* $i \in I$, C_i *and* C_i' *are equivalent by a change of variable, and* C_i' *is of Lipschitz class with ratio l.*

We can now apply these results to the study of geodesics of a metric space (giving the name "geodesic of E" to every simple rectifiable arc whose length is $\leqslant$ the length of every other arc having the same end points).

11.6. Theorem. *Let* E *be a compact metric space, and let* A *and* B *be disjoint closed subsets of* E.

If there exist rectifiable curves in E *with endpoints in* A *and* B, *respectively, and if k denotes the infimum of their lengths, then there also exists a simple arc with length k and endpoints in* A *and* B, *respectively.*

Indeed, let l denote any finite number such that $k < l$. Let K be the subset of $\mathscr{C}([0, 1], E)$ consisting of the mappings f of Lipschitz class with ratio l such that $f(0) \in A$, $f(1) \in B$; K is equicontinuous and closed in $\mathscr{C}([0, 1], E)$, hence compact by Ascoli's theorem (Chapter I, Section 23).

Corollary 11.5 shows that $k = \inf_{f \in K} L(f)$; therefore by Lemma 11.3 there exists $f_0 \in K$ such that

$$L(f_0) = \inf_{f \in K} L(f) = k.$$

This mapping f_0 is not necessarily one-to-one, but the use of an intrinsic parametrization by $[0, k]$ will eliminate this deficiency:

For every $t \in [0, 1]$, let $\varphi(t)$ be the total variation of f_0 on $[0, t]$. For all $t_1, t_2 \in [0, 1]$ we have

$$d(f_0(t_1), f_0(t_2)) \leqslant |\varphi(t_1) - \varphi(t_2)|. \tag{1}$$

Therefore the relation $\varphi(t_1) = \varphi(t_2)$ implies $f_0(t_1) = f_0(t_2)$, which shows that f_0 is a function of φ, that is, of the form $f_0 = g \circ \varphi$. Then inequality (1) can be written as

$$d(g(u_1), g(u_2)) \leqslant |u_1 - u_2|,$$

where

$$u_1 = \varphi(t_1) \quad \text{and} \quad u_2 = \varphi(t_2).$$

Thus g is of Lipschitz class with ratio 1 on $[0, k]$; g is called the *intrinsic parametrization* associated with f_0.

The total variation of g is $\leqslant k$, but since

$$g(0) = f_0(0) \in \text{A} \quad \text{and} \quad g(k) = f_0(1) \in \text{B},$$

the total variation of g is $\geqslant k$; thus it is exactly equal to k, and the total variation of g on every interval $[u_1, u_2]$ is $(u_2 - u_1)$.

We assert that g is one-to-one; indeed, if there existed u_1, u_2 with $u_1 < u_2$ such that $g(u_1) = g(u_2)$, then by removing from the curve the arc corresponding to the interval (u_1, u_2) we would obtain a curve with end points in A and B, respectively, and whose length would be

$$k - (u_2 - u_1) < k.$$

EXAMPLE. Let Δ be the closed disc $x^2 + y^2 \leqslant r^2$ of $\mathbf{R}^2$; let f be a continuous mapping of Δ into $\mathbf{R}$, and let E be the graph of f. The metric subspace E of $\mathbf{R}^3$ is homeomorphic to Δ, hence compact.

If f is of Lipschitz class, then through any two points p and q of E there passes a rectifiable arc in E, namely the image of the line segment joining the projections of p and q on Δ.

Therefore by Theorem 11.6 a geodesic of E passes through p and q.

Let us call the image of the interior of Δ the *interior* of E, and the image of the circle $x^2 + y^2 = r^2$ the *frontier* of E, and let O denote the image of the center of Δ.

The lengths of the arcs of E joining O to a point of the frontier have an infimum $\geqslant r$; on the other hand, the length of the geodesics joining O to q tends to 0 as q tends to O. It follows that if q is taken in a suitable neighborhood of O, every geodesic joining O and q is interior to E. We can therefore state:

11.7. Proposition. *If p is a point of an open Lipschitz surface S of $\mathbf{R}^3$ of the form $z = f(x, y)$, then for every point q of S close enough to p there exists a geodesic of S with endpoints p and q.*

IV. THE STONE-WEIERSTRASS THEOREM
(Section 12)

We are here going to establish several theorems which will show us that every family of numerical functions, on a compact space, which is sufficiently rich and which is closed under certain operations, can be used to uniformly approximate every continuous function on this space.

Let X be a compact space, and $\mathscr{C}(X, \mathbf{R})$ the algebra of continuous mappings of X into $\mathbf{R}$, taken with the topology of uniform convergence.

We will say that a subset A of $\mathscr{C}(X, \mathbf{R})$ is a *lattice* if for all $f, g \in A$, the envelopes $\sup(f, g)$ and $\inf(f, g)$ also belong to A.

12.1. Proposition. *If* A *is a lattice subset of* $\mathscr{C}(X, \mathbf{R})$, *then for every* $f \in \mathscr{C}(X, \mathbf{R})$, *the statement that* $f \in \bar{A}$ *is equivalent to the statement that for every* $x, y \in X$, f *is the limit on* $\{x, y\}$ *of elements of* A.

PROOF. Indeed, let f be a continuous function which can be thus approximated on every set $\{x, y\}$, and let ϵ be a number > 0.

Then for any $x, y \in X$ there exists $g_{x,y} \in A$ such that

$$|f(x) - g_{x,y}(x)| < \epsilon; \tag{1}$$

$$|f(y) - g_{x,y}(y)| < \epsilon. \tag{2}$$

We put

$$\omega_{x,y} = \{z : g_{x,y}(z) < f(z) + \epsilon\}.$$

Since the function $g_{x,y} - f$ is continuous, the set $\omega_{x,y}$ is open, and it contains y by relation (2); therefore for every fixed x, the $\omega_{x,y}$ constitute an open covering of X. We can therefore find a finite subcovering (ω_{x,y_i}).
Put

$$g_x = \inf_i(g_{x,y_i});$$

then $g_x < f + \epsilon$ on X; and $g_x(x) > f(x) - \epsilon$ from (1).
Put

$$\omega_x = \{z : g_x(z) > f(z) - \epsilon\}.$$

Since the function $g_x - f$ is continuous, the set ω_x is open, and it contains x. Therefore the ω_x constitute an open covering of X, and we can find a finite subcovering (ω_{x_i}).
We now put

$$g = \sup_j(g_{x_j});$$

then $g \in A$; $g < f + \epsilon$, and $g > f - \epsilon$ on X.

We have therefore found a $g \in A$ which uniformly approximates f to within ϵ.

EXAMPLE.   Let X be a compact set in $\mathbf{R}^n$ and let A be the set of traces on X of continuous functions f on $\mathbf{R}^n$ which are piecewise affine (that is, there exists a finite covering of $\mathbf{R}^n$ by convex polyhedra on each of which f is affine). This set A is clearly a lattice, and for all x and y there exist functions $f \in A$ which take any assigned values at x and y. Therefore

$$\bar{A} = \mathscr{C}(X, \mathbf{R}).$$

12.2. Lemma.   *Every closed subalgebra A of $\mathscr{C}(X, \mathbf{R})$ is a lattice.*

PROOF.   By virtue of the relations

$$\sup(f, g) = \tfrac{1}{2}[(f + g) + |f - g|]; \quad \inf(f, g) = \tfrac{1}{2}[(f + g) - |f - g|],$$

it suffices to prove that if $f \in A$, then also $|f| \in A$.

To do this, we shall show that $|f|$ is the uniform limit of polynomials in f of the form $\sum_1^n a_p f^p$; we can clearly restrict ourselves to the case where $\|f\| \leqslant 1$.

But for every $\epsilon > 0$ we have

$$0 \leqslant (x^2 + \epsilon^2)^{1/2} - |x| \leqslant \epsilon.$$

On the other hand,

$$x^2 + \epsilon^2 = 1 + \epsilon^2 + (x^2 - 1) = (1 + \epsilon^2)(1 + u),$$

where $u = (x^2 - 1)/(1 + \epsilon^2)$.

For every $x \in [-1, 1]$ we have

$$|u| \leqslant (1 + \epsilon^2)^{-1} < 1;$$

therefore the Taylor series* of $(1 + u)^{1/2}$ converges uniformly to $(1 + u)^{1/2}$ when $x \in [-1, 1]$; there thus exists a polynomial $P(x)$ such that

$$|(x^2 + \epsilon^2)^{1/2} - P(x)| \leqslant \epsilon \qquad \text{for all} \quad x \in [-1, 1].$$

In particular, we therefore have $|P(0)| \leqslant 2\epsilon$, so that if finally we put $Q = P - P(0)$, then

$$\big|Q(x) - |x|\big| \leqslant \epsilon + 2\epsilon + \epsilon = 4\epsilon \qquad \text{for all} \quad x \in [-1, 1].$$

---

* There exist proofs of Lemma 12.2 which avoid the use of Taylor's formula (see Problem 16).

Since Q does not have a constant term, $Q(f) \in A$; and since we have assumed $\|f\| \leqslant 1$, then

$$\| Q(f) - |f| \| \leqslant 4\epsilon.$$

12.3. Definition. LET A BE A FAMILY OF MAPPINGS OF A SET X INTO A SET Y. THEN A IS SAID TO *SEPARATE* THE POINTS OF X IF, FOR ANY $x, y \in X$ WITH $x \neq y$, THERE EXISTS AN $f \in A$ SUCH THAT $f(x) \neq f(y)$.

We can now state the desired fundamental theorem:

12.4. Theorem (of Stone-Weierstrass). *Let* A *be a subalgebra of* $\mathscr{C}(X, \mathbf{R})$ *such that*:

1. A *separates the points of* X;
2. *For every* $x \in X$ *there exists an* $f \in A$ *such that* $f(x) \neq 0$.

Then

$$\bar{A} = \mathscr{C}(X, \mathbf{R}).$$

PROOF. By virtue of Lemmas 12.1 and 12.2, it suffices to show that for all $x, y \in X$ with $x \neq y$, and for all scalars α, β, there exists an $f \in A$ with $f(x) = \alpha$ and $f(y) = \beta$.

If there exists a $g \in A$ with $g(x) \neq g(y)$ and $g(x), g(y) \neq 0$, we put

$$f = a_1 g + a_2 g^2.$$

The existence of scalars a_1, a_2 such that $f(x) = \alpha, f(y) = \beta$ is guaranteed by the condition

$$g(x)g^2(y) - g(y)g^2(x) = g(x)g(y)(g(y) - g(x)) \neq 0,$$

which is satisfied by hypothesis.

But there exists such a g; for there exists g_1 such that $g_1(x) \neq g_1(y)$; if $g_1(x)$ and $g_1(y)$ are $\neq 0$, we take $g = g_1$; if, however, $g_1(x) = 0$ for example, there exists g_2 such that $g_2(x) \neq 0$, and we take $g = g_1 + \epsilon g_2$, where $\epsilon \neq 0$ and is so small that $g(x) \neq g(y)$ and $g(y) \neq 0$.

REMARK 1. It is convenient in applications to formulate this theorem as follows:

If a family (f_i) of elements of $\mathscr{C}(X, \mathbf{R})$ separates the points of X, and if the f_i do not all vanish at any one point of X, then every $f \in \mathscr{C}(X, \mathbf{R})$ is the uniform limit of polynomials (without constant terms) with respect to the f_i.

REMARK 2. If A contains the constants, condition 2 of Theorem 12.4 is satisfied.

12.5. Corollary. *Let* A *be a subalgebra (over the field* **C***) of* $\mathscr{C}(X, \mathbf{C})$ *such that*:

1. A *separates the points of* X;
2. *For every* $x \in X$, *there exists an* $f \in A$ *such that* $f(x) \neq 0$;
3. *For every* $f \in A$, *we also have* $\bar{f} \in A$ *(where* $\bar{f}$ *denotes the conjugate of* f *)*.

Then

$$\bar{A} = \mathscr{C}(X, \mathbf{C}).$$

Indeed, the subalgebra A_r (over **R**) of the real-valued functions in A satisfies conditions 1 and 2 of Theorem 12.4, for if f separates x and y, the same is true of $\mathscr{R}(f)$ or $\mathscr{R}(if)$, and if $f(x) \neq 0$, the same is true of $\mathscr{R}f(x)$ or $\mathscr{R}(if)(x)$.

Therefore

$$\bar{A}_r = \mathscr{C}(X, \mathbf{R}); \qquad \text{hence} \qquad \overline{A_r + iA_r} = \mathscr{C}(X, \mathbf{C}).$$

Condition 3 of the corollary is essential. Indeed, let us take for X the unit disk of **C**, and let A be the set of traces on X of polynomials in the complex variable z. The algebra A satisfies conditions 1 and 2, but not condition 3. One can verify that $\bar{A} \neq \mathscr{C}(X, \mathbf{C})$, for example by noting that for every $f \in A$, hence also for every $f \in \bar{A}$, $f(0)$ is the mean of f over the unit circle, which is not true for every $f \in \mathscr{C}(X, \mathbf{C})$.

APPLICATION 1.　Let X be a compact subset of $\mathbf{R}^n$; the family (f_i) of the n coordinate functions $x \rightarrow x_i$ separates the points of X. Therefore every function $f \in \mathscr{C}(X, \mathbf{C})$ is the uniform limit of polynomials in n variables with complex coefficients (with a constant term if $O \in X$; without constant term, if one wishes, if $O \notin X$).

APPLICATION 2.　Let X be the unit circle $|z| = 1$ of **C**; the function $z \rightarrow z$ separates the points of X and does not vanish on X. Therefore the algebra generated by z and $\bar{z}$ is everywhere dense on $\mathscr{C}(X, \mathbf{C})$. Let φ denote the mapping $t \rightarrow e^{it}$ of **R** into X. For every $f \in \mathscr{C}(X, \mathbf{C})$, $f \circ \varphi$ is a continuous function on **R**, periodic with period 2π, and we know (see Volume 1, Chapter III) that every continuous periodic function with period 2π on **R** is of this form.

Since f is the uniform limit of polynomials in z and $\bar{z}$, $f \circ \varphi$ is the uniform limit of polynomials in e^{it} and e^{-it}; in other words, every continuous complex-valued function on **R** which is periodic with period 2π is the uniform limit of trigonometric polynomials $\sum_{-n}^{n} a_p e^{ipt}$.

Extension of continuous functions

Let X be a topological space, Y a closed subset of X, and f a continuous mapping of Y into **R**. The question presents itself of determining whether f can be extended to a continuous mapping of X into **R**. We shall see that the Stone-Weierstrass theorem furnishes an easy answer when X is compact and metrizable.

12.6. Proposition. *If* Y *denotes a closed subset of a compact metric space* X, *every* $f \in \mathscr{C}(Y, \mathbf{R})$ *is the restriction to* Y *of an element of* $\mathscr{C}(X, \mathbf{R})$.

Proof. 1. $\mathscr{C}(X, \mathbf{R})$ separates the points of X since, if $a, b \in X$ with $a \neq b$, the continuous function $x \to d(a, x)$ separates a and b. Therefore Theorem 12.4 shows that for every $g \in \mathscr{C}(Y, \mathbf{R})$ and for every $\epsilon > 0$, there exists $g_\epsilon \in \mathscr{C}(X, \mathbf{R})$ such that $| g_\epsilon(y) - g(y) | < \epsilon$ for every $y \in Y$. We shall assume in addition that g and g_ϵ have the same infimum and supremum (if this is not the case, we replace g_ϵ by $\sup(\alpha, \inf(\beta, g_\epsilon))$, where α and β are the infimum and supremum, respectively, of g).

2. Let us define a sequence $(g^{(n)})$ of elements of $\mathscr{C}(X, \mathbf{R})$ recursively by the following conditions:

$$g^{(1)} = f_{1/2} ; \qquad g^{(n)} = \left(f - \sum_1^{n-1} g^{(i)}\right)_{1/2^n} \qquad \text{for} \quad n > 1.$$

We deduce that

$$\left| f(y) - \sum_1^n g^{(i)}(y)\right| \leqslant (\tfrac{1}{2})^n \qquad \text{on} \quad Y;$$

$$| g^{(n)}(x)| \leqslant (\tfrac{1}{2})^{n-1} \qquad \text{on} \quad X.$$

It follows from this that on the one hand the series with general term $g^{(n)}$ converges uniformly on X, and on the other hand that its sum g is equal to f on Y.

V. FUNCTIONS DEFINED ON AN INTERVAL OF R

The existence of an order structure and an affine structure on the intervals of **R** makes it possible to define, for functions on such intervals, various notions related to these structures, such as that of the limit from the left or right, monotonicity, differentiability, and convexity.

We are here going to examine these various notions.

13. LEFT AND RIGHT LIMITS

Let us recall (Chapter I, Section 8) that if I is an interval of **R**, E is a separated topological space, and f is a mapping of I into E, then f is said to have a right limit at the point a of I if $\lim_{x>a,x\to a} f(x)$ exists.

This limit is denoted by $f(a_+)$; $f(a_-)$ is defined in a similar way.

13.1. Definition. THE POINT a IS SAID TO BE A DISCONTINUITY OF THE *FIRST KIND* OF f IF, ON THE ONE HAND, $f(a_-)$ AND $f(a_+)$ EXIST, AND ON THE OTHER HAND, WE DO NOT HAVE $f(a_-) = f(a) = f(a_+)$.

EXAMPLE 1. The mapping $x \to$ (integer part of x) of **R**$_+$ into **R**$_+$ has the integers 1, 2, ... as its discontinuities of the first kind.

EXAMPLE 2. The mapping f of **R**$^+$ into **R**$^+$ defined by:

$$f(x) = 0 \qquad \text{for } x = 0 \text{ and for } x \text{ irrational,}$$

$$f(x) = q^{-1} \qquad \text{if } x \text{ is the irreducible fraction } p/q,$$

has as its discontinuities of the first kind all the rational points $\neq 0$.

EXAMPLE 3. The mapping f of **R** into **R** defined by $f(x) = 0$ if x is rational, and $f(x) = 1$ if x is irrational, has no discontinuities of the first kind.

An example will show us that if no restrictions are placed on E, then every point of I can be a discontinuity of the first kind:

Let E denote the product **R** $\times \{1, 2, 3\}$, with the lexicographic order defined as follows:

For every $x \in$ **R** we take $(x, 1) < (x, 2) < (x, 3)$, and for every $x, y \in$ **R** such that $x < y$, we take $(x, i) < (y, j)$ for any $i, j \in \{1, 2, 3\}$.

Let E be taken with the order topology, and let f denote the mapping $x \to (x, 2)$ of **R** into E.

One can verify that E is locally compact and that for every $x \in$ **R**,

$$f(x_-) = (x, 1) \qquad \text{and} \qquad f(x_+) = (x, 3)\,.$$

However, this kind of singular occurrence cannot take place if E is metrizable:

13.2. Proposition. *If f is a mapping of an interval I of* **R** *into a metric space* E, *the set of points of discontinuity of the first kind of f is at most countable.*

Indeed, let D_n be the set of points of discontinuity of the first kind of f at which the oscillation of f is $\geq n^{-1}$. Then D_n has only isolated points, for if a denotes an accumulation point of D_n, a is the limit of a monotone sequence of distinct points of D_n; if for example this sequence is decreasing, then $f(a_+)$ cannot exist, therefore $a \notin D_n$.

Since D_n has only isolated points, it is at most countable; and since $D = \bigcup D_n$, D is at most countable.

Z There exist functions which are discontinuous at every point and have no discontinuities of the first kind; this is the case for Example 3 above.

13.3. Definition. LET f BE A MAPPING OF AN INTERVAL I OF **R** INTO A METRIC SPACE E.

1. f IS SAID TO BE *REGULATED* IF ITS POINTS OF DISCONTINUITY ARE ALL OF THE FIRST KIND.

2. f IS SAID TO BE A *STEP FUNCTION* IF THERE EXISTS A FINITE PARTITION OF I INTO SUBINTERVALS (SOME OF WHICH MAY BE ONE POINT) ON EACH OF WHICH f IS CONSTANT.

Proposition 13.2 shows that the set of points of discontinuity of a regulated function is at most countable. It is evident, incidentally, that every step function is regulated, but the converse is false, as every continuous function is regulated.

13.4. Proposition. *The collection of regulated functions is closed under uniform limit.*

Indeed, suppose f is the uniform limit of regulated functions f_n; for every $a \in I$, $f_n(a_+)$ and $f_n(a_-)$ exist, hence the same is true of $f(a_+)$ and $f(a_-)$.

Let us note here that if the metric space E is a normed vector space, the set of regulated functions in $\mathscr{F}(I, E)$ is a vector subspace of $\mathscr{F}(I, E)$.

13.5. Proposition. *Suppose the interval I is compact, while the metric space E is arbitrary.*

Then the class of regulated functions and the class of uniform limits of step functions are identical.

PROOF. Since every step function is regulated, Proposition 13.4 shows that the same is true of every uniform limit of step functions.

Conversely, let f be a regulated function, and let ϵ be a number >0. For every $x \in I$ there exist two nonempty intervals (α_x, x) and (x, β_x) on each of which the oscillation of f is $<\epsilon$. Since I is compact, there exists a finite covering of I by intervals of the form (α_x, β_x); hence there exists a finite partition of I into intervals I_n, some of them possibly consisting of one point, on each of which the oscillation of f is $<\epsilon$. The function f_ϵ which is constant on each interval I_n and which coincides with f at the midpoint of each I_n clearly approximates f to within ϵ.

Corollary. *Every regulated mapping of a compact* I *into a metric space* E *is bounded.*

14. MONOTONE FUNCTIONS

If f is an increasing mapping of an interval I into **R**, then for every $a \in$ I we have

$$f(a_-) = \sup_{x<a} f(x); \qquad f(a_+) = \inf_{x>a} f(x).$$

Thus *every increasing function* (and similarly every decreasing function) *is a regulated function*; in particular, the set of its points of discontinuity is at most countable.

Therefore every difference of two increasing functions, in other words every function of bounded variation (Chapter I, Proposition 24.8) is regulated. This result might lead us to expect that, conversely, every regulated numerical function is of bounded variation; this is not so, as there exist even continuous functions on $[0, 1]$ with unbounded variation.

EXAMPLES.   It is well to be familar with several classical examples of increasing functions of a paradoxical nature, which serve as guide lines in trying to discover mathematical propositions.

EXAMPLE 1.   Let $A = \{a_1, a_2, ..., a_n, ...\}$ be a countable set of points of the open interval $(0, 1)$ such that $\bar{A} = [0, 1]$, and let (α_n) be an infinite sequence of numbers >0, with sum 1.

For every $x \in [0, 1]$ we put

$$f(x) = \sum_{a_n < x} \alpha_n \, .$$

In other words, the sum is taken over all n such that $a_n < x$. It is immediate that f is strictly increasing on $[0, 1]$, with $f(0) = 0$ and $f(1) = 1$, and that the set of its points of discontinuity is A.

EXAMPLE 2.   We now put $f([0, 1]) = B$, where f is the function defined in the preceding example. The mapping f^{-1} of B onto $[0, 1]$ is strictly increasing; one can verify:

(a)   That f^{-1} can be extended in a unique way to an increasing mapping g of $[0, 1]$ onto $[0, 1]$;

(b)   That g is continuous;

(c)   That the sum of the lengths of the intervals of $[0, 1]$ on which g is constant is equal to 1, which implies that the change of g takes place on a set of "measure zero" in a sense which will be made precise in the theory of integration.

15. THEOREMS OF FINITE INCREASE

We shall not review here the elementary classical properties of the derivatives of a function of a real variable. On the other hand, we shall prove several theorems of "finite increase" which enable one to pass from a local to a global situation and which will advantageously replace the classical theorem of finite increase (the mean value theorem), which is valid only for real-valued differentiable functions.

In all of what follows, I denotes an arbitrary interval of **R**, and D a finite or countable subset of I; in the more classical results, this set D is either empty, or consists of the end points of I.

15.1. Lemma.   *Let f be a continuous mapping of I into **R** such that, for every x interior to I with $x \notin D$ and for every $\delta > 0$, there exists $y \in (x, x + \delta)$ such that $f(x) \leqslant f(y)$.*

Then f is increasing on I.

PROOF.   Let $u, v \in I$, with $u < v$, and let k be any number such that

$$k < f(u); \qquad k \notin f(D).$$

Let A be the set of $x \in [u, v]$ such that $k \leqslant f(x)$; this set is nonempty since it contains u, and is closed since f is continuous; therefore it contains the number $\alpha = \sup A$.

Suppose $\alpha < v$; we cannot have $k < f(\alpha)$, for then α would be in the interior of A; therefore $k = f(\alpha)$. But $\alpha \notin D$ since $f(\alpha) = k \notin f(D)$; therefore by the hypothesis of the lemma there exists $\beta \in (\alpha, v)$ such that $f(\alpha) \leqslant f(\beta)$; hence $\beta \in A$, which contradicts $\alpha = \sup A$.

We therefore have $\alpha = v$, in other words $k \leqslant f(v)$; since $f(D)$ is at most countable, there exist numbers k arbitrarily close to $f(u)$; therefore $f(u) \leqslant f(v)$.

In other words, f is increasing.

15.2. Lemma.   *Let φ be a continuous mapping of I into a metric space E, and let g be a continuous increasing mapping of I into **R**.*

Suppose that for every x in the interior of I, with $x \notin D$, and for every $\delta > 0$, there exists $y \in (x, x + \delta)$ such that

$$d(\varphi(y), \varphi(x)) \leqslant g(y) - g(x). \tag{1}$$

Then for all u, $v \in I$, with $u < v$, we have

$$d(\varphi(v), \varphi(u)) \leqslant g(v) - g(u).$$

Indeed, given u and v, we put

$$f(x) = g(x) - d(\varphi(u), \varphi(x)) \qquad \text{for every} \quad x \in [u, v].$$

Then for all $x, y \in [u, v]$ such that $x < y$ and such that (1) is satisfied, we have

$$f(x) - f(y) = g(x) - g(y) + d(\varphi(u), \varphi(y)) - d(\varphi(u), \varphi(x))$$
$$\leqslant g(x) - g(y) + d(\varphi(y), \varphi(x)) \leqslant 0.$$

Therefore, by Lemma 15.1, f is increasing on $[u, v]$; hence

$$0 \leqslant f(v) - f(u), \qquad \text{that is} \qquad d(\varphi(u), \varphi(v)) \leqslant g(v) - g(u).$$

To now obtain statements of a more classical nature, we give a definition:

15.3. Definition. Let φ be a mapping of I into a normed space E. Then φ is said to be *differentiable from the right* (or *right differentiable*) at the point a of I (where a is not the right end point of I) if the element $h^{-1}(\varphi(a + h) - \varphi(a))$ of E tends to a limit as $h \to 0$ along values > 0. This limit is called the right derivative of φ at a, and is denoted by $\varphi_r{}'(a)$.

We can then write

$$\Delta\varphi = \varphi(a + h) - \varphi(a) = h(\varphi_r{}'(a) + \delta(h)),$$

where $\lim_{h \to 0} \delta(h) = 0$. Thus for every $\epsilon > 0$ we have

$$h(\| \varphi_r{}'(a)\| - \epsilon) \leqslant \| \Delta\varphi \| \leqslant h(\| \varphi_r{}'(a)\| + \epsilon)$$

for all $h > 0$ sufficiently small.

In particular, φ is right continuous at the point a.

Differentiability from the left is defined similarly; if φ is differentiable from the right and left at the point a, with the derivatives equal, then φ is said to be differentiable at a.

15.4. Theorem. *If the continuous numerical function φ is right differentiable at every point of $I \doteq D$, and if $m \leqslant \varphi_r{}'(x) \leqslant M$ for every $x \in I \doteq D$, then*

$$m(v - u) \leqslant \varphi(v) - \varphi(u) \leqslant M(v - u) \qquad \text{for} \quad u < v.$$

The inequalities are strict when f is not affine on $[u, v]$.

PROOF.   Let us first show that if $\varphi_r'(x) \geqslant 0$ for every $x \notin D$, then φ is increasing. Indeed, given $\epsilon > 0$, for every $x \notin D$ we have, when h is sufficiently small,

$$\varphi(x + h) - \varphi(x) \geqslant -\epsilon h.$$

Therefore the function $f : x \rightarrow \varphi(x) + \epsilon x$ satisfies the conditions of Lemma 15.1; hence it is increasing. Since this is true for all $\epsilon > 0$, φ itself is increasing.

But the functions $\varphi_1 : x \rightarrow Mx - \varphi(x)$ and $\varphi_2 : x \rightarrow \varphi(x) - mx$ have right derivatives $\geqslant 0$ at the points of $I \doteq D$; hence they are increasing, which implies the desired inequalities.

Finally, if f is not affine with derivative M on $[u, v]$, the increasing function $Mx - \varphi(x)$ is not constant on $[u, v]$, whence

$$Mu - \varphi(u) < Mv - \varphi(v).$$

A similar argument holds for $\varphi(x) - mx$.

15.5. Theorem.   *Let φ be a continuous mapping of I into a normed space E, and let g be a continuous increasing mapping of I into* **R**.
Suppose that φ and g are right differentiable at every point of $I \doteq D$, and that

$$\| \varphi_r'(x)\| \leqslant g_r'(x).$$

Then for all $u, v \in I$ with $u < v$ we have

$$\| \varphi(v) - \varphi(u)\| \leqslant g(v) - g(u).$$

PROOF.   Given a number $\epsilon > 0$, for every x in the interior of I, with $x \notin D$, there exist $h > 0$ arbitrarily small such that

$$\| \varphi(x + h) - \varphi(x)\| \leqslant h(\| \varphi_r'(x)\| + \epsilon) \leqslant h(g_r'(x) + \epsilon)$$
$$\leqslant g(x + h) - g(x) + 2\epsilon h.$$

By virtue of Lemma 15.2 applied to the functions φ and $x \rightarrow g(x) + 2\epsilon x$, we therefore have

$$\| \varphi(v) - \varphi(u)\| \leqslant g(v) - g(u) + 2\epsilon(v - u).$$

This relation holds for all $\epsilon > 0$, which implies the desired relation.

15.6. Corollary.   *If $\| \varphi_r'(x)\| \leqslant M$ for every $x \in I \doteq D$, then φ is of Lipschitz class with ratio M on I.*

Z All the results which we have just established concern functions defined on an interval I of **R**; we shall see later that certain of them can be extended to the case where I is replaced by a convex subset of **R**^{n}, by making use of the fact that any two points of a convex set are the endpoints of a line segment contained in the convex set.

But we shall show by an example that it is not possible to replace I by a general metric space:

Let J be the subset of the Euclidean plane **R**^{2} defined as follows: J is the union of the two line segments $[(1, 0), (0, k)]$ and $[(-1, 0), (0, k)]$.

We define the mapping φ of J into **R** as the restriction to J of the linear form $(x_1, x_2) \to kx_1$.

It is easily verified that if J is taken with the Euclidean metric, then φ is of Lipschitz class with ratio 1 in the neighborhood of each point of J. But the smallest number k' such that φ is of Lipschitz class with ratio k' is k, which can be arbitrarily large.

2. The proof of Lemma 15.1 only uses the fact that $f(D)$ does not contain any interval; one could therefore hope to enlarge the class of sets D entering into the assertions obtained. But careful examples show that such an extension would be of no convenience and little interest; thus, for example, the continuous increasing function g constructed in 13.5 has derivative zero, hence $\leqslant 0$, except at the points of a closed set of "measure zero," and yet is increasing and nonconstant.

3. In all of our results, the right derivatives have played a priviledged role; one can evidently replace right by left in these results. Besides, in general the functions studied will have a two-sided derivative at every point of I $\dot-$ D.

16. DEFINITION OF CONVEX FUNCTIONS. IMMEDIATE PROPERTIES

In Section 8 we have seen the importance of the operation "upper envelope" in creating new classes of functions; this operation will arise once again in connection with convex functions, which will turn out to be identical with the upper envelopes of affine functions.

16.1. Definition. LET f BE A *FINITE* NUMERICAL FUNCTION, DEFINED ON AN INTERVAL I OF **R**.

THEN f IS SAID TO BE *CONVEX* IF, FOR ALL $x_1, x_2 \in$ I, EVERY POINT $M(x)$ OF THE GRAPH Γ OF f SUCH THAT $x \in [x_1, x_2]$ LIES BELOW* THE

* The terms "below" and "above" are used, here and in the sequel, in the weak sense; for example, the graph of f is included in the set of points lying above the graph of f as well as in the set of points lying below the graph of f.

LINE SEGMENT JOINING $M(x_1)$ AND $M(x_2)$ (WHERE $M(x)$ DENOTES THE POINT $(x, f(x))$); IN OTHER WORDS:

$$f(\alpha_1 x_1 + \alpha_2 x_2) \leqslant \alpha_1 f(x_1) + \alpha_2 f(x_2)$$

FOR ALL α_1, $\alpha_2 \geqslant 0$ SUCH THAT $\alpha_1 + \alpha_2 = 1$.

For example, every affine function $x \to ax + b$ is convex.

16.2. Proposition. *To say that f is convex is equivalent to saying that the set $A(f)$ of points of the plane $\mathbf{R}^2$ situated above the graph of f is convex.*

Indeed, if f is convex and if P_1 and P_2 are points of $A(f)$ with abscissas x_1 and x_2, the segment $M(x_1)M(x_2)$ lies above Γ, hence so does the segment P_1P_2 since P_1 and P_2 lie above $M(x_1)$ and $M(x_2)$, respectively.

Conversely, if $A(f)$ is convex and if $M(x_1)$ and $M(x_2)$ are two points of Γ, these points belong to $A(f)$; the segment $M(x_1)M(x_2)$ belongs to $A(f)$, and therefore lies above Γ.

16.3. Definition. A FINITE NUMERICAL FUNCTION f DEFINED ON AN INTERVAL I OF **R** IS SAID TO BE *STRICTLY CONVEX* IF FOR ALL x_1, $x_2 \in I$, EVERY POINT $M(x)$ OF THE GRAPH Γ OF f SUCH THAT $x \in (x_1, x_2)$ LIES *STRICTLY* BELOW THE SEGMENT $M(x_1)$ $M(x_2)$.

This is equivalent to saying that f is convex and that its graph Γ does not contain three colinear points. For if M_1, M_2, M_3 are three colinear points of Γ with abscissas x_1, x_2, x_3 and $x_1 < x_2 < x_3$, then for every $x \in [x_1, x_3]$ the point $M(x)$ lies on the segment M_1M_3, for otherwise one would have, for example, $x_1 < x < x_2$ with $M(x)$ lying strictly below M_1M_2, which would imply that M_2 lies strictly above $M(x)M_3$, which is impossible.

Therefore to say that f is strictly convex in I is equivalent to saying that f is convex and that there does not exist any open subinterval of I on which f is affine.

16.4. Definition. A FINITE NUMERICAL FUNCTION f DEFINED ON AN INTERVAL I OF **R** IS SAID TO BE *CONCAVE* IF $(-f)$ IS CONVEX.

This amounts to saying that the set of points of the plane lying below the graph of f is convex.

Operations on convex functions

16.5. Proposition. (a) *Every linear combination with positive coefficients of convex functions is convex.*

(b) *Every pointwise limit of convex functions is convex.*

(c) *Every finite upper envelope of convex functions is convex.*

PROOF.   Assertions (a) and (b) follow from the inequalities

$$f_i(\alpha_1 x_1 + \alpha_2 x_2) \leqslant \alpha_1 f_i(x_1) + \alpha_2 f_i(x_2),$$

which are preserved by positive linear combination and by passage to the limit.

To prove (c), let (f_i) be a family of convex functions, with upper envelope f (assumed everywhere finite). Each of the sets $A(f_i)$ is convex; we know that $A(f) = \bigcap_i A(f_i)$; therefore $A(f)$ is convex. In other words (Proposition 16.2) f is convex.

16.6. Corollary.   *Every finite numerical function on* I *which is the upper envelope of affine functions is convex.*

17. CONTINUITY AND DIFFERENTIABILITY OF CONVEX FUNCTIONS

17.1. Proposition.   *To say that f is convex is equivalent to saying that the function p,*

$$p(x, y) = \frac{f(x) - f(y)}{x - y} \qquad (\text{where } x \neq y),$$

is increasing with respect to each of the variables.

Indeed, $p(x, y)$ is the slope of the line $M(x)M(y)$, and the condition of the proposition is equivalent to the assertion that if a, b, c are three points of I with $a < c < b$, then

$$\text{slope } M(a)M(c) \leqslant \text{slope } M(a)M(b) \leqslant \text{slope } M(c)M(b),$$

which amounts to saying that $M(c)$ lies below the segment $M(a)M(b)$ (Fig. 7).

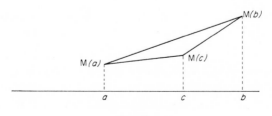

FIG. 7

17.2. Corollary. *To say that f is both convex and concave is equivalent to saying that f is affine.*

We note, in fact, that the concavity of f is characterized by the decreasing nature of p in each variable.

Thus if f is convex and concave, p is a constant; we therefore have

$$f(x) - f(y) = k(x - y).$$

Hence f is affine. The converse is obvious.

17.3. Proposition. *Every function f which is convex in an open interval* I *has a right derivative and a left derivative at every point of* I *(hence is continuous), and if a < b, then*

$$f_l'(a) \leqslant f_r'(a) \leqslant \frac{f(b) - f(a)}{a - b} \leqslant f_l'(b) \leqslant f_r'(b).$$

PROOF. Indeed, let $x < a < y$ and put

$$p(t) = \frac{f(t) - f(a)}{t - a}.$$

Proposition 17.1 shows that $p(x) \leqslant p(y)$.

Therefore the infimum of the $p(y)$ (where $a < y$) is finite and equal to $\lim_{y \to a} p(y)$; similarly the supremum of the $p(x)$ (where $x < a$) is finite and equal to $\lim_{x \to a} p(x)$. Therefore $f_r'(a)$ and $f_l'(a)$ exist, and

$$p(x) \leqslant f_l'(a) \leqslant f_r'(a) \leqslant p(y).$$

Letting $y = b$ in this relation, we obtain several of the desired inequalities; the rest are obtained by interchanging the roles of a and b.

Z 1. A function which is convex in a *closed* interval $[a, b]$ need not be continuous at the endpoints; for example, the function f which equals 0 in the interior of $[a, b]$ and 1 at the end points is convex in $[a, b]$ but not continuous.

2. A function which is convex in a bounded open interval may be unbounded; this is the case for the function $(1 - x^2)^{-1}$ on the interval $(-1, 1)$.

3. A function which is continuous and convex on a closed interval may be nondifferentiable at the end points; this is the case for the function $-(1 - x^2)^{1/2}$ on $[-1, 1]$. Nevertheless there is then a generalized derivative which equals $-\infty$ at a and $+\infty$ at b.

17.4. Corollary. *The functions f_l' and f_r' are increasing, and the set of points of* I *at which f is not differentiable is at most countable.*

PROOF.   That f_l' is increasing, for example, is contained in the inequalities of Proposition 17.3. These inequalities also show that if $a < b$, the intervals $(f_l'(a), f_r'(a))$ and $(f_l'(b), f_r'(b))$ are disjoint; therefore there cannot be more than countably many such intervals which are nonempty; in other words, the sets of points x at which $f_l'(x) \neq f_r'(x)$ is at most countable.

17.5. Definition.   LET f BE A CONVEX FUNCTION IN AN OPEN INTERVAL I, WITH GRAPH Γ. EVERY LINE Δ PASSING THROUGH A POINT $M(a)$ OF Γ AND LYING BELOW Γ IS CALLED A *SUPPORTING LINE* AT THE POINT $M(a)$.

17.6. Proposition.   *There exists at least one supporting line at every point of the graph of a function which is convex in an open interval.*

Indeed, the inequalities of Proposition 17.3 show that in order for Δ to be a supporting line at $M(a)$, it is necessary and sufficient that its slope p satisfy the relation

$$f_l'(a) \leqslant p \leqslant f_r'(a).$$

In particular, if f is differentiable at a, the only supporting line at $M(a)$ is the tangent.

17.7. Corollary.   *Every function f which is convex in an open interval is the upper envelope of a family of affine functions.*

Indeed, it suffices to take those affine functions whose graphs are supporting lines of the graph of f.

This corollary is the converse of Corollary 16.6.

18. CRITERIA FOR CONVEXITY

Proposition 17.1 already furnishes a convenient criterion for convexity; here is another:

18.1. Proposition.   *Let f be a finite numerical function on an open interval* I, *and let* D *be an at most countable subset of* I. *In order that f be convex, it is necessary and sufficient that f be continuous, have a right derivative f_r' at every point of* I $\dot{-}$ D, *and that f_r' be increasing on* I $\dot{-}$ D.

PROOF. By Corollary 17.4, we already know that the condition is necessary. Conversely, suppose it is satisfied. Let a, b, c be points of I with $a < b < c$; we put

$$k_1 = \sup_{x \leqslant b} f_r'(x) \qquad \text{and} \qquad k_2 = \inf_{v \geqslant b} f_r'(x).$$

Theorem 15.4 shows that

$$f(b) - f(a) \leqslant k_1(b - a) \qquad \text{and} \qquad k_2(c - b) \leqslant f(c) - f(b).$$

Since $k_1 \leqslant k_2$, we therefore have

$$\frac{f(b) - f(a)}{b - a} \leqslant \frac{f(c) - f(b)}{c - b}.$$

This relation shows that $M(c)$ lies below the segment $M(a)M(b)$. Therefore f is convex.

18.2. Corollary. *If a function f has a second derivative f'' at every point of the open interval I, the convexity of f is equivalent to the relation $f'' \geqslant 0$.*

Here is a criterion which enables one to pass from a local statement to a global one.

18.3. Proposition. *Let f be a finite numerical function on an open interval I. If every point of I is interior to an interval in which f is convex, then f is convex in I.*

Indeed, the local convexity implies that f_r' exists at every point of I, and is locally increasing. Every interval $[u, v]$ of I can be covered by a finite number of open intervals, on each of which f_r' is increasing; it follows at once that $f_r'(u) \leqslant f_r'(v)$. Therefore f_r' is increasing on I. By virtue of Proposition 18.1, f is therefore convex.

Finally, here is a criterion which is of little more than historical interest:

18.4. Proposition. *Let f be a finite numerical function which is continuous (or even only lower semicontinuous) on an open interval I.*
If for all a, $b \in$ I we have

$$f\left(\frac{a + b}{2}\right) \leqslant \frac{1}{2}(f(a) + f(b)),$$

then f is convex.

PROOF. Suppose a, $b \in$ I with $a < b$; let $y = d(x)$ be the equation of the line $M(a)M(b)$. If we did not have $f(x) \leqslant d(x)$ on $[a, b]$, the set ω of points x of $[a, b]$ at which $f(x) > d(x)$ would be nonempty and open, since $f - d$ is lower semicontinuous. Let (α, β) be a connected component of ω; then $f(x) > d(x)$ on (α, β) and $f(x) - d(x) \leqslant 0$ for $x = \alpha$ or β. Therefore

$$f\left(\frac{\alpha + \beta}{2}\right) > d\left(\frac{\alpha + \beta}{2}\right) = \frac{1}{2}(d(\alpha) + d(\beta)) \geqslant \frac{1}{2}(f(\alpha) + f(\beta))$$

or

$$f\left(\frac{\alpha + \beta}{2}\right) > \frac{1}{2}(f(\alpha) + f(\beta)),$$

contrary to hypothesis.

Z There exist everywhere discontinuous functions on **R** for which $f(x + y) = f(x) + f(y)$ identically; such a function satisfies the inequality of Proposition 18.4 and yet is not convex, for otherwise it would be continuous.

19. CONVEX FUNCTIONS ON A SUBSET OF A VECTOR SPACE

The criterion for convexity of Proposition 16.2 suggests a convenient procedure for defining the convexity of a numerical function defined on a subset X of a vector space E over the field **R**.

19.1. Definition.   LET f BE A FINITE NUMERICAL FUNCTION, DEFINED ON A SUBSET X OF A VECTOR SPACE E (OVER **R**).
WE SAY THAT f IS CONVEX IF THE SET $A_X(f)$ OF POINTS OF THE VECTOR SPACE E $\times$ **R** LYING ABOVE THE GRAPH OF f IS CONVEX.

19.2. Proposition.   *In order that a finite numerical function f defined on a subset X of a vector space E be convex, it is necessary and sufficient that X be a convex set and that the restriction of f to every segment I of X be convex.*

PROOF.   The condition is necessary, for if f is convex, the set $A_X(f)$ is convex; hence X, which is its projection on E, is also convex. On the other hand, for every segment I $\subset$ X the set $A_I(f)$ is the intersection of $A_X(f)$ with the convex set I $\times$ **R**; hence $A_I(f)$ is convex.
The condition is sufficient, for, let P_1 and P_2 be points of $A_X(f)$ and let p_1 and p_2 be their projections on X. If the restriction of f to the segment I $= [p_1 p_2]$ is convex, the segment $[P_1 P_2]$ belongs to $A_I(f)$, hence also to $A_X(f)$.
Several of the propositions established for convex functions of a real variable extend at once to these generalized convex functions. In particular, linear combinations with coefficients $\geqslant 0$ of convex func-

tions, the limits of convex functions, and the upper envelopes of convex functions are convex functions.

If we restrict ourselves to convex functions defined on an open convex subset X of $\mathbf{R}^n$, other properties can be generalized. For example, such an f is continuous and there exists at least one supporting hyperplane at every point of the graph of f. We shall not prove these last two properties.

19.3. Proposition. *If f is convex, the set $\{x : f(x) \leqslant 0\}$ is convex.*

More generally, if f is convex and g is concave, the set of points x such that $f(x) \leqslant g(x)$ is convex.

Indeed, if f is convex and if $f(a) \leqslant 0$, $f(b) \leqslant 0$, we also have $f(x) \leqslant 0$ for every $x \in [a, b]$; therefore the set in question is convex.

The second statement follows from the first on noting that $f - g$ is convex.

A similar result holds for the set $\{x : f(x) < g(x)\}$.

EXAMPLES.   The solid ellipsoid in $\mathbf{R}^n$ defined by $\Sigma\, x_p{}^2/a_p{}^2 \leqslant 1$ is convex.

Similarly, the set of $x \in \mathbf{R}^n$ such that $\Sigma\, \alpha_i \|\, x - a_i \,\| \leqslant 1$ is convex when the α_i are $\geqslant 0$.

19.4. Proposition. *Let X (Y) be a convex subset of a vector space E (F); let f be a convex function on Y, and let φ be an affine mapping of X into Y. Then $f \circ \varphi$ is a convex function on X.*

This is an immediate consequence of the relation

$$\varphi(\alpha_1 x_1 + \alpha_2 x_2) = \alpha_1 \varphi(x_1) + \alpha_2 \varphi(x_2) \qquad \text{when} \qquad \alpha_1 + \alpha_2 = 1.$$

EXAMPLE.   If f is a convex function on Y, the function on Y^2 defined by $(x, y) \to f(x - y)$ is convex since the mapping $(x, y) \to x - y$ is linear.

Positive-homogeneous convex functions

19.5. Definition.   LET f BE A NUMERICAL FUNCTION DEFINED ON A SUBSET X OF A VECTOR SPACE E (OVER $\mathbf{R}$). THEN f IS SAID TO BE *POSITIVE--HOMO-GENEOUS* IF X IS A CONE WITH VERTEX O AND IF $f(\lambda x) = \lambda f(x)$ FOR EVERY $x \in X$ AND $\lambda > 0$.

19.6. Proposition. *Let f be a finite positive-homogeneous numerical function defined on a convex cone X of a vector space E.*

1. *In order that f be a convex function, it is necessary and sufficient that* $f(x_1 + x_2) \leqslant f(x_1) + f(x_2)$ *for all* x_1, $x_2 \in X$.

2. *When in addition* $f \geqslant 0$, *then for f to be convex it is necessary and sufficient that the set* B *of points x of* X *at which* $f(x) \leqslant 1$ *be convex*.

PROOF.   1.   If f is convex, then for all x_1, $x_2 \in X$ we have

$$f(x_1 + x_2) = 2f\left(\frac{x_1 + x_2}{2}\right) \leqslant 2\left[f\left(\frac{x_1}{2}\right) + f\left(\frac{x_2}{2}\right)\right] = f(x_1) + f(x_2).$$

Conversely, if $f(u_1 + u_2) \leqslant f(u_1) + f(u_2)$ for all u_1, $u_2 \in X$, then for all α_1, $\alpha_2 \geqslant 0$ we have

$$f(\alpha_1 x_1 + \alpha_2 x_2) \leqslant f(\alpha_1 x_1) + f(\alpha_2 x_2) = \alpha_1 f(x_1) + \alpha_2 f(x_2).$$

Therefore f is convex.

2.   Let B be the set of $x \in X$ such that $f(x) \leqslant 1$.

If f is convex, Proposition 19.3 shows that B is convex. Conversely, suppose that $f \geqslant 0$ and B is convex.

If x_1, $x_2 \in X$, and if $k_1 > f(x_1)$, $k_2 > f(x_2)$, then

$$k_1^{-1}x_1 \in B \qquad \text{and} \qquad k_2^{-1}x_2 \in B.$$

Thus, since B is convex, the barycenter $(k_1 + k_2)^{-1}(x_1 + x_2)$ of these points also belongs to B; therefore

$$f(x_1 + x_2) \leqslant k_1 + k_2 \qquad \text{when} \quad k_1 > f(x_1) \quad \text{and} \quad k_2 > f(x_2).$$

It follows that

$$f(x_1 + x_2) \leqslant f(x_1) + f(x_2).$$

Thus f is convex.

EXAMPLE.   For every scalar $\alpha > 0$, the function f

$$(x_p) \rightarrow \left(\sum |x_p|^\alpha\right)^{1/\alpha}$$

is positive-homogeneous on $\mathbf{R}^n$. But if $\alpha \geqslant 1$, each of the functions $|x_p|^\alpha$ is convex; hence f^α is convex and the set $\{x : f(x) \leqslant 1\}$ is convex; therefore f is convex.

Twice-differentiable convex functions

Let f be a numerical function defined on a convex open subset X of $\mathbf{R}^n$. We assume that f has continuous second partial derivatives.

For every $a \in X$ and every $\alpha \in \mathbf{R}^n$, the mapping $\varphi : t \rightarrow f(a + t\alpha)$, which is defined on an open interval of $\mathbf{R}$ containing 0, has a second derivative at 0:

$$\varphi''(0) = \sum \alpha_i \alpha_j \frac{\partial^2 f}{\partial x_i \, \partial x_j} (a).$$

But the convexity of f is equivalent to that of its restrictions to the segments of X, that is, to that of the functions φ. This convexity is also expressed (Corollary 18.2) by the relation $\varphi''(0) \geqslant 0$ for all a, α; we can therefore state:

19.7. Proposition. *In order that a numerical function f with continuous second partial derivatives defined on an open convex set X in $\mathbf{R}^n$ be convex, it is necessary and sufficient that for every $a \in X$ the quadratic form*

$$\sum \alpha_i \alpha_j \frac{\partial^2 f}{\partial x_i \, \partial x_j} (a) \qquad be \ \geqslant 0.$$

Z 1. It should be noted that the relations $\partial^2 f / \partial x_i{}^2 \geqslant 0$ by no means suffice for the convexity of f. For example, the function $(x^2 + 3xy + 2y^2)$ is not convex in any open convex subset of $\mathbf{R}^2$.

2. If f is defined on an open nonconvex subset X of $\mathbf{R}^n$ and satisfies the condition of Proposition 19.7, then it is convex in every open convex subset of X, but cannot in general be extended to a convex function on a convex set containing X. An example is the function $f(x, y) = (y - x^2)^2 + x^4$ on the subset of $\mathbf{R}^2$ defined by $y < 4x^2$.

20. THE MEAN RELATIVE TO A MONOTONE FUNCTION

Even elementary analysis uses various averaging operations such as the arithmetic, geometric, quadratic, or harmonic mean. We are going to generalize these elementary notions and indicate some inequalities based on convexity.

To simplify the language, we shall here call every finite family $\mu = (\alpha_i , x_i)_{i \in I}$, where $x_i \in E$ and the α_i are numbers > 0, a *discrete measure* on the set E. We say that μ is carried by a subset X of E if X contains all the points x_i .

The total mass of $\mu = (\alpha_i , x_i)_{i \in I}$ is the number $\| \mu \| = \Sigma \alpha_i$. If φ denotes a mapping of E into another set F, and if $\mu = (\alpha_i , x_i)_{i \in I}$ is carried by E, we call the discrete measure $\varphi(\mu) = (\alpha_i , \varphi(x_i))_{i \in I}$ on F the image of μ under φ; clearly $\| \varphi(\mu) \| = \| \mu \|$.

If E is a vector space, the barycenter of μ is the point $\| \mu \|^{-1} \Sigma \alpha_i x_i$ of E, which we shall denote by $\mathscr{M}_1(\mu)$; for every scalar $k > 0$, the measure $k\mu = (k\alpha_i, x_i)_{i\in I}$ has the same barycenter as μ; in particular, for $k = \|\mu\|^{-1}$ the measure $k\mu$ has total mass 1, which is sometimes convenient.

The barycenter $\mathscr{M}_1(\mu)$ belongs to every convex set which carries μ; in particular, if $E = \mathbf{R}$, then

$$\inf(x_i) \leqslant \mathscr{M}_1(\mu) \leqslant \sup(x_i).$$

20.1. Definition. LET f BE A STRICTLY MONOTONE CONTINUOUS NUMERICAL FUNCTION ON AN INTERVAL A OF $\mathbf{R}$; LET $\mu = (\alpha_i, x_i)_{i\in I}$ BE A DISCRETE MEASURE ON A, AND LET f^{-1} DENOTE THE FUNCTION INVERSE TO f.

THE *MEAN OF μ RELATIVE TO* f IS DEFINED AS THE NUMBER $f^{-1}(\mathscr{M}_1(f(\mu)))$, THAT IS, THE NUMBER a SUCH THAT

$$\left(\sum_i \alpha_i\right) f(a) = \sum_i \alpha_i f(x_i).$$

WE SHALL DENOTE THIS NUMBER a BY $\mathscr{M}_f(\mu)$.

The existence of the number a follows from the fact that $\mathscr{M}_1(f(\mu)) \in f(A)$; its uniqueness follows from the fact that f is injective. It is clear that $\mathscr{M}_f(\mu) \in A$, and more precisely that

$$\inf(x_i) \leqslant \mathscr{M}_f(\mu) \leqslant \sup(x_i).$$

We also note for future use that $\mathscr{M}_f = \mathscr{M}_{-f}$.

EXAMPLE 1.   If we take for f the identity mapping $x \to x$ of $\mathbf{R}$ into $\mathbf{R}$, then

$$\mathscr{M}_f(\mu) = \mathscr{M}_1(\mu);$$

this mean will be called the *arithmetic* mean because, in the case where the α_i are equal, we have

$$\mathscr{M}_1(\mu) = n^{-1}\left(\sum x_i\right),$$

where n is the number of elements of I.

More generally, we will denote by $\mathscr{M}_r$ the mean relative to the numerical function $x \to x^r$, defined on $\mathbf{R}_+$ if $r > 0$, and on $\mathbf{R}_+^*$ if $r < 0$. For example, $\mathscr{M}_{-1}$ will be the *harmonic* mean, $\mathscr{M}_2$ the *quadratic* mean.

EXAMPLE 2.   For reasons which will be better understood shortly,

$\mathcal{M}_0$ denotes the mean relative to the function $x \rightarrow \log x$ defined on $\mathbf{R}_+{}^*$. When all the α_i are equal to 1, the relation

$$n \log a = \sum \log x_i = \log \left(\prod x_i \right)$$

shows that $\mathcal{M}_0(\mu) = (\prod x_i)^{1/n}$, that is, the geometric mean of the x_i. This is why $\mathcal{M}_0$ will be called the *geometric* mean.

COMPARISON OF MEANS. For every continuous strictly monotone function f on A, $\mathcal{M}_f$ is a numerical function on the set of discrete measures on A. We propose to investigate under what conditions $\mathcal{M}_f = \mathcal{M}_g$ or, more generally, $\mathcal{M}_f \leqslant \mathcal{M}_g$.

20.2. Lemma. *Let f be a convex numerical function on an interval A of $\mathbf{R}$. Then for every discrete measure μ on A*

$$f(\mathcal{M}_1(\mu)) \leqslant \mathcal{M}_1(f(\mu)).$$

The equality holds only if f is affine on the smallest interval which carries μ.

PROOF. If $\mu = (\alpha_i, x_i)_{i \in I}$, let G be the barycenter of the measure $(\alpha_i, M(x_i))_{i \in I}$, where $M(x_i)$ denotes the point of the graph Γ of f with abscissa x_i.

The coordinates x, y of G are

$$x = \mathcal{M}_1(\mu) \qquad \text{and} \qquad y = \mathcal{M}_1(f(\mu)).$$

Since f is convex, the set $A(f)$ is convex, and therefore contains the barycenter G; in other words, G lies above the graph of f, which is expressed by the relation $f(x) \leqslant y$, and which is just the desired inequality.

If f is affine on the interval $[\inf(x_i), \sup(x_i)]$, G evidently lies on the graph of f, hence $f(x) = y$. If f is not affine on the above interval, denote $\inf(x_i)$ by x_1, and $\sup(x_i)$ by x_2; for every $x \in (x_1, x_2)$, $M(x)$ lies strictly above Γ; this is in particular the case for the barycenter of the discrete measure $\nu' = (\alpha_i, M(x_i))_{i=1.2}$; we also put $\nu'' = (\alpha_i, M(x_i))_{i \neq 1.2}$.

A well-known property of barycenters shows that G belongs to the segment joining the barycenters of ν' and ν''; since both of these lie above Γ, and one of them strictly above Γ, G lies strictly above Γ; in other words, $f(x) < y$.

EXAMPLE. If f is strictly convex, then for every μ which is not carried by a single point we have

$$f(\mathcal{M}_1(\mu)) < \mathcal{M}_1(f(\mu)).$$

20.3. Corollary. *Let f be a continuous numerical function which is strictly increasing on an interval* A *of* **R**; *then*

$$(\mathscr{M}_1 \leqslant \mathscr{M}_f) \Leftrightarrow (f \text{ is convex}); \qquad (\mathscr{M}_f \leqslant \mathscr{M}_1) \Leftrightarrow (f \text{ is concave}).$$

When f is decreasing, the analogous criteria are obtained by interchanging the words "convex" and "concave."

In these various cases (f convex or concave) $\mathscr{M}_1(\mu) = \mathscr{M}_f(\mu)$ only if f is affine on an interval which carries μ.

PROOF.   Suppose f is increasing. If f is convex, Lemma 20.2 shows that

$$f(\mathscr{M}_1(\mu)) \leqslant \mathscr{M}_1(f(\mu)), \qquad \text{whence} \qquad \mathscr{M}_1(\mu) \leqslant f^{-1}(\mathscr{M}_1(f(\mu))) = \mathscr{M}_f(\mu).$$

Conversely, if $\mathscr{M}_1 \leqslant \mathscr{M}_f$, which can be expressed by

$$f(\mathscr{M}_1(\mu)) \leqslant \mathscr{M}_1(f(\mu)) \qquad \text{for every} \quad \mu,$$

then in particular we have, for all μ of the form $(\alpha_i, x_i)_{i=1.2}$ with $\alpha_1 + \alpha_2 = 1$,

$$f(\alpha_1 x_1 + \alpha_2 x_2) \leqslant \alpha_1 f(x_1) + \alpha_2 f(x_2),$$

that is, f is convex.

It follows from Lemma 20.2 that if f is convex, $\mathscr{M}_1(\mu) = \mathscr{M}_f(\mu)$ only if f is affine on an interval which carries μ.

The case where f is concave is treated similarly. If f is decreasing, then $-f$ is increasing, and since $\mathscr{M}_f = \mathscr{M}_{-f}$, the stated equivalences follow from those which have just been established.

20.4. Theorem. *Let f and g be continuous strictly monotone functions on an interval* A *of* **R**.

1. $\mathscr{M}_f = \mathscr{M}_g$ *is equivalent to the relation*

$$g = \alpha f + \beta, \qquad where \qquad \alpha, \beta \in \mathbf{R}, \quad with \quad \alpha \neq 0.$$

2.   *The relation $\mathscr{M}_f \leqslant \mathscr{M}_g$ is equivalent to the assertion that either g is increasing and $g \circ f^{-1}$ is convex, or g is decreasing and $g \circ f^{-1}$ is concave.*

In these two cases, when $g \circ f^{-1}$ is strictly convex or concave, $\mathscr{M}_f(\mu) = \mathscr{M}_g(\mu)$ holds only when μ is carried by a single point.

PROOF.   1.   The relation $\mathscr{M}_f = \mathscr{M}_g$ means that for every measure $(\alpha_i, x_i)_{i \in I}$ such that $\sum \alpha_i = 1$, we have

$$f^{-1}\left(\sum \alpha_i f(x_i)\right) = g^{-1}\left(\sum \alpha_i g(x_i)\right).$$

If we put

$$h = g \circ f^{-1} \quad \text{and} \quad y_i = f(x_i),$$

this relation becomes

$$h\left(\sum \alpha_i y_i\right) = \sum \alpha_i (h \circ f)(x_i) = \sum \alpha_i h(y_i)$$

or

$$\mathscr{M}_1(f(\mu)) = \mathscr{M}_h(f(\mu)).$$

Since the discrete measure $f(\mu)$ can be an arbitrary discrete measure on $f(A)$, this relation is written simply as $\mathscr{M}_1 = \mathscr{M}_h$. Corollary 20.3 shows that this implies that h is both convex and concave, hence affine; in other words, we have

$$(g \circ f^{-1})(y) = \alpha y + \beta \quad \text{with} \quad \alpha \neq 0,$$

or, putting $f^{-1}(y) = x$,

$$g(x) = \alpha f(x) + \beta.$$

2.   We now study the inequality $\mathscr{M}_f \leqslant \mathscr{M}_g$, assuming to begin with f and g are increasing. A calculation parallel to the preceding shows that the relation $\mathscr{M}_f \leqslant \mathscr{M}_g$ is equivalent to $\mathscr{M}_1 \leqslant \mathscr{M}_h$ which, by virtue of Corollary 20.3, is equivalent to saying that $h = g \circ f^{-1}$ is convex.

If f is increasing and g decreasing, since $\mathscr{M}_g = \mathscr{M}_{-g}$, the inequality $\mathscr{M}_f \leqslant \mathscr{M}_g$ expresses the convexity of the function $-g \circ f^{-1}$, hence the concavity of $g \circ f^{-1}$.

The other two cases are deduced from this by observing that the two functions $u \to g(u)$ and $u \to g(-u)$ are simultaneously either convex or concave.

When h is strictly convex or concave, Corollary 20.3 shows that $\mathscr{M}_1(f(\mu)) = \mathscr{M}_h(f(\mu))$ only if $f(\mu)$, hence also μ, is carried by a single point, which proves the last assertion.

20.5. A practical criterion. *Suppose that f and g have second derivatives with f' and g' everywhere $\neq 0$; then*

$$(\mathscr{M}_f \leqslant \mathscr{M}_g) \Leftrightarrow (f''/f' \leqslant g''/g').$$

Proof.   Since replacing f by $-f$ or g by $-g$ leaves invariant all the quantities entering into the relation to be established, we can consider only the case of f, g increasing.

The relation $\mathscr{M}_f \leqslant \mathscr{M}_g$ is then equivalent to the convexity of $g \circ f^{-1}$; let us put

$$F(y) = (g \circ f^{-1})(y) \quad \text{and} \quad y = f(x).$$

Then

$$\frac{dF}{dy} = \frac{dF}{dx}\frac{dx}{dy} = \frac{g'(x)}{f'(x)}.$$

The convexity of F is expressed by dF/dy being an increasing function of y or, since f is increasing with respect to x, by g'/f' being an increasing function of x, that is $(g''f' - g'f'') \geqslant 0$, or $f''/f' \leqslant g''/g'$.

EXAMPLE.   Put

$$f_r(x) = x^r \quad \text{and} \quad f_0(x) = \log x.$$

Then for all r

$$f_r''/f_r' = (r - 1)x^{-1} \quad \text{on} \quad (0, \infty).$$

But $(r - 1)x^{-1}$ is an increasing function of r; therefore $\mathscr{M}_r$ *is also an increasing function of r.* More precisely, since $(r - 1)x^{-1}$ is a strictly increasing function of r, then if $r < r'$ and if μ is not carried by a point,

$$\mathscr{M}_r(\mu) < \mathscr{M}_{r'}(\mu).$$

We note here that the case $r = 0$ is not exceptional, which justifies the notation adopted.

In particular we obtain the classical inequalities:

harmonic mean $\leqslant$ geometric mean $\leqslant$ arithmetic mean $\leqslant$ quadratic mean.

REMARK.   Criterion 20.5 is particularly interesting for, in the family of functions being considered, it shows that each of the classes of functions f which give the same mean is characterized by the quotient f''/f'; these quotients constitute a vector space of functions on A, whose natural order goes over into the order on the family of means.

20.6. Proposition.   Hölder's inequality.   *Let $\alpha, \beta, ..., \lambda$ be   a   finite sequence   of   numbers >0 such   that $\alpha + \beta + \cdots + \lambda = 1$,   and   let $(a_i)_{i \in I}$, $(b_i)_{i \in I}$, ..., $(l_i)_{i \in I}$ be a sequence of the same length of finite families of numbers $\geqslant 0$.*
    Then

$$\sum_i a_i^{\alpha} b_i^{\beta} \cdots l_i^{\lambda} \leqslant \left(\sum a_i\right)^{\alpha} \left(\sum b_i\right)^{\beta} \cdots \left(\sum l_i\right)^{\lambda}. \tag{1}$$

The equality holds only when either all the elements of one family are zero or all of the families are proportional.

PROOF. If all the elements of one family are zero, the relation becomes $0 = 0$. In the contrary case, we can write

$$\frac{\sum a_i^\alpha b_i^\beta \cdots l_i^\lambda}{(\sum a_i)^\alpha (\sum b_i)^\beta \cdots (\sum l_i)^\lambda} = \sum \left(\frac{a_i}{\sum a_i}\right)^\alpha \left(\frac{b_i}{\sum b_i}\right)^\beta \cdots \left(\frac{l_i}{\sum l_i}\right)^\lambda. \qquad (2)$$

But the relation $\mathscr{M}_0 \leqslant \mathscr{M}_1$ shows that

$$A^\alpha B^\beta \cdots L^\lambda \leqslant \alpha A + \beta B + \cdots + \lambda L,$$

with equality only if $A = B = \cdots = L$; the right side of (2) is therefore bounded from above by

$$\sum \left(\alpha \frac{a_i}{\sum a_i} + \beta \frac{b_i}{\sum b_i} + \cdots + \lambda \frac{l_i}{\sum l_i}\right) = \alpha + \beta + \cdots + \lambda = 1,$$

with equality only if, for all i,

$$\frac{a_i}{\sum a_i} = \frac{b_i}{\sum b_i} = \cdots = \frac{l_i}{\sum l_i},$$

which asserts the proportionality of the families (a_i), (b_i), ...

Another form of Hölder's inequality

Let r be a number >0; we replace, in (1), a_i by $\omega_i a_i^{r/\alpha}$, b_i by $\omega_i b_i^{r/\beta}$, ..., where the ω_i are >0, obtaining

$$\sum \omega_i (a_i b_i \cdots l_i)^r \leqslant \left(\sum \omega_i a_i^{r/\alpha}\right)^\alpha \left(\sum \omega_i b_i^{r/\beta}\right)^\beta \cdots .$$

With a change of notation for the exponents, this relation can be written as

$$\left(\sum \omega_i (a_i b_i \cdots l_i)^r\right)^{1/r} \leqslant \left(\sum \omega_i a_i^{p_1}\right)^{1/p_1} \left(\sum \omega_i b_i^{p_2}\right)^{1/p_2} \cdots ,$$

where $p_1, p_2, \ldots > 0$ with

$$1/p_1 + 1/p_2 + \cdots = 1/r.$$

This relation can be written more concisely as

$$\mathscr{M}_r(ab \cdots l) \leqslant \mathscr{M}_{p_1}(a)\mathscr{M}_{p_2}(b) \cdots .$$

A particularly important case is that in which $r = 1$ and where there are only two families.

20.7. Minkowski's inequality. This inequality says simply that a certain positive-homogeneous function is convex in $\mathbf{R}^n$:

Given numbers α_1, α_2, ..., $\alpha_n \geqslant 0$ and a number $p \geqslant 1$, we consider the function f defined on $\mathbf{R}^n$ by

$$x = (x_i) \rightarrow \left(\sum \alpha_i \mid x_i \mid^p \right)^{1/p}.$$

The function f is clearly positive-homogeneous and, as in the example following Proposition 19.6, is convex. We therefore have the inequality (of Minkowski)

$$\left(\sum \alpha_i \mid x_i + y_i \mid^p \right)^{1/p} \leqslant \left(\sum \alpha_i \mid x_i \mid^p \right)^{1/p} + \left(\sum \alpha_i \mid y_i \mid^p \right)^{1/p}.$$

When the α_i are >0, with $p > 1$, f is strictly convex (except on the rays issuing from the origin O), and therefore the inequality is strict when the families (x_i) and (y_i) are not proportional.

This inequality extends at once to x_i, y_i complex.

PROBLEMS

Note: The rather difficult problems are marked with an asterisk.

NUMERICAL FUNCTIONS DEFINED ON AN ARBITRARY SET

*1. Let $(x_i)_{i \in I}$ and $(y_j)_{j \in J}$ be finite families of real numbers $\geqslant 0$ such that

$$\sum_I x_i = \sum_J y_j .$$

Show that there exists a finite family $(z_{ij})_{(i,j) \in I \times J}$ of real numbers $\geqslant 0$ such that

$$x_i = \sum_j z_{ij} \quad \text{for every} \quad i \in I$$

and

$$y_j = \sum_i z_{ij} \quad \text{for every} \quad j \in J.$$

*2. Extend the preceding result to families of elements $\geqslant 0$ of the ordered space $\mathscr{F}(E, \mathbf{R})$, where E is an arbitrary set.

NUMERICAL FUNCTIONS DEFINED ON A TOPOLOGICAL SPACE

3. Let f be a numerical function defined on $\mathbf{R}^2$, such that for every x the mapping $y \rightarrow f(x, y)$ is increasing, and for every y the mapping $x \rightarrow f(x, y)$ is increasing. Show that f tends to a limit when x and $y \rightarrow +\infty$, in a sense which it is required to make precise.

4. Let f be a numerical function defined on $\mathbf{R}$, and define A as the set of points a of $\mathbf{R}$ such that

$$\limsup_{x \rightarrow a, x > a} f(x) \neq \limsup_{x \rightarrow a, x < a} f(x).$$

Show that A is at most countable.

***5.** Let f be a numerical function defined on $\mathbf{R}$. Show that the set of points a of $\mathbf{R}$ such that $\lim_{x \rightarrow a, x \neq a} f(x)$ exists and is different from $f(a)$ is at most countable.

***6.** Let f be a numerical function defined on $\mathbf{R}$. One says that f has a *relative maximum* at a point $a \in \mathbf{R}$ if there exists a neighborhood V of a such that $f(x) \leqslant f(a)$ for every $x \in V$. Let A be the set of all such points a. Show that $f(A)$ is at most countable.

7. Let $(f_i)_{i \in I}$ be an equicontinuous family of finite numerical functions defined on a metric space E.

(a) Show that the functions $\sup_{i \in I} f_i$ and $\inf_{i \in I} f_i$ are uniformly continuous.

(b) Show that the family (f_J) of finite functions of the form $\sup_{i \in J} f_i$ or $\inf_{i \in J} f_i$, where J is an arbitrary subset of I, is equicontinuous.

SEMICONTINUOUS NUMERICAL FUNCTIONS

8. Let f and g be lower semicontinuous mappings of a topological space E into $\mathbf{R}$. Show that if $f + g$ is continuous, then f and g are also.

***9.** Let f be a finite numerical lower semicontinuous function on the interval $[0, 1]$.

(a) Show that f is the upper envelope of the continuous functions $g \leqslant f$.

(b) Show that f is the limit of an increasing sequence of continuous functions.

***10.** Extend the preceding result to every finite and lower semi-continuous function f on a metric space with a countable base.

11. Let f be a numerical lower semicontinuous function defined on a topological space E. Show that for every nonempty subset A of E we have

$$\sup_{x \in \bar{A}} f(x) = \sup_{x \in A} f(x).$$

12. For every rational number $r = p/q$ in irreducible form ($q > 0$) put $f(r) = q$; show that f is lower semicontinuous on $\mathbf{Q}$ and that at every point $r \in \mathbf{Q}$, the oscillation of f is $+\infty$.

*13. Let E be a metric space and let K be a compact subset of $\mathbf{R} \times$ E. For every $x \in \mathbf{R}$ we put $q(x) =$ diameter of the set of points of K with abscissa x. Show that $q(x)$ is an upper semicontinuous function.

14. Let f be a numerical function defined on a topological space E. Show that the set of points of E at which the oscillation of f is $\geqslant \lambda$ (where $\lambda > 0$) is closed.

Deduce from this that the set of points of continuity of f is a countable intersection of open sets.

*15. Let f be a continuous numerical function defined on the square $C = [0, 1]^2$; f is said to be piecewise affine if there exists a finite covering of C by triangles, on each of which f is affine. Let $\mathscr{P}$ be the vector space of these functions, taken with the topology of uniform convergence. Let $\alpha(f)$ be the ordinary area of the graph of f in the Euclidean space $\mathbf{R}^3$. Show that $\alpha(f)$ is lower semicontinuous on $\mathscr{P}$.

STONE-WEIERSTRASS THEOREM

16. It is required to show, using an induction argument, that there exists a sequence (p_n) of real polynomials which is increasing on the interval $[0, 1]$ and which converges uniformly to $\sqrt{t}$ on this interval. To show this, put

$$p_{n+1}(t) = p_n(t) + \tfrac{1}{2}(t - p_n^2(t)) \quad \text{and} \quad p_1 = 0,$$

and show that the sequence (p_n) thus defined recursively has the required properties.

17. Let E be a compact space and let (f_i), where $i = 1, 2, ..., n$, be a family of n elements of $\mathscr{C}(E, \mathbf{R})$ which separates the points of E. Show that E is homeomorphic with a subset of $\mathbf{R}^n$.

18. Let a_1, a_2, a_3 be three noncolinear points of $\mathbf{R}^2$. We denote by f_i the function $x \to \| x - a_i \|$. Show that every continuous numerical function on $\mathbf{R}^2$ is the limit of a sequence of polynomials (without constant terms) in f_1, f_2, f_3 or in the squares of these functions, which converges uniformly on every compact set in $\mathbf{R}^2$.

THEOREMS OF FINITE INCREASE

19. Let f be a finite and continuous numerical function on an interval $I = [a, b]$ of $\mathbf{R}$.

One says that f is *increasing to the right* at a point $x_0 \in \overset{\circ}{I}$ if there exists a number $x_1 > x_0$ such that $f(x_0) \leqslant f(x)$ for all $x \in [x_0, x_1]$. Decrease to the right is similarly defined.

Show that if $f(a) = f(b) = 0$, there exists a point c_1 of $\overset{\circ}{I}$ at which f is increasing to the right, and a point c_2 of $\overset{\circ}{I}$ at which f is decreasing to the right (same for left).

20. Let f be a continuous and differentiable numerical function on an interval $[a, b]$. Show, using the classical theorem of Rolle, that even if f' is not continuous, f' assumes all the values lying between $f'(a)$ and $f'(b)$ (show that for every λ such that $f'(a) < \lambda < f'(b)$ there exists an $x \in [a, b]$ such that one of the chords $M(a)M(x)$ and $M(x)M(b)$ has slope λ). Deduce from this that $f'([a, b])$ is connected.

21. Let f be a continuous and differentiable numerical function on an *open* interval (a, b). If $\alpha = \lim_{x \to a} f'(x)$ exists and is finite, show that $\lim_{x \to a} f(x)$ exists and that f has a continuous extension to $[a, b)$ which is right differentiable at a, with derivative equal to α.

CONVEX FUNCTIONS

22. Let $(f_i)_{i \in I}$ be a family of convex functions on an open interval I of $\mathbf{R}$. Show that if the family (f_i) is uniformly bounded from above and if there exists a $c \in I$ such that the set $(f_i(c))$ is bounded from below, the family (f_i) is equicontinuous on every compact interval of I.

23. Let (f_n) be a sequence of convex functions on an open interval I of $\mathbf{R}$ which converges pointwise to a finite function f. Show by using the preceding problem that the convergence is uniform on every compact interval of I.

***24.** Extend the preceding problems to convex functions on a convex subset X of $\mathbf{R}^2$ (or more generally of $\mathbf{R}^n$).

25. Let f and g be convex functions on a convex subset X of a vector space; show that if $(f + g)$ is affine on X, then f and g are also.

26. Let f be a convex function on a compact interval $[a, b]$ and such that $f_r'(a)$ and $f_l'(b)$ are finite. Show that f is the restriction to $[a, b]$ of a convex function on **R**.

27. Let g be a continuous numerical function of the pair (x, t), where $a \leqslant x \leqslant b$ and $\alpha \leqslant t \leqslant \beta$. If g is a convex function of x for every t, prove the convexity of the function

$$f(x) = \int_\alpha^\beta g(x, t)\, dt.$$

28. Let f be a convex function on **R** and let φ be a continuous function $\geqslant 0$ on **R**, which vanishes off a compact set.

(a) Show that the function $F(x) = \int_{\mathbf{R}} f(x - t)\varphi(t)\, dt$ is convex on **R**.

(b) Let ψ be the function defined by

$$\psi(t) = 0 \qquad\qquad \text{for } |t| \geqslant 1;$$
$$\psi(t) = k \exp[(t^2 - 1)^{-1}] \qquad \text{for } |t| < 1,$$

where k is such that the integral of ψ over **R** equals 1. Show that ψ has derivatives of all orders on **R**.

(c) Show that the convex function

$$f_a(x) = a \int_{-\infty}^{+\infty} f(x - t)\psi(at)\, dt = a \int_{-\infty}^{+\infty} f(t)\psi(a(x - t))\, dt$$

is infinitely differentiable and that f_a converges to f uniformly on every compact interval of **R** as $a \to +\infty$.

29. Let f be an increasing convex function in $(0, +\infty)$. Show that either $f = $ constant or $\lim_{x \to +\infty} f(x) = +\infty$.

30. Let f be a convex function in an interval $[a, +\infty)$. Show that $f(x)/x$ tends to a finite limit or to $+\infty$ as $x \to +\infty$. Show that when this limit is $\leqslant 0$, the function f is decreasing on $[a, +\infty)$.

*31. Let f be a convex function in the interval $[0, +\infty)$.

(a) Show that the function φ defined by

$$\varphi(x) = f(x) - xf_r'(x) \qquad \text{(the y intercept of the right tangent)}$$

is decreasing.

(b) Show that if $\lim_{x \to +\infty} \varphi(x)$ is a finite number β, the same is true of $\alpha = \lim_{x \to +\infty} f(x)/x$ and that $f(x) - (\alpha x + \beta)$ is $\geqslant 0$ and tends to 0 as $x \to +\infty$.

32. Extend Proposition 18.4 to semicontinuous functions f such that for all a, $b \in I$ there exists an $x \in (a, b)$ for which $M(x)$ lies below the segment $M(a)M(b)$.

33. Let f be a strictly increasing (decreasing) function on an open interval I of **R**. Show that for f to be convex it is necessary and sufficient that its inverse f^{-1} be concave (convex).

34. Let f be a continuous finite numerical function on an interval I of **R**. Show that if for every $a \in I$ there exists an open interval (of a line in **R**^{2}) containing $M(a)$ and lying below the graph of f, then f is convex.

35. Using the properties of the projective transformation $(x, y) \rightarrow (x^{-1}, yx^{-1})$ of the halfplane $x > 0$ onto itself, show that if f is convex for $x > 0$ the same is true of the function $x \rightarrow xf(x^{-1})$ and conversely.
   Then give another proof using Problem 28.

36. (a) Using Problem 28, show that if f and g are positive, convex, and increasing (or decreasing) on the same interval I, the product fg is convex.

   (b) Using the same method, state a criterion for $f \circ g$ to be convex.

37. Let f be a positive function on an interval I $\subset$ **R**. We shall say that f is *logarithmically convex* if $\log f$ is convex in I.
   Show that if f is logarithmically convex, f is convex.
   Show that if f and g are logarithmically convex, so is fg.
   Use Problem 28 here, as well as in the following problems.

*38. Show that the sum of two logarithmically convex functions is logarithmically convex.

39. Let $f(x, t)$ be a finite numerical function >0, defined and continuous on the product I $\times$ J of two open intervals I and J of **R** and such that, for every $t \in$ J, $f(x, t)$ is logarithmically convex with respect to x.
   Show that if, for every $x \in$ I, the integral

$$g(x) = \int_J f(x, t) \, dt$$

is convergent, then g is logarithmically convex. Use Problem 38.

40. Let

$$\Gamma(x) = \int_0^\infty e^{-t} t^{x-1} \, dt.$$

Show, by using Problem 39, that for every $x > 0$ this integral is finite and that the function Γ is logarithmically convex on $(0, \infty)$.
   Show that $\Gamma(n + 1) = n!$ for every integer n.

41. Let $\mathcal{K}$ be the set of functions which are concave and positive in an open interval (a, b).

(a) Show that $\mathcal{K}$ is ordered by the relation

$$f \prec g \quad \text{if} \quad g - f \in \mathcal{K}.$$

(b) We will say that a function $f \in \mathcal{K}$ is *extremal* if every relation $f \prec g$, where $g \in \mathcal{K}$, implies that $g = \lambda f$ with $\lambda \in [0, 1]$.

Show that the only extremal elements of $\mathcal{K}$ are the traces of functions f which vanish at a and b and are affine on two intervals $[a, c]$, $[c, b]$ (where $c \in (a, b)$), or of functions which are affine on (a, b) and vanish at a or b.

(c) Show, by using Problem 28, that $\mathcal{K}$ is a lattice for the order $\prec$.

MEANS AND INEQUALITIES

42. Show that the area of a triangle of perimeter $2p$ is maximum when its sides a, b, c are equal (use the relation $\mathcal{M}_0 \prec \mathcal{M}_1$ and the expression for the area as a function of p, $(p - a)$, $(p - b)$, $(p - c)$).

43. Show that the volume of a rectangular parallelepiped of given area is a maximum when it is a cube.

44. Let a_1, a_2, ..., a_n be numbers > 0, and let a be their geometric mean. Show that

$$(1 + a_1)(1 + a_2) \cdots (1 + a_n) \geqslant (1 + a)^n,$$

with the equality holding only if the a_i are equal.

45. Let μ be a discrete measure on $(0, \infty)$. Show that the function $r \to (\mathcal{M}_r(\mu))^r$ is logarithmically convex.

46. Let φ be a continuous numerical function on an open interval I of **R**, and let $a \in I$.

(a) Show that there exists a strictly increasing function Φ (and only one) on $(0, \infty)$ such that

$$\Phi'' = \varphi\Phi'; \qquad \Phi(a) = 0; \qquad \Phi'(a) = 1.$$

(b) If μ denotes an arbitrary discrete measure on I, we put

$$\mathrm{I}(\varphi) = \Phi(\mathcal{M}_\Phi(\mu)).$$

Show that the function I is logarithmically convex in the vector space $\mathscr{C}(\mathrm{I}, \mathbf{R})$.

47. For every $f \in \mathscr{C}([0, 1], \mathbf{R})$ and every $p > 0$ we put

$$N_p(f) = \left(\int_0^1 |f(x)|^p \, dx \right)^{1/p}.$$

(a) Show that if $p > 1$, N_p is a convex function on $\mathscr{C}([0, 1], \mathbf{R})$. From now on we assume that f is fixed and > 0.

(b) Show that the function $p \to N_p(f)$ is increasing and infinitely differentiable.

(c) Show that $(N_p(f))^p$ is a logarithmically convex function of p.

(d) Show that $N_p(f)$ is a logarithmically convex function of p^{-1} (use Problem 35).

48. With the notation of Problem 47, show that if $p^{-1} + q^{-1} = 1$, then

$$N_1(fg) \leqslant N_p(f)N_q(g).$$

*49. Let $\varphi, \psi, \ldots$ denote strictly increasing continuous functions on $[0, \infty)$, and for every $f \in \mathscr{C}([0, 1], \mathbf{R})$ with $f \geqslant 0$ define $\mathscr{M}_\varphi(f)$ by the relation

$$\varphi(\mathscr{M}_\varphi(f)) = \int_0^1 \varphi(f(x)) \, dx.$$

Show that $\mathscr{M}_\varphi \leqslant \mathscr{M}_\psi$ is equivalent to the convexity of $\psi \circ \varphi^{-1}$.

50. Let φ be a continuous strictly increasing function on an interval $[0, a]$, with $\varphi(0) = 0$, and let ψ be the inverse of φ.
Show that for all x, y such that $x \in [0, a]$, $y \in [0, \varphi(a)]$,

$$xy \leqslant \int_0^x \varphi(t) \, dt + \int_0^y \psi(t) \, dt,$$

with the equality holding only if $y = \varphi(x)$.

51. With the same notation, we denote by Φ and Ψ the primitives of φ and ψ which vanish at 0 (i.e., $\Phi(0) = \Psi(0) = 0$ and $\Phi' = \varphi$, $\Psi' = \psi$).
Now let f and g be functions which are continuous on $[0, 1]$ and have values in $[0, a]$ and $[0, \varphi(a)]$, respectively. Show that

$$\int_0^1 f(u)g(u) \, du \leqslant \int_0^1 \Phi(f(u)) \, du + \int_0^1 \Psi(g(u)) \, du.$$

DEFINITIONS AND AXIOMS

UPPER ENVELOPE. The *upper envelope* of a family $(f_i)_{i \in I}$ of numerical functions on a set E is the function

$$f = \sup_{i \in I} f_i$$

defined by

$$f(x) = \sup_{i \in I} f_i(x) \qquad \text{for every} \quad x \in E.$$

LIMIT SUPERIOR. Let f be a numerical function on a set E, and let $\mathscr{B}$ be a filter base on E.

The *limit superior* of f along $\mathscr{B}$ is defined as the supremum of $\bar{f}(\mathscr{B})$ (where $\bar{f}(\mathscr{B}) = \bigcap_{B \in \mathscr{B}} \overline{f(B)}$), and is denoted by $\lim_{\mathscr{B}} \sup f$.

LOWER SEMICONTINUITY. A numerical function f defined on a topological space E is said to be *lower semicontinuous* at the point a if for every $\lambda < f(a)$ there exists a neighborhood V of a such that $\lambda < f(V)$.

CONVEX FUNCTIONS OF ONE VARIABLE. Let f be a finite numerical function defined on an interval I of **R**. Then f is said to be *convex* if, for all x_1, $x_2 \in T$, every point $M(x)$ of the graph of f such that $x \in [x_1, x_2]$ lies below the segment $M(x_1)M(x_2)$.

CONVEX FUNCTIONS ON A SUBSET OF A VECTOR SPACE. Let f be a finite numerical function defined on a subset of a vector space E (over **R**).

Then f is said to be *convex* if the set of points of the vector space E $\times$ **R** lying above the graph of f is convex.

POSITIVE-HOMOGENEOUS FUNCTIONS. Let f be a numerical function defined on a subset X of a vector space E (over **R**). Then f is said to be *positive-homogeneous* if X is a cone with vertex O and if

$$f(\lambda x) = \lambda f(x) \qquad \text{for every} \quad x \in X \quad \text{and every} \quad \lambda > 0.$$

THE MEAN RELATIVE TO A MONOTONE FUNCTION. Let f be a continuous strictly monotone numerical function on an interval A of **R**, and let $\mu = (\alpha_i, x_i)_{i \in I}$ be a discrete measure on A.

The *mean of μ relative to f* is defined as the number a such that

$$\left(\sum_i \alpha_i \right) f(a) = \sum_i \alpha_i f(x_i);$$

the number a is denoted by $\mathscr{M}_f(\mu)$.

TRACE OF A MAPPING. If f is a mapping of a space E into a space F, and X is a subset of E, then the *trace of f on* X (or *restriction of f to* X) is the mapping g of X into F defined by $g(x) = f(x)$, $x \in X$.

BIBLIOGRAPHY

BOURBAKI, N., *Fonctions d'une variable réelle*, Chapters I, II, III (Actualités scientifiques et industrielles, No. 1074). Hermann, Paris.

HARDY, G. H., LITTLEWOOD, J. E., and POLYA, G., *Inequalities*. Cambridge Univ. Press, London and New York, 1952.

CHAPTER III

Topological Vector Spaces

We have emphasized in Chapter I, Section 22, the interest in putting topologies on spaces of functions, and have given several examples of such topologies.

We are now going to systematically study the most useful of these spaces, namely those which have the structure of a vector space over **R** or **C**.

I. GENERAL TOPOLOGICAL VECTOR SPACES. EXAMPLES

1. DEFINITION AND ELEMENTARY PROPERTIES OF TOPOLOGICAL VECTOR SPACES

In Chapter I, Section 14, we defined the notions of a topological group, ring, and field by a condition of compatibility between the topology and the algebraic structure. A vector space over **R** or **C** has not only an addition, but also a multiplication by the elements of **R** or **C**; we are thus led, if we wish to define a useful topology on such a space, to also bring in the topology of the underlying field.

To simplify the statements, we shall denote the underlying field by **K** whenever no properties particular to **R** or **C** are involved.

1.1. Definition. LET E BE A SET HAVING BOTH THE STRUCTURE OF A VECTOR SPACE OVER THE FIELD **K** AND AT THE SAME TIME A TOPOLOGY; WE SAY THAT THESE TWO STRUCTURES ARE *COMPATIBLE* IF:

1. THE TOPOLOGY OF E IS COMPATIBLE WITH THE ADDITIVE GROUP STRUCTURE OF E.

2. THE MAPPING $(\lambda, x) \to \lambda x$ OF THE TOPOLOGICAL SPACE **K** $\times$ E INTO E IS CONTINUOUS.

THE SET E WITH THESE TWO COMPATIBLE STRUCTURES IS CALLED A *TOPOLOGICAL VECTOR SPACE* (ABBREVIATED TVS), *REAL* OR *COMPLEX* ACCORDING AS **K** IS **R** OR **C**.

183

We note at this point that if E is a TVS over **C**, the fact that **R** is a subfield of **C** implies that the topology of E is also compatible with its TVS structure over **R**. This remark will enable us, when it is useful, and regardless of what **K** is, to use the properties of E regarded as a vector space over **R**, for example, the properties of its convex subsets.

EXAMPLE 1.   We mention without proof, since it will be a consequence of later results, that the product **K**^{n}, and the space $\mathscr{C}([0, 1], \mathbf{K})$ taken with the topology of uniform convergence, are topological vector spaces.

EXAMPLE 2.   On the other hand, the vector space $\mathscr{C}(\mathbf{R}, \mathbf{R})$ of continuous numerical functions on **R**, with the topology of uniform convergence (associated with the ecart $d(f, g) = \sup |f(x) - g(x)|$), is not a topological vector space. In fact, its topology is indeed compatible with its group structure, but λf is not a continuous function of the pair (λ, f) since, for example, if f is an unbounded function, λf does not converge uniformly to the function O as $\lambda \to 0$.

1.2. Proposition.   *The compatibility of a topology and a vector space structure on a set* E *can be expressed by the following conditions*:

1   *The mapping* $(x, y) \to (x + y)$ *of* E × E *into* E *is continuous.*

2.   *For every* $a \in$ E, *the mapping* $\lambda \to \lambda a$ *of* **K** *into* E *is continuous at the point* $\lambda \doteq 0$.

3.   *For every* $\alpha \in \mathbf{K}$, *the mapping* $x \to \alpha x$ *of* E *into* E *is continuous at the point* $x =$ O.

4.   *The mapping* $(\lambda, x) \to \lambda x$ *of* **K** × E *into* E *is continuous at the point* (0, O).

PROOF.   By Definition 1.1, if the structures are compatible, then conditions 1–4 are clearly satisfied.

Conversely, suppose these conditions are satisfied; the relation

$$\lambda x = \alpha a + (\lambda - \alpha)a + \alpha(x - a) + (\lambda - \alpha)(x - a)$$

shows that when $\lambda \to \alpha$ and $x \to a$ (which implies $(\lambda - \alpha) \to 0$ and $(x - a) \to$ O), then

$$\lambda x \to \alpha a + 0a + \alpha O + OO = \alpha a.$$

Thus the mapping $(\lambda, x) \to \lambda x$ is continuous.

In particular, the mapping $x \to (-1)x = -x$ is continuous; and since by hypothesis addition is continuous, the topology is indeed compatible with the additive group structure of E.

1.3. Proposition. *Let* E *be a topological vector space. For every scalar* $\alpha \neq 0$ *and every* $b \in$ E, *the dilation* $x \to \alpha x + b$ *is a homeomorphism of* E *with itself.*

PROOF. Every dilation is bijective and the mapping inverse to a dilation is itself a dilation. But it follows from Definition 1.1 that every dilation is continuous; hence it is a bicontinuous bijection of E to E.

1.4. Corollary. 1. *Every dilation of* E *carries every open* (*closed*) *set in* E *onto an open* (*closed*) *set in* E.

2. *The family* $\mathscr{V}_a$ *of neighborhoods of a point* $a \in$ E *is the image, under the translation* $x \to x + a$, *of the family* $\mathscr{V}$ *of neighborhoods of the point* O.

This is a direct consequence of the fact that every dilation, hence in particular every translation, is a homeomorphism of E with itself.

We recall that the second property is true in every topological group; it shows that the topology of E is known whenever one knows the family of neighborhoods of the point O.

1.5. Proposition. *Let* P *be a subset of a topological vector space* E.

If P *is a vector subspace of* E (*respectively, a convex set or a cone*), *the same is true of its closure* $\bar{P}$ *in* E.

PROOF. We recall first that if f is a continuous mapping of one topological space A into another B, then for every $X \subset A$ one has $f(\bar{X}) \subset \overline{f(X)}$; indeed, $X \subset f^{-1}(\overline{f(X)})$ which is closed, hence also $\bar{X} \subset f^{-1}(\overline{f(X)})$, from which the desired inclusion follows.

Now let P be a vector subspace of E; let λ, $\mu \in \mathbf{K}$ and let f be the mapping $(x, y) \to \lambda x + \mu y$ of E $\times$ E into E; f carries P $\times$ P into P. But since it is continuous, it carries $\bar{P} \times \bar{P} = \overline{P \times P}$ into $\bar{P}$; in other words, for all $x, y \in \bar{P}$ we have $\lambda x + \mu y \in \bar{P}$, that is, $\bar{P}$ is a vector subspace of E.

The analogous result concerning convex subsets of E is obtained by using those mappings f for which λ, $\mu \geqslant 0$ and $\lambda + \mu = 1$.

The result concerning cones with vertex O is obtained by using the mappings f of E into E of the form $x \to \lambda x$, where $\lambda > 0$.

1.6. Corollary. *In a topological vector space, every hyperplane* H *is either closed or everywhere dense.*

Indeed, by Proposition 1.5, and taking account of the fact that every vector subspace of E containing H is either E or H, either $\bar{H} = H$ or $\bar{H} = E$.

Continuous linear mappings

1.7. Proposition. *Let* E *and* F *be topological vector spaces over the same field* **K**.

1. *In order that a linear mapping of* E *into* F *be continuous, it is sufficient that it be continuous at the point* O *of* E.

2. *The set* $\mathscr{L}(E, F)$ *of continuous linear mappings of* E *into* F *is a vector subspace of the vector space* $\mathscr{F}(E, F)$ *of mappings of* E *into* F.

PROOF. The first statement is a special case of a characterization of continuous representations in topological groups (see Chapter I, Section 14).

To prove the second statement, let f, $g \in \mathscr{L}(E, F)$, and let λ, $\mu \in \mathbf{K}$; the linear mapping $x \rightarrow \lambda f(x) + \mu g(x)$ of E into F is continuous since f and g are continuous and since the mapping $(u, v) \rightarrow \lambda u + \mu v$ of $F \times F$ into F is continuous; in other words, $\lambda f + \mu g \in \mathscr{L}(E, F)$.

In general, the space $\mathscr{L}(E, E)$ of continuous linear mappings of E into E is denoted by $\mathscr{L}(E)$, and its elements are called continuous linear *operators* in E.

Continuous linear functionals

1.8. The most important continuous linear mappings are those with values in **K**; in other words, the continuous linear functionals. The space $\mathscr{L}(E, \mathbf{K})$ is denoted by E′ and is called the *topological dual* of E.

Clearly $E' \subset E^*$, where E^* denotes the algebraic dual of E, that is, the set of linear functionals on E.

In general $E' \neq E^*$, that is, in general there exist discontinuous linear functionals on E (see Problem 69).

For every linear functional f, the hyperplane $f^{-1}(0)$ is the inverse image under f of the closed set $\{0\} \subset \mathbf{K}$; therefore if f is continuous, this hyperplane is closed in E. One can prove, conversely, that if $f^{-1}(0)$ is closed, then f is continuous (see Problem 8). Here is another convenient characterization:

1.9. Proposition. *To say that a linear functional* f *on* E *is continuous is equivalent to saying that there exists a nonempty open set in* E *on which* f *is bounded.*

PROOF. If f is continuous, the continuity of f at O implies the existence of a neighborhood of O, hence also a nonempty open set, for all elements x of which $|f(x)| \leqslant 1$.

Conversely, let X be a nonempty open set in E on which $|f(x)| \leqslant k$, and let a be a point of X. The translate $X - a$ of X contains O and is therefore a neighborhood of O, and for every $x \in X - a$ we have

$$f(x) \in f(X - a) = f(X) - f(a), \qquad \text{whence} \qquad |f(x)| \leqslant k + f(a).$$

Thus for every $\epsilon > 0$ there exists a neighborhood V of O on which $|f(x)| \leqslant \epsilon$, namely the image of $X - a$ under the dilation

$$x \to \epsilon(k + (f(a)|)^{-1}x.$$

In other words, f is continuous at the point O, hence everywhere by Proposition 1.7.

1.10. *Total subsets*

We recall that if X is a subset of a vector space E, the smallest vector subspace of E containing X is the set F of linear combinations of elements of X; F is called the subspace generated by X.

If, now, E is a TVS, Proposition 1.5 shows that the closure $\bar{F}$ of F is also a vector subspace of E; $\bar{F}$ is called the *closed subspace of* E *generated by* X.

When $\bar{F} = E$, that is, when F is everywhere dense on E, one says that X is *total* in E. In other words, X is total in E if for every $x \in E$ there exist, in every neighborhood of x, points of E which are linear combinations of elements of X.

For example, every basis of E is a total subset of E; but it is essential to note that a set X can be total in E without generating E. For example, in $\mathscr{C}([0, 1], \mathbf{R})$ the set X of monomials generates the vector space F of polynomials, which is distinct from $\mathscr{C}([0, 1], \mathbf{R})$ but everywhere dense on it by virtue of the Stone-Weierstrass theorem. We shall encounter other examples of total sets, in particular in the study of Hilbert spaces.

2. TOPOLOGY ASSOCIATED WITH A FAMILY OF SEMINORMS

The topologies on the function spaces studied in Chapter I, Section 22, were defined by metrics or more generally by ecarts. When dealing with spaces having a vector space structure, we are led to require of these metrics and ecarts that they be compatible, in a sense to be specified, with the vectorial structure of these spaces. We are thus led to single out the important notion of a seminorm and to study the topologies defined by a family of seminorms.

2.1. Definition. LET E BE A VECTOR SPACE OVER **K**. BY A *SEMINORM* ON E IS MEANT A MAPPING p OF E INTO **R** SUCH THAT:

S_1 : $p(x) \geqslant 0$ FOR EVERY $x \in E$;

S_2 : $p(\lambda x) = |\lambda| p(x)$ FOR EVERY $x \in E$ AND EVERY $\lambda \in \mathbf{K}$;

S_3 : $p(x + y) \leqslant p(x) + p(y)$ FOR ALL $x, y \in E$.

WE CALL p A *NORM* IF IN ADDITION $p(x) \neq 0$ FOR EVERY $x \neq O$.

In studying a well-specified seminorm on a space E, we generally denote $p(x)$ by $\| x \|$.

2.2. EXAMPLE. If f denotes a linear functional on E, $|f|$ is a seminorm on E; indeed,

$$|f| \geqslant 0; \qquad |f(\lambda x)| = |\lambda f(x)| = |\lambda| |f(x)|$$

and

$$|f(x + y)| = |f(x) + f(y)| \leqslant |f(x)| + |f(y)|.$$

In order that this seminorm be a norm, it is necessary that $f(x)$ vanish only for $x = O$, hence that E be one-dimensional; conversely, if E is one-dimensional and if $f \neq O$, then $|f|$ is a norm.

2.3. *Immediate properties and operations*

1. For every seminorm p on E, $p(O) = 0$.

2. Every seminorm p on a vector space E over **C** is also a seminorm on E regarded as a vector space over **R**. In particular, p being subadditive and positive-homogeneous, it is convex in E (see Proposition 19.6 of Chapter II).

We now indicate various operations which enable one to construct seminorms from other seminorms; these operations are very similar to those which we have studied in connection with ecarts (Chapter I, Section 15).

3. Every *linear positive* (that is, with coefficients $\geqslant 0$) combination of seminorms is again a seminorm. In particular, every finite sum of norms is a norm.

For example, in $\mathbf{C}^n$, the function $x \to$ (coordinate x_i) is a linear functional, hence $|x_i|$ is a seminorm; the same is thus true of $\Sigma_i |x_i|$, and since the latter vanishes only if $x = O$, it is a norm.

4. Every (everywhere finite) limit of seminorms is a seminorm.

5. For every family (p_i) of seminorms whose upper envelope p is everywhere finite, p is a seminorm.

Indeed, p clearly satisfies S_1 and S_2; moreover, for every i we have

$$p_i(x + y) \leqslant p_i(x) + p_i(y) \leqslant p(x) + p(y),$$

whence

$$p(x + y) = \sup p_i(x + y) \leqslant p(x) + p(y).$$

For example, let $\mathscr{B}(A, \mathbf{K})$ be the vector space of bounded mappings of a set A into $\mathbf{K}$. For every $a \in A$ the mapping $f \to f(a)$ of $\mathscr{B}(A, \mathbf{K})$ into $\mathbf{K}$ is linear; therefore by Example 2.2 the function $p_a : f \to |f(a)|$ is a seminorm.

Now let X be an arbitrary nonempty subset of A; since every $f \in \mathscr{B}(A, \mathbf{K})$ is bounded, the function $\sup_{a \in X} p_a$ is finite, and therefore a seminorm; it is called the seminorm of uniform convergence on X.

6. Let E and F be vector spaces over the same field $\mathbf{K}$, φ a linear mapping of E into F, and p a seminorm on F; then $p \circ \varphi$ is a seminorm on E; the verification of this is immediate.

Example 2.2 rests on this procedure; here is another example. Let F_1 and F_2 be vector spaces over $\mathbf{K}$, and p_1 a seminorm on F_1; then the function $(x_1, x_2) \to p_1(x_1)$ defined on $F_1 \times F_2$ is a seminorm on $F_1 \times F_2$.

7. Finally, here is an operation analogous to that on ecarts studied in Chapter I; 15.2.6:

Let $(p_1, p_2, ..., p_n)$ be a finite sequence of seminorms on a vector space E, and let φ be an increasing, convex, and positive-homogeneous mapping of $(\mathbf{R}_+)^n$ into $\mathbf{R}_+$.

Then the function $\varphi(p_1, p_2, ..., p_n)$ is a seminorm on E: Property S_1 is evident; S_2 follows from the positive-homogeneity of φ; finally S_3 follows from the fact that φ is increasing and subadditive.

For example, for every number $\alpha \geqslant 1$, $(\sum p_i^\alpha)^{1/\alpha}$ is a seminorm.

2.4. Ecart associated with a seminorm

Let E be a vector space with a seminorm p; for all $x, y \in E$ we put

$$d(x, y) = p(x - y).$$

It is immediate that

1. $d(x, y) \geqslant 0$ and $d(x, x) = 0$;
2. $d(x, y) = d(y, x)$ since $p(x - y) = p(y - x)$;
3. $d(x, y) \leqslant d(x, z) + d(z, y)$;

indeed, this inequality can be written as

$$p(x - y) \leqslant p(x - z) + p(z - y);$$

but

$$(x - y) = (x - z) + (z - y),$$

hence the last inequality follows from S_3.

These three properties show that d is an ecart on E; it is immediate that this ecart is invariant under translation and that, more generally, it is multiplied by $|\alpha|$ under a dilation $x \rightarrow \alpha x + b$.

This ecart is finite; in order that it be a metric, it is therefore sufficient that $p(x - y) = 0$ imply $x - y = O$; in other words, that the seminorm on E be a norm.

2.5. Balls associated with a seminorm

We maintain the preceding notation. The set $B(a, \rho)$ of points $x \in E$ such that $d(a, x) < \rho$ is called the *open p-ball* with center a and radius ρ (where $a \in E$ and $\rho > 0$); the closed p-balls are defined in the same way, by replacing $<$ by $\leqslant$. We will call the ball $B(O, 1)$ the *unit p-ball*.

It is immediate that the dilation $x \rightarrow \alpha x + b$ transforms $B(O, \rho)$ into $B(b, |\alpha|\rho)$; it is therefore sufficient to study the balls with center O.

2.6. Proposition 1. *Every open p-ball* B *with center* O *is a convex set which is invariant under each of the isometries* $x \rightarrow \alpha x$, *where* $|\alpha| = 1$.

2. *In order that p be a norm, it is necessary and sufficient that* $B(O, \rho)$ *contain no vector subspace of dimension* 1.

PROOF. 1. Since p is convex, the set $B(O, \rho)$ of x such that $p(x) < \rho$ is convex (Proposition 19.3, Chapter II).

The relation $p(\alpha x) = |\alpha| p(x)$ shows that if $|\alpha| = 1$, the dilation $x \rightarrow \alpha x$ is a bijective isometry of $B(O, \rho)$ with itself.

2. If there exists $a \neq O$ in E such that $p(a) = 0$, then all the points λa belong to $B(O, \rho)$; while if $p(a) \neq 0$, there exists a λ such that $\lambda a \notin B(O, \rho)$, for example $\lambda = 2\rho/p(a)$.

A similar assertion holds for the closed balls with radius $\rho > 0$.

Finally, we note that the closed ball $B(O, 0)$ is a vector subspace of E, which reduces to $\{O\}$ only if p is a norm.

2.7. Balls associated with a family of seminorms

In Chapter I, Section 16, we defined and studied the topology associated with a metric on an arbitrary set E. Therefore if E is a vector space with a norm, the metric associated with this norm defines a topology on E. We shall make a detailed study of such topologies in Sections 4–6; for the moment, more generally, we are going to define the topology associated with a family of seminorms on a vector space.

Let E be a vector space, and let $\mathscr{P} = (p_i)_{i \in I}$ be a family, finite or infinite, of seminorms on E. We denote by $B_i(a, \rho)$ the open p_i-ball with center a and radius ρ.

We will call every finite intersection of open p_i-balls with center a an *open $\mathscr{P}$-ball with center a* (the intersection of two open $\mathscr{P}$-balls with center a is thus also a $\mathscr{P}$-ball with center a).

The consideration of the particular case in which the elements of $\mathscr{P}$ are the multiples λp (where $\lambda > 0$) of a seminorm p shows that one cannot speak of the radius of a $\mathscr{P}$-ball.

Definition of a $\mathscr{P}$-topology

Let us now say that a subset X of E is "open" if either X $= \varnothing$, or for every $x \in$ X there exists an open $\mathscr{P}$-ball, with center x, contained in X.

It is immediate that the collection of these "open sets" satisfies axioms O_1, O_2, O_3 of a topological space; we can therefore give the following definition:

2.8. Definition. LET E BE A VECTOR SPACE, AND LET $\mathscr{P}$ BE AN ARBITRARY FAMILY OF SEMINORMS ON E. THEN THE *TOPOLOGY ASSOCIATED WITH THE FAMILY $\mathscr{P}$*, OR THE $\mathscr{P}$-*TOPOLOGY*, IS DEFINED AS THE TOPOLOGY ON E WHOSE OPEN SETS ARE THE SETS X EACH OF WHOSE POINTS IS THE CENTER OF AN OPEN $\mathscr{P}$-BALL CONTAINED IN X.

Let us show that for this topology, every open p_i-ball is an open set; indeed, let $x \in B_i(a, \rho)$; the open ball $B_i(x, \epsilon)$, where $\epsilon = \rho - p_i(a - x)$, is contained in $B_i(a, \rho)$, for the relation

$$p_i(x - y) < \rho - p_i(a - x)$$

implies

$$p_i(a - y) \leqslant p_i(a - x) + p_i(x - y) < \rho.$$

It follows from this, by axiom O_2, that every open $\mathscr{P}$-ball is an open set; by axiom O_1, every union of open $\mathscr{P}$-balls is therefore an open set.

Conversely, the definition of an open set implies that every open set is the union of open $\mathscr{P}$-balls. Hence *the open sets in E and the unions of open $\mathscr{P}$-balls are identical*.

The definition of the $\mathscr{P}$-topology shows that every neighborhood of a point a contains an open $\mathscr{P}$-ball with center a; hence every point

a of E has a neighborhood base of open $\mathscr{P}$-balls with center a, that is, sets of the form $a + B$, where B is an open $\mathscr{P}$-ball with center O.

2.9. Proposition. *Every $\mathscr{P}$-topology on a vector space E is compatible with the vector space structure of E.*

PROOF. We will verify conditions 1–4 of Proposition 1.2; to do this, let us denote by B an open arbitrary $\mathscr{P}$-ball with center O.

1. For all $a, b \in$ E, the balls $a + \frac{1}{2}$ B and $b + \frac{1}{2}$ B are neighborhoods of a and b and, taking into account the convexity of B, we have

$$(a + \tfrac{1}{2}B) + (b + \tfrac{1}{2}B) = (a + b) + \tfrac{1}{2}(B + B) \subset (a + b) + B,$$

whence the continuity of the mapping $(x, y) \to (x + y)$ at the point (a, b).

2. If $B = \bigcap_{i \in J} B_i(O, \rho_i)$, the condition $\lambda a \in B$ takes the form $|\lambda| \, p_i(a) \leqslant \rho_i$ for all $i \in$ J, or $|\lambda| \leqslant \inf_{i \in J} (\rho_i p_i(a)^{-1})$, that is, $|\lambda| \leqslant k$ where $k > 0$.

3. The condition $\alpha x \in$ B is satisfied for every x if $\alpha = 0$; otherwise it can be written as $x \in \alpha^{-1}B$, and $\alpha^{-1}B$ is a neighborhood of O.

4. The condition $\lambda x \in$ B is satisfied whenever $|\lambda| \leqslant 1$ and $x \in$ B.

Convergence criterion for a filter base

In a metric space E, to say that a sequence (x_n) of points of E converges to a point a of E is equivalent to saying that

$$\lim_{n \to \infty} d(a, x_n) = 0.$$

In particular, if E is a normed space taken with the metric associated with the norm p, this condition assumes the form

$$\lim_{n \to \infty} p(a - x_n) = 0.$$

We are going to see that this condition extends in a simple way to $\mathscr{P}$-topologies.

2.10. Proposition. *Let $\mathscr{B}$ be a filter base on a vector space E with a $\mathscr{P}$-topology. To say that $\mathscr{B}$ converges to a point a of E is equivalent to saying that, for every $p \in \mathscr{P}$, $\lim_{\mathscr{B}} p(x - a) = 0$.*

PROOF. The open $\mathscr{P}$-balls with center a constitute a neighborhood base of a; therefore the convergence of $\mathscr{B}$ to a is equivalent to the assertion that for every open $\mathscr{P}$-ball B with center a, there exists an $X \in \mathscr{B}$ contained in B.

On the other hand, to say that $\lim_{\mathscr{B}} p(x - a) = 0$ is equivalent to saying that for every $\epsilon > 0$, there exists an $X \in \mathscr{B}$ contained in the ball $\{x : p(x - a) < \epsilon\}$.

Therefore to say that $\lim_{\mathscr{B}} p(x - a) = 0$ for every $p \in \mathscr{P}$ is equivalent to saying that for every finite family of balls of the form

$$\{x : p_i(x - a) < \epsilon_i\},$$

there exists an $X \in \mathscr{B}$ contained in each of them, and hence in their intersection. Since every open $\mathscr{P}$-ball with center a is such an intersection, we have established the stated equivalence.

2.11. EXAMPLE. Let (f_i) be a family of linear functionals on a vector space E; the family of seminorms $|f_i|$ defines a $\mathscr{P}$-topology on E which is called the *weak topology associated with the family of linear functionals* f_i. If $\mathscr{B}$ is a filter base on E, it amounts to the same thing to say that

$$\lim_{\mathscr{B}} f_i(x - a) = 0 \qquad \text{or that} \qquad \lim_{\mathscr{B}} |f_i(x - a)| = 0.$$

Therefore, by Proposition 2.10, to say that $\mathscr{B}$ converges to a in the weak topology associated with the linear functionals f_i is equivalent to saying that, for every f_i,

$$\lim_{\mathscr{B}} f_i(x - a) = 0, \qquad \text{or again that} \qquad \lim_{\mathscr{B}} f_i(x) = f(a).$$

Criterion for the continuity of a linear functional

2.12. Proposition. *Let E be a vector space with a $\mathscr{P}$-topology. Then the continuity of a linear functional f on E is equivalent to the existence of a finite subfamily $(p_i)_{i \in J}$ of $\mathscr{P}$ and a constant $k > 0$ such that*

$$|f| \leqslant k \sup_{i \in J}(p_i).$$

PROOF. The above relation implies that $|f(x)| \leqslant k$ on the intersection of the open balls $\{x : p_i(x) < 1\}_{i \in J}$. Hence by Proposition 1.9, f is continuous.

2.   Conversely, if f is continuous, there exists an open $\mathscr{P}$-ball B with center O on which $|f(x)| \leqslant 1$.

For every $x \in E$, there exists a $\lambda > 0$ such that $x \in \lambda B$, and for such a λ we have $|f(x)| \leqslant \lambda$. But B is of the form

$$B = \bigcap_{i \in J} \{x : p_i(x) < \epsilon_i\}.$$

We therefore have $|f(x)| \leqslant \lambda$ for every $\lambda > 0$ such that $p_i(x) < \lambda \epsilon_i$, i.e., such that

$$\epsilon_i^{-1} p_i(x) < \lambda \qquad \text{(for every } i \in \text{J).}$$

It follows that

$$|f(x)| \leqslant \sup_{i \in \text{J}}(\epsilon_i^{-1} p_i(x)),$$

whence

$$|f| \leqslant k \sup_{i \in \text{J}} p_i \qquad \text{(where } k = \sup_{i \in \text{J}} \epsilon_i^{-1}).$$

Subspace and product space

2.13. Let E be a vector space, and let F be a vector subspace of E. For every seminorm p on E, the trace of p on F is a seminorm q on F; and for every $a \in$ F, the trace on F of the open p-ball with center a and radius ρ is the open q-ball with center a and radius ρ.

Therefore for every family (p_i) of seminorms on E, the trace on F of the topology associated with the family (p_i) is identical with the topology associated with the family (q_i) of the traces of the p_i on F.

2.14. Let E and F be vector spaces over the same field **K**, and let (p_i), (q_j) be families of seminorms on E and F, respectively. The spaces E and F have corresponding $\mathscr{P}$-topologies; therefore the product E $\times$ F has both a vector space structure and a topology which is the product of the topologies of E and F (Chapter I, Section 20).

On the other hand, the functions $(x, y) \rightarrow p_i(x)$ and $(x, y) \rightarrow q_j(y)$ constitute (see 2.3.6) a family of seminorms on E $\times$ F with which is associated a $\mathscr{P}$-topology. We shall see that this $\mathscr{P}$-topology is identical with the product of the topologies of E and F.

Indeed, the open balls with center O associated with the seminorms on E $\times$ F are finite intersections of open balls of the form

$$\{(x, y) : p_i(x) < \epsilon_i\} \text{ or } \{(x, y) : q_j(y) < \epsilon_j\};$$

in other words, these balls are simply the products of an open ball with center O in E, and an open ball with center O in F. Since these products constitute a neighborhood base of O for the product topology, the stated identity is proved.

This result clearly extends to every finite product of vector spaces.

Criterion for separation

2.15. Proposition. *In order that a $\mathscr{P}$-topology on a vector space* E *be separated, it is necessary and sufficient that for every* $x \neq$ O *of* E, *there exist a seminorm* $p \in \mathscr{P}$ *such that* $p(x) \neq 0$.

PROOF.   1.   If there exists an $x \neq O$ such that $p(x) = 0$ for every $p \in \mathscr{P}$, every open $\mathscr{P}$-ball with center O contains x; therefore x and O cannot be separated by disjoint open neighborhoods.

2.   Suppose that for every $x \neq O$ of E, there exists $p \in \mathscr{P}$ such that $p(x) \neq 0$; the open p-balls $B(O, \rho)$ and $B(x, \rho)$, where $\rho = \frac{1}{2} p(x)$, are disjoint. Hence O and x can be separated by disjoint open sets.

More generally, any two distinct points are of the form y, $y + x$, where $x \neq O$, and with the preceding notation they can be separated by the open p-balls $B(y, \rho)$ and $B((y + x), \rho)$.

Metrizable $\mathscr{P}$-topologies

2.16. Proposition.   *Let $\mathscr{P}$ be a finite or countable family of seminorms on E.*

1.   *If $\mathscr{P}$ is finite, the topology associated with each of the seminorms*

$$\sup p_i, \qquad \left(\sum p_i^2\right)^{1/2}, \qquad \sum p_i,$$

is identical with the $\mathscr{P}$-topology.

2.   *If $\mathscr{P} = (p_n)_{n \in \mathbb{N}}$, the $\mathscr{P}$-topology is identical with the topology on E associated with the ecart*

$$d(x, y) = \sum_n 2^{-n} p_n'(x - y), \qquad \text{where} \qquad p_n' = \inf(1, p_n).$$

PROOF.   1.   If $\mathscr{P}$ has r elements, then

$$\sup p_i \leqslant \left(\sum p_i^2\right)^{1/2} \leqslant \sum p_i \leqslant r \sup p_i.$$

Hence the ecarts associated with the three seminorms in question define the same topology on E (Proposition 16.7, Chapter I).

On the other hand, the balls $\bigcap_i B_i(O, \epsilon)$ of E constitute a neighborhood base of O; but such a ball is simply the ball with radius ϵ associated with the seminorm $p = \sup p_i$. Hence the p-topology and the $\mathscr{P}$-topology are identical.

2.   Put

$$d_r(x, y) = \sum_{n \leqslant r} 2^{-n} p_n'(x - y).$$

The relation $d(x, y) < \epsilon$ implies $d_r(x, y) < \epsilon$; therefore the d_r-ball with center O and radius ϵ contains the d-ball with the same center and radius.

Conversely, the relation $d_r(x, y) < \tfrac{1}{2}\epsilon$ implies

$$d(x, y) < \tfrac{1}{2}\epsilon + \sum_{r+1}^{\infty} 2^{-n};$$

therefore the d-ball with radius ϵ contains the d_r-ball with radius $\tfrac{1}{2}\epsilon$ for every r such that $\epsilon 2^{r-1} \geqslant 1$.

But the open d_r-balls with center O constitute a neighborhood base of O in the $\mathscr{P}$-topology, since for every r the topologies associated with d_r and with $\Sigma_{n \leqslant r}\, p_n$ are identical; whence the desired identity.

Note finally that d is not the ecart associated with a seminorm, since d is bounded; this is not related to the method of proof adopted, for there exist $\mathscr{P}$-topologies defined by a countable family of seminorms which are not definable by a single seminorm (see Problem 17).

2.17.   Corollary. *If $\mathscr{P}$ is finite or countable, and if the $\mathscr{P}$-topology is separated, then this topology is metrizable.*

Indeed, we have just seen that in these two cases the $\mathscr{P}$-topology is definable by an ecart; if it is separated, this ecart is a metric.

2.18. *The role of $\mathscr{P}$-topologies*

There exist topological vector spaces whose topology is not a $\mathscr{P}$-topology (see Problem 3), but such spaces have not, to the present time, played any role in Analysis.

Indeed, on the one hand, the class of $\mathscr{P}$-topologies suffices for most of the needs of Analysis, and on the other hand, it is the only known class of topological vector spaces for which one is able to establish worthwhile and useful theorems.

Vector spaces with a $\mathscr{P}$-topology are often called *locally convex spaces* because in such a space the point O has a neighborhood base consisting of convex neighborhoods, and because one can show, conversely, that the topology of every TVS having the latter property is a $\mathscr{P}$-topology.

3. CLASSICAL EXAMPLES OF TOPOLOGICAL VECTOR SPACES

We shall now study several classical types of topological vector spaces; they will all be spaces with $\mathscr{P}$-topologies. In other words, in each case it will be a question of defining a family of seminorms adapted to the phenomena which it is desired to bring out.

3.1. Let us recall the vector space $\mathscr{B}(X, \mathbf{K})$ of *bounded* mappings of an arbitrary set X into $\mathbf{K}$, with the norm of uniform convergence:

$$\|f\| = \sup_{x \in X} |f(x)|.$$

When X is a compact topological space, the space $\mathscr{C}(X, \mathbf{K})$ of continuous functions is a particularly important subspace of $\mathscr{B}(X, \mathbf{K})$.

3.2. Let $\mathscr{C}^r([0, 1], \mathbf{K})$ be the space of mappings of $[0, 1]$ into $\mathbf{K}$ which have continuous derivatives up to order r inclusive (where $r \in \mathbf{N}$). We define on this space the topology of uniform convergence for each derivative of order $\leqslant r$, by defining the family of seminorms p_i according to

$$p_i(f) = \sup_{t \in [0,1]} |f^{(i)}(t)| \qquad (\text{where } i = 0, 1, ..., r).$$

By Proposition 2.16, this topology can also be defined by the single norm

$$p(f) = \sum_0^r p_i(f).$$

One can similarly define a topology on the space $\mathscr{C}^r([0, 1]^n, \mathbf{K})$ of mappings of the interval $[0, 1]^n$ into $\mathbf{K}$ which have continuous partial derivatives up to order r inclusive, by the following seminorms:

$$p_i(f) = \sup |\,\mathrm{D}^i f(t)|$$

where $i = (i_1, i_2, ..., i_n)$, $i_j \geqslant 0$, $\Sigma_j i_j \leqslant r$, and

$$\mathrm{D}^i \equiv \frac{\partial^{i_1 + i_2 + \cdots + i_n}}{\partial x_1^{i_1} \partial x_2^{i_2} \cdots \partial x_n^{i_n}}.$$

Note that for $r = 0$, the spaces $\mathscr{C}^r([0, 1]^n, \mathbf{K})$ and $\mathscr{C}([0, 1]^n, \mathbf{K})$ are identical.

3.3. We denote by $\mathscr{C}^\infty([0, 1]^n, \mathbf{K})$ the space of infinitely differentiable functions on $[0, 1]^n$ with values in $\mathbf{K}$, with the seminorms p_i defined in 3.2.

By Proposition 2.16, the topology associated with this family can be defined by a metric; however, to verify the convergence of a filter base, it is much more simple and intuitive to apply the criterion of Proposition 2.10 than to use this metric.

3.4. Here is a family of spaces analogous to the preceding: Let K be a compact set in $\mathbf{R}^n$; we denote by $\mathscr{D}_\mathrm{K}^r(\mathbf{R}^n, \mathbf{K})$, or more concisely by $\mathscr{D}_\mathrm{K}^r$

when there is no chance for ambiguity, the space of mappings of $\mathbf{R}^n$ into $\mathbf{K}$ which have continuous partial derivatives up to order r inclusive, and which are zero off the compact set K.

As in Section 3.2, we give this space the topology associated with the seminorms

$$p_i(f) = \sup_{t \in \mathbf{R}^n} | D^i f(t)|.$$

The space $\mathscr{D}^r([0, 1]^n, \mathbf{K})$ is similarly defined.

3.5. Let p be a real number $\geqslant 1$; for every infinite sequence $x = (x_i)$ of elements of $\mathbf{K}$, we define the positive, finite or infinite number $\| x \|$ by

$$\| x \|^p = \sum_i | x_i |^p.$$

From Minkowski's inequality (Chapter II, Section 20.7) we deduce that

$$\left(\sum_0^n | x_i + y_i |^p \right)^{1/p} \leqslant \left(\sum_0^n | x_i |^p \right)^{1/p} + \left(\sum_0^n | y_i |^p \right)^{1/p} \leqslant \| x \| + \| y \|,$$

whence

$$\| x + y \| \leqslant \| x \| + \| y \|.$$

It follows from this inequality and the obvious relation $\| \lambda x \| = | \lambda | \, \| x \|$ that the set of x such that $\| x \| < \infty$ is a vector space, and that $\| x \|$ is a seminorm on this space. Moreover $\| x \|$ vanishes only if $x_i = 0$ for all i; hence $\| x \|$ is a norm on this space.

This space (real or complex) with this norm is denoted by l^p. In particular, the space l^1 can be identified with the space of absolutely convergent series; as for l^2, we shall meet it again in the study of Hilbert spaces.

3.6. Here now is an important space which we will only be able to define in full generality when we are familiar with the theory of integration:

Let p again be a real number $\geqslant 1$; for every $f \in \mathscr{C}([0, 1], \mathbf{K})$ we define the positive real number $\| f \|$ by

$$\| f \|^p = \int_0^1 | f(t)|^p \, dt.$$

Let us associate, with every finite increasing sequence $\sigma = (t_1, t_2, ..., t_n)$

of points of $[0, 1]$, where $t_1 = 0$ and $t_n = 1$, the expression $\|f\|_\sigma$ defined by

$$\|f\|_\sigma^p = \sum_i (t_{i+1} - t_i) |f(t_i)|^p.$$

Minkowski's inequality shows that $\|f + g\|_\sigma \leqslant \|f\|_\sigma + \|g\|_\sigma$.

But when the modulus of σ (Chapter I, Section 24.6) tends to 0, $\|f\|_\sigma$ tends to $\|f\|$; we deduce from this that $\|f + g\| \leqslant \|f\| + \|g\|$.

This inequality, coupled with the fact that $\|\lambda f\| = |\lambda| \|f\|$ and that $\|f\|$ is zero only if $f = O$, shows that $\|f\|$ is a norm on $\mathscr{C}([0, 1], \mathbf{K})$; for $p = 1$ it is called the norm of convergence in the mean; for $p = 2$ it is called the norm of convergence in quadratic mean (or, of mean square convergence).

In the following two examples we deal with the topology of uniform convergence on every compact set.

3.7.   Let X be a separated topological space; for every compact $K \subset X$, every $f \in \mathscr{C}(X, \mathbf{K})$ is bounded on K; therefore, if we put

$$p_K(f) = \sup_{x \in K} |f(x)|,$$

p_K is a seminorm on $\mathscr{C}(X, \mathbf{K})$. The $\mathscr{P}$-topology defined on $\mathscr{C}(X, \mathbf{K})$ by the family (p_K) is called the topology of uniform convergence on every compact set (or, more concisely, *compact uniform convergence*). For every $f \neq O$, there exists a compact set K such that $p_K(f) \neq 0$; hence this topology is separated.

By Proposition 2.10, if $(f_i)_{i \in I}$ is a family of elements of $\mathscr{C}(X, \mathbf{K})$ and if $\mathscr{B}$ is a filter base on I, to say that the f_i converge in this topology to f along $\mathscr{B}$ means that, for every compact $K \subset X$, the f_i converge uniformly to f on K.

It is often convenient to replace the family (p_K) by a subfamily which defines the same topology: If (K_j) denotes a family of compact sets in X which is absorbing in the sense that every compact set K is contained in some K_j, one can verify that the family (p_{K_j}) defines the same topology as does the family of all the p_K.

For every vector subspace E of $\mathscr{C}(X, \mathbf{K})$, the trace on E of the topology of $\mathscr{C}(X, \mathbf{K})$ is also called the topology of compact uniform convergence.

For example, let D be a domain (open connected set) in $\mathbf{C}^n$, and let $\mathscr{H}(D)$ be the vector space of functions which are holomorphic in D. The most useful topology on $\mathscr{H}(D)$ is the topology of uniform convergence on every compact set; from the fact that there exists a countable and absorbing family of compact sets in D (verify this), it follows that the topology on $\mathscr{H}(D)$ can be defined by a countable family of ecarts;

since moreover this topology is separated, it is metrizable (see Proposition 2.16).

3.8.   Let A be an open set in $\mathbf{R}^n$, and let r be an integer $\geqslant 0$; we denote by $\mathscr{E}^r(A, \mathbf{K})$ the vector subspace of $\mathscr{C}(A, \mathbf{K})$ consisting of the functions which have continuous partial derivatives up to order r inclusive.

For every compact $K \subset A$ and every D^i (see Section 3.2) of order $|i| = i_1 + i_2 + \cdots + i_n \leqslant r$, we put

$$p_{K,i}(f) = \sup_{t \in K} |D^i f(t)|.$$

The topology defined on $\mathscr{E}^r(A, \mathbf{K})$ by the family of seminorms $p_{K,i}$ is called the topology of compact uniform convergence for all the derivatives of order $\leqslant r$.

As in the preceding example, one can require that the compact sets K belong to a countable absorbing family; hence the topology of $\mathscr{E}^r(A, \mathbf{K})$ is metrizable.

The space $\mathscr{E}^\infty(A, \mathbf{K})$ is similarly defined; its topology is also metrizable.

3.9.   We denote by $\mathscr{D}^r(\mathbf{R}^n, \mathbf{K})$ the subspace of $\mathscr{C}(\mathbf{R}^n, \mathbf{K})$ consisting of the functions which vanish off some compact set, and which have continuous partial derivatives up to order r inclusive.

The topology of this space is defined by the family of seminorms $p_{\varphi,i}$ given by

$$p_{\varphi,i}(f) = \sup_{t \in \mathbf{R}^n} |\varphi(t) D^i f(t)|,$$

where D^i is as previously, and φ is any element of $\mathscr{C}(\mathbf{R}^n, \mathbf{K})$.

It can be shown that, in contrast with the preceding topologies, the topology thus defined is not metrizable.

One could similarly define a topology on $\mathscr{D}^\infty(\mathbf{R}^n, \mathbf{K})$, but in fact the topology on this space which is useful is defined by other seminorms.

Here now are two examples of weak topologies.

3.10.   Once again let $\mathscr{F}(X, \mathbf{K})$ be the space of mappings of a set X into **K**. For every $a \in X$, the function $f \to f(a)$ is a linear functional; the topology on $\mathscr{F}(X, \mathbf{K})$ defined by the family of seminorms $f \to |f(a)|$ is called the *topology of pointwise convergence on* X. This is a weak topology; hence (see Example 2.11) to say that a family of functions f_i converges pointwise to a function f (along a filter base) is equivalent to saying that, for every $x \in X$, the $f_i(x)$ converge to $f(x)$ in **K**.

3.11.   Let E be a topological vector space, and E' its topological dual. The weak topology on E associated with the family of (continuous) linear functionals $l \in E'$ is called the *weak topology of* E. This topology is separated whenever there exists, for every $x \in E$, $x \neq O$, an $l \in E'$

such that $l(x) \neq 0$; in other words, whenever, in the sense of Definition 12.3 of Chapter II, the continuous linear functionals on E separate the points of E.

To say that (x_i) converges weakly to $x \in$ E is equivalent to saying that, for every $l \in$ E', the $l(x_i)$ converge to $l(x)$.

We shall meet this weak topology again, for example in the study of Hilbert spaces.

Similarly, the dual E' of a TVS E has a very useful weak topology, namely, that associated with the family of linear functionals $\varphi_a : l \rightarrow l(a)$, where a is an arbitrary point of E; it is often denoted by $\sigma($E', E$)$.

Less classical examples of TVS's will be found in Problems 5, 30, 32, 59, etc.

Use of these topological vector spaces

A well-chosen topology on a vector space E of functions, in addition to furnishing a convenient language, leads to the possibility of utilizing all the notions and results of the theory of TVS's.

It leads in addition to the definition of new mathematical entities consisting of the elements of the dual E'. Here are two important examples:

3.12. Let X be a compact topological space; the elements of the dual of $\mathscr{C}($X, **R**$)$ taken with the uniform topology are called *real Radon measures*.

The best known of these measures is the Lebesgue measure on $[0, 1]$ defined (for X $= [0, 1]$) by the continuous linear functional

$$f \rightarrow \int_0^1 f(t)\, dt.$$

We shall come back to the Radon measures in the study of integration.

3.13. The elements of the dual of $\mathscr{D}^r(\mathbf{R}^n, \mathbf{R})$ are called *real distributions of order r*. They are a special case of the distributions of L. Schwartz. The distributions of order 0 are the Radon measures on $\mathbf{R}^n$.

II. NORMED SPACES

Normed spaces were introduced into analysis after Hilbert spaces and have been much studied, in particular by Banach, even before the development of a general theory of topological vector spaces.

Although their importance diminished after the discovery of topologies associated with a family of seminorms, they still constitute a powerful tool, and their study is relatively simple.

4. TOPOLOGY ASSOCIATED WITH A NORM; CONTINUOUS LINEAR MAPPINGS

4.1. Definition. A VECTOR SPACE E WITH A NORM IS CALLED A *NORMED* SPACE. A NORMED SPACE E IS CALLED A *BANACH SPACE* IF IT IS COMPLETE FOR THE METRIC ASSOCIATED WITH THE NORM.

For example, the space $\mathscr{C}([0, 1], \mathbf{K})$ with the norm of uniform convergence is a Banach space since it is complete (Chapter I, 22.7); on the other hand, the same space with the norm of mean convergence is not complete (argue as in 14.7 below).

Let us recall that the sum and the upper envelope of every finite family of norms is also a norm.

Recall also that the metric associated with a norm p on E is defined by

$$d(x, y) = p(x - y).$$

With this metric is associated a topology which is called the topology of the normed space E; by Proposition 2.9 this topology is compatible with the vector space structure of E. We are going to reprove this result while at the same time making it more precise.

4.2. Proposition. *Let* E *be a normed space over* **K**.

1. *The mapping* $(\lambda, x) \to \lambda x$ *of* $\mathbf{K} \times E$ *into* E *is continuous.*

2. *The mapping* $(x, y) \to x + y$ *of* $E \times E$ *into* E *is of Lipschitz class with ratio 2.*

3. *The mapping* $x \to \| x \|$ *of* E *into* **R** *is of Lipschitz class with ratio 1.*

Proof. 1. We have

$$\Delta(\lambda x) = (\lambda + \Delta\lambda)(x + \Delta x) - \lambda x = \Delta\lambda \cdot x + \lambda \Delta x + \Delta\lambda \cdot \Delta x,$$

from which

$$\| \Delta(\lambda x)\| \leqslant | \Delta\lambda | \cdot \| x \| + | \lambda | \cdot \| \Delta x \| + | \Delta\lambda | \cdot \| \Delta x \|.$$

Thus $\| \Delta(\lambda x) \|$ tends to 0 as $| \Delta\lambda |$ and $\| \Delta x \|$ tend to 0, which implies the continuity of the mapping $(\lambda, x) \to \lambda x$.

However, this mapping is not uniformly continuous when E has points $\neq O$; indeed, let $a \neq O$ in E, and take $x = \lambda a$. The mapping

$(\lambda, \lambda) \rightarrow \lambda^2$ is not uniformly continuous, hence neither is the mapping $(\lambda, x) \rightarrow \lambda \cdot \lambda a = \lambda^2 a$.

2. The relations

$$\Delta(x + y) = (x + \Delta x) + (y + \Delta y) - (x + y) = \Delta x + \Delta y;$$

$$\| \Delta x + \Delta y \| \leqslant \| \Delta x \| + \| \Delta y \|$$

show that the mapping $(x, y) \rightarrow x + y$ is of Lipschitz class with ratio 2 (for the usual norms on $E \times E$).

3. The relation $\big| \, \| x + \Delta x \| - \| x \| \, \big| \leqslant \| \Delta x \|$ shows that the function $\| x \|$ is of Lipschitz class with ratio 1.

Continuous linear mappings

The fact that in every normed space the origin has a neighborhood base consisting of the homothetic images of a given ball makes possible a simple characterization of the continuous linear mappings of one normed space into another.

4.3. Proposition. *Let* E *and* F *be normed spaces, and* f *a linear mapping of* E *into* F. *The following three assertions are equivalent*:

1. *f is continuous.*

2. *f is bounded on every bounded subset of* E.

3. *There exists a constant* $k > 0$ *such that, for every* $x \in E$,

$$\| f(x) \| \leqslant k \| x \|.$$

When one of these conditions is satisfied, f is of Lipschitz class.

PROOF. We first recall that a subset X of a metric space is said to be bounded if its diameter is finite; in a normed space, this condition can be expressed more simply by the statement that X is contained in some ball with center O.

$1 \Rightarrow 2$. The continuity of f at O implies the existence of an open ball $B(O, \rho)$ in E whose image under f is contained in the unit ball of F. By the homogeneity of f, the image under f of every ball in E with center O is contained in a ball of F; the same is therefore true of every bounded subset X of E.

$2 \Rightarrow 3$. The unit sphere $S = \{x : \| x \| = 1\}$ of E is bounded; therefore $f(S)$ is bounded, in other words, there exists a constant $k \geqslant 0$ such that

$$\| f(x) \| \leqslant k = k \| x \| \qquad \text{for every} \quad x \in S.$$

But every point $y \in E$ is of the form λx, where $x \in S$ and $\lambda \geqslant 0$; therefore the relation $\lambda \| f(x) \| \leqslant k\lambda \| x \|$ can be written as

$$\| f(y) \| \leqslant k \| y \| \qquad \text{for every} \quad y \in E.$$

$3 \Rightarrow 1.$ Indeed, $\| f(x) \| \leqslant k \| x \|$ implies

$$\| f(u) - f(v) \| = \| f(u - v) \| \leqslant k \| u - v \|.$$

Thus f is of Lipschitz class with ratio k, and hence continuous.

Equivalent norms

We have seen in Chapter I, Section 16 that the same topology can be defined by inequivalent metrics d_1 and d_2, that is, such that $d_1(x, y)$ and $d_2(x, y)$ do not tend to 0 simultaneously. We shall see that this singular occurrence cannot take place for metrics associated with norms.

4.4. Definition. Two norms on a vector space E are said to be EQUIVALENT IF THE TOPOLOGIES ASSOCIATED WITH THESE NORMS ARE IDENTICAL.

This is evidently an equivalence relation; we denote it by $\sim$.

4.5. Proposition. *Let p_1 and p_2 be norms on a vector space E.*

$$(p_1 \sim p_2) \Leftrightarrow (\exists k_1, k_2 \in \mathbf{R}_+ \quad \text{such that} \quad p_2 \leqslant k_1 p_1 \quad \text{and} \quad p_1 \leqslant k_2 p_2).$$

PROOF. This is a consequence of Proposition 4.3. Indeed, to say that $p_1 \sim p_2$ is the same as saying that the linear mapping $x \to x$ of E taken with the norm p_1 into E taken with the norm p_2 is continuous, and similarly with p_1, p_2 interchanged; that is, there exist two numbers k_1, $k_2 \geqslant 0$ such that

$$p_2(x) \leqslant k_1 p_1(x) \quad \text{and} \quad p_1(x) \leqslant k_2 p_2(x) \qquad \text{for every} \quad x \in E.$$

These numbers k_1, k_2 are clearly > 0.

Z We shall show in Section 7 that all the norms on a finite-dimensional vector space are equivalent. On the other hand, here is an example of an infinite-dimensional vector space on which there exist two inequivalent norms.

The space in question is $\mathscr{C}([0, 1], \mathbf{K})$ with the norm p_1 of uniform convergence, and the norm p_2 defined by

$$p_2(f) = \int_0^1 | f(t) | \, dt.$$

Clearly $p_2 \leqslant p_1$; on the other hand, if we denote by f_n the monomial $t \to t^n$, then

$$p_1(f_n) = 1 \qquad \text{whereas} \qquad p_2(f_n) = (n + 1)^{-1}.$$

Therefore there exists no constant k such that $p_1 \leqslant kp_2$.

Choice of a norm on $\mathscr{L}(\mathsf{E}, \mathsf{F})$

Let us try to find a norm on the vector space $\mathscr{L}(\mathrm{E}, \mathrm{F})$ of continuous linear mappings of E into F which characterizes the size of an element f of $\mathscr{L}(\mathrm{E}, \mathrm{F})$. It is out of the question to use the norm of uniform convergence on all of E, since, apart from the mapping O, no $f \in \mathscr{L}(\mathrm{E}, \mathrm{F})$ is bounded on E. On the other hand, we have characterized the continuous linear mappings f by the property of being bounded on the unit ball B of E; moreover, two elements of $\mathscr{L}(\mathrm{E}, \mathrm{F})$ which coincide on this ball are identical. We are thus led to use the norm of uniform convergence on the ball B, in other words, to put for every $f \in \mathscr{L}(\mathrm{E}, \mathrm{F})$,

$$\| f \| = \sup_{\|x\| \leqslant 1} \| f(x) \|.$$

This is evidently a seminorm (see 2.3, Nos. 5 and 6); and since $f = \mathrm{O}$ if $f(x) = \mathrm{O}$ for every $x \in \mathrm{B}$, it is a norm.

The proof of the implication $(2 \Rightarrow 3)$ in Proposition 4.3 shows that $\| f \|$ is the smallest constant $k \geqslant 0$ such that $\| f(x) \| \leqslant k \| x \|$ for every $x \in \mathrm{E}$; in particular, one can therefore write $\| f(x) \| \leqslant \| f \| \| x \|$. To sum up:

4.6. **Proposition.** *The function $f \to \| f \|$ is a norm on $\mathscr{L}(\mathrm{E}, \mathrm{F})$. For every $f \in \mathscr{L}(\mathrm{E}, \mathrm{F})$, $\| f \|$ is the smallest number $k \geqslant 0$ such that $\| f(x) \| \leqslant k \| x \|$ for every $x \in \mathrm{E}$.*

Z If the norms of E and F are replaced by equivalent norms, it is immediate that $\| f \|$ is replaced by an equivalent norm. Thus the topology of $\mathscr{L}(\mathrm{E}, \mathrm{F})$ depends only on the topology of E and of F.

When the norms of E and F are specified, the norm which we have defined on $\mathscr{L}(\mathrm{E}, \mathrm{F})$ is the usual norm. It is especially convenient by virtue of the simplicity of its definition and by virtue also of the following property:

Let E, F, G be normed spaces, and let $f \in \mathscr{L}(\mathrm{E}, \mathrm{F})$, $g \in \mathscr{L}(\mathrm{F}, \mathrm{G})$; the relation

$$\| g(f(x)) \| \leqslant \| g \| \| f(x) \| \leqslant \| g \| \| f \| \| x \|$$

shows that

$$\| g \circ f \| \leqslant \| g \| \| f \|.$$

Thus the norm chosen is well suited to the composition of linear mappings.

Nevertheless it might be convenient in certain cases to replace this norm by other equivalent norms. For example, let us associate, with every linear mapping f of $\mathbf{K}^n$ into itself defined by a matrix (a_{ij}) for the canonical basis in $\mathbf{K}^n$, the sum

$$\|f\| = \sum_{i,j} |a_{ij}|.$$

This is a norm which is sometimes used on $\mathscr{L}(\mathbf{K}^n)$; incidentally, it also satisfies the inequality $\|g \circ f\| \leqslant \|g\| \|f\|$.

4.7. Proposition. *When F is complete, so is $\mathscr{L}(E, F)$.*

PROOF.   Let B be the closed unit ball of E. We have defined the norm of an element f of $\mathscr{L}(E, F)$ as the norm (for uniform convergence) of the trace of f on B.

But the trace of f on B is a bounded affine mapping g of B into F such that $g(O) = O$, and conversely one can verify that every bounded affine mapping g of B into F such that $g(O) = O$ can be extended in a unique way to a linear mapping of E into F which, being bounded on B, is continuous.

In other words, if $\mathscr{A}(B, F)$ denotes the vector space of bounded affine mappings g of B into F such that $g(O) = O$, the mapping $f \to$ (trace of f on B) is an isomorphism of $\mathscr{L}(E, F)$ onto $\mathscr{A}(B, F)$ which preserves the norm.

Since F is complete, so is $\mathscr{C}(B, F)$ (see Chapter I, 22.7). Since $\mathscr{A}(B, F)$ is closed in $\mathscr{C}(B, F)$ (as every uniform limit of bounded affine mappings is affine and bounded), $\mathscr{A}(B, F)$ is complete; hence $\mathscr{L}(E, F)$ is complete.

In particular, since $\mathbf{K}$ is complete, we can state:

4.8. Corollary. *The dual E' of every normed space is complete.*

Extension of a continuous linear mapping

We proved in Chapter I (Theorem 20.14) that a uniformly continuous mapping of an everywhere dense subset X of a metric space E into a *complete* metric space F can be extended in a unique way to a continuous mapping of E into F.

This general result leads to the following assertion:

4.9. Proposition. *Let X be an everywhere dense vector subspace of a normed space E, and let f be a continuous linear mapping of X into a* **complete** *normed space F.*

Then there exists a unique continuous mapping g of E *into* F *whose restriction to* X *is f; this mapping g is linear, and* $\| g \| = \| f \|$.

PROOF.   The inequality $\| f(u) - f(v) \| \leqslant \| f \| \| u - v \|$ shows that f is of Lipschitz class with ratio $\| f \|$; hence by Theorem 20.14 of Chapter I, f has a unique continuous extension g to E, and g is of Lipschitz class with ratio $\| f \|$.

Let us verify that g is linear. Let $x, y \in$ E; they are the respective limits of two sequences (x_n) and (y_n) of points of X. For every $n \in$ **N** and all scalars λ, μ we have

$$g(\lambda x_n + \mu y_n) = \lambda g(x_n) + \mu g(y_n).$$

But addition and multiplication by scalars are continuous in E and in F, and g is moreover continuous; thus each term in this relation tends to a limit as $n \to \infty$, and we have

$$g(\lambda x + \mu y) = \lambda g(x) + \mu g(y).$$

In other words, g is linear.

The fact that g is of Lipschitz class with ratio $\| f \|$ allows us to write

$$\| g(x) \| \leqslant \| f \| \| x \|.$$

In other words, $\| g \| \leqslant \| f \|$; but on the other hand, g is an extension of f. Hence $\| f \| \leqslant \| g \|$, which gives the desired equality.

4.10.   Corollary.   *Every continuous linear mapping f of a vector subspace* X *of a normed space* E *into a complete normed space* F *can be extended in a unique way to a continuous linear mapping of* $\bar{X}$ *into* F.

Indeed, by Proposition 1.5, $\bar{X}$ is a vector subspace of E; since X is everywhere dense on $\bar{X}$, one can apply Proposition 4.9.

EXAMPLE.   Since **K** is complete, assertions 4.9 and 4.10 apply to the extension of continuous linear functionals.

4.11.   REMARK.   The following example will show why it is essential that F be complete.

Let E be an infinite-dimensional complete normed space, and let X = F be a vector subspace of E which is everywhere dense on, but distinct from E (for example E = $\mathscr{C}([0, 1],$ **K**) and X is the subspace consisting of all the polynomials). We take for f the identity mapping of X into F. One can verify that f has no continuous extension to all of E.

4.12. *Examples of continuous linear mappings*

1.   Let $\varphi \in \mathscr{C}([0, 1], \mathbf{K})$; the linear mapping $f \rightarrow \varphi f$ of $\mathscr{C}([0, 1], \mathbf{K})$ into itself is continuous and of norm $\| \varphi \|$. In order that it be an isomorphism of $\mathscr{C}([0, 1], \mathbf{K})$ onto itself, it is necessary and sufficient that φ not vanish at any point of $[0, 1]$.

2.   For every $f \in \mathscr{C}([0, 1], \mathbf{K})$, let Pf denote the primitive of f which vanishes at the point 0. The linear mapping $f \rightarrow Pf$ of $\mathscr{C}([0, 1], \mathbf{K})$ into itself is injective and has norm 1.

3.   Let A and B be compact spaces, and let φ be a continuous mapping of A into B. The mapping $f \rightarrow f \circ \varphi$ of $\mathscr{C}(B, \mathbf{K})$ into $\mathscr{C}(A, \mathbf{K})$ is linear and has norm 1.

4.   Let (k_n) be a sequence of elements of $\mathbf{K}$ such that $| k_n | \leqslant k < \infty$; the mapping $(x_n) \rightarrow (k_n x_n)$ of l^p into itself is linear and has norm $\leqslant k$.

5.   The mapping $(x_n) \rightarrow (x_n')$, where $x_n' = x_{n+1}$, of l^p into itself is linear and has norm 1.

Here, now, are two examples of linear mappings which are not continuous.

6.   Let E be the normed subspace of $\mathscr{C}([0, 1], \mathbf{K})$ (taken with its usual norm) consisting of the functions f which have a continuous derivative f'.

The linear mapping $f \rightarrow f'$ of E into $\mathscr{C}([0, 1], \mathbf{K})$ is not continuous since, for example, if we put $f_n(x) = n^{-1} \sin nx$, the sequence (f_n) converges to O whereas the sequence (f_n') does not converge to O.

7.   Let p_1 be the norm of mean convergence on $\mathscr{C}([0, 1], \mathbf{K})$ and let p_2 be its usual norm. The identity mapping of this space taken with the norm p_1 into the same space taken with the norm p_2 is not continuous.

Z   One observes that in Examples 6 and 7 of discontinuous linear mappings, the spaces on which they are defined are incomplete. This is not accidental; one can in fact show (see Problem 62) that when a linear mapping of a Banach space into a normed space possesses a certain degree of regularity, it is necessarily continuous. To be sure, one can by using the axiom of choice define discontinuous linear functionals on every infinite-dimensional Banach space, but this involves the construction of a family of functionals rather than the effective construction of one functional.

In short, one can expect that every linear mapping of a Banach space into a normed space, constructed by the procedures currently used in Analysis, will be continuous.

5. STABILITY OF ISOMORPHISMS

Let us first give a precise statement of what we mean by an iso-morphism.

5.1. Definition. LET E AND F BE NORMED SPACES, AND LET f BE A LINEAR MAPPING OF E INTO F. THEN f IS CALLED AN *ISOMORPHISM* IF IT IS INJECTIVE, AND IF BOTH f AND THE INVERSE MAPPING f^{-1} OF $f(E)$ ONTO E ARE CONTINUOUS.

Thus, we do not require that $f(E) = F$.

5.2. Proposition. *To say that a linear mapping f of E into F is an iso-morphism is equivalent to saying that there exist constants k_1, $k_2 > 0$ such that*

$$k_1\| x \| \leqslant \| f(x) \| \leqslant k_2 \| x \|$$

for every $x \in E$.

PROOF. Suppose f is an isomorphism; the continuity of f implies the existence of k_2; that of f^{-1} implies the existence of k_1 (the best constant k_1 being $\| f^{-1} \|^{-1}$).

Conversely, if $k_1 \| x \| \leqslant \| f(x) \|$, then f is injective and f^{-1} is continuous; if moreover $\| f(x) \| \leqslant k_2 \| x \|$, then f is continuous.

EXAMPLE. One can verify in Example 2 of 4.12 that the mapping $f \to Pf$ is continuous but is not an isomorphism.

5.3. Corollary. *The subset I of $\mathcal{L}(E, F)$ consisting of the isomorphisms is open.*

PROOF. Suppose f is an isomorphism, and therefore satisfies a relation of the kind in Proposition 5.2; then for every $g \in \mathcal{L}(E, F)$ such that $\| g \| < k_1$ we have

$$(k_1 - \| g \|)\| x \| \leqslant \| f(x) + g(x) \| \leqslant (k_1 + k_2)\| x \|.$$

Since $k_1 - \| g \| > 0$, $f + g$ is an isomorphism.

Corollary 5.3 exhibits a certain stability of isomorphisms, since it shows that a linear mapping f which is an isomorphism remains an isomorphism after the addition of a "small" continuous linear mapping. This result can be generalized a bit as follows:

5.4. Proposition. *Let A be an arbitrary metric space, let f be an injection of A into a normed space F which multiplies distances by at least a factor $K > 0$ (in other words, f^{-1} is of Lipschitz class with ratio K^{-1}), and let*

g be another mapping of A *into* F *which is of Lipschitz class with ratio*
$k < K$.

Then the mapping $f + g$ *of* A *into* F *is injective and multiplies distances
by at least a factor* $(K - k)$.

This is an immediate consequence of the relation

$$\|(f + g)(x) - (f + g)(y)\| = \|(f(x) + f(y)) + (g(x) - g(y))\|$$
$$\geqslant (K - k)\, d(x, y).$$

Let us add that if f is of Lipschitz class, so is $f + g$.

The results which follow will assume that the space F is complete,
and will lead later to important applications.

We remark, to begin with, that if f denotes the identity mapping of a
complete normed space F into itself, and if g denotes a linear mapping
of F into F of norm < 1, not only is $f + g$, by Proposition 5.2, an
isomorphism, it also carries F onto F. Indeed, for every $a \in$ F the equation $f(x) + g(x) = a$ can also be written as $x = a - g(x)$, and since
the mapping $x \to a - g(x)$ is contractive, this equation has a solution
(by Theorem 21.1, Chapter I).

What we are now going to do is replace f by an isomorphism of a
complete space E onto another such space F, and replace g by a mapping
of Lipschitz class with sufficiently small ratio, and then "localize" these
mappings f and g.

5.5. Lemma. *Let* ω *be an open set in a Banach space* F, *and let* g' *be a
mapping of* ω *into* F *which is of Lipschitz class with ratio* $k' < 1$. *Then
the image of* ω *under the mapping* $\gamma : y \to y + g'(y)$ *is open in* F.

More precisely, the image under γ *of every closed ball* $B(b, \rho) \subset \omega$
contains the closed ball $B(\gamma(b), (1 - k')\rho)$.

PROOF.   It clearly suffices to prove the second part of the assertion.
To simplify the notation, we assume by a translation of ω (respectively,
$\gamma(\omega)$) that $b = O$ (respectively, $\gamma(b) = O$).

We want to show that for every $c \in$ F such that $\|c\| \leqslant (1 - k')\rho$,
the equation $x + g'(x) = c$ has a solution such that $\|x\| \leqslant \rho$. But this
equation can be written as $x = c - g'(x)$; the mapping $x \to c - g'(x)$
is of Lipschitz class with ratio $k' < 1$ and maps $B(O, \rho)$ into itself,
since if $\|x\| \leqslant \rho$, then

$$\|c - g'(x)\| \leqslant \|c\| + \|g'(x)\| \leqslant (1 - k')\rho + k'\rho = \rho.$$

Since $B(O, \rho)$ is a complete metric space, Theorem 21.1 of Chapter I (the idea of successive approximations) shows that the equation has a solution.

5.6. Lemma.   *Let* A *be a metric space; let f be an injection of* A *into a Banach space* F *which multiplies distances by at least a number* K > 0, *and such that f*(A) *is open in* F, *and let g be another mapping of* A *into* F *which is of Lipschitz class with ratio k* $<$ K. *Then the image of* A *under f* $+$ *g is an open set in* F.

PROOF.   We put $g' = g \circ f^{-1}$; then g' is a mapping of the open set $\omega = f(A)$ in F into F, and is of Lipschitz class with ratio $k' = k/K$, which ratio is by hypothesis < 1.

If we denote by f' the identity mapping in F, then

$$(f + g)(A) = (f + g)(f^{-1}(\omega)) = (f' + g')(\omega).$$

Lemma 5.5 now shows that $(f' + g')(\omega)$ is an open set in F, which is the desired result.

5.7. Theorem.   *Let* E *and* F *be Banach spaces, and let f be a bijective isomorphism of* E *onto* F. *Let* A *be an open set in* E, *and g a mapping of* A *into* F *which is of Lipschitz class with ratio k.*

When $k < \|f^{-1}\|^{-1}$, *then f* $+$ *g is injective, both it and its inverse are of Lipschitz class, and* $(f + g)(A)$ *is open in* F.

This is a special case of Lemma 5.6; indeed, since f is an isomorphism of E onto F, $f(A)$ is open in F, and f multiplies distances by at least $K = \|f^{-1}\|^{-1}$. Proposition 5.4 shows that $f + g$, which is clearly of Lipschitz class, multiplies distances by at least $K - k$; therefore its inverse is of Lipschitz class with ratio $(K - k)^{-1}$.

This theorem will be extremely valuable to us in the study of continuously differentiable functions, for the proof of theorems concerning implicit functions.

Z   A simple example will show us that the completeness of F is essential in the assertions 5.5–5.7.

Let F be the vector subspace of $\mathscr{C}([0, 1], \mathbf{R})$ consisting of the restrictions to $[0, 1]$ of real polynomials; let g be the mapping of F into itself which associates with every polynomial $x \in$ F the polynomial $t \to x(t^2)$. Then $\|g\| = 1$; therefore for every k such that $0 < k < 1$, kg is of Lipschitz class with ratio $k < 1$. The image of F under the mapping $x \to x + kg(x)$ is a vector subspace of F which is distinct from F since it contains only polynomials of even degree; hence it contains no open subset of F.

6. PRODUCT OF NORMED SPACES;
CONTINUOUS MULTILINEAR MAPPINGS

Let $(E_i)_{i \in I}$ be a *finite* family of normed spaces over the same field **K**, whose norms we shall uniformly denote by $\| x \|$, and let E be the product vector space of the E_i.

We have seen in 2.14 that the topology on E associated with the family of seminorms $\| x_i \|$ is identical with the product of the topologies of the E_i.

The seminorms $\sup \| x_i \|$, $\Sigma \| x_i \|$, and $(\Sigma \| x_i \|^2)^{1/2}$ are equivalent and each of them defines the same topology on E as does the family of $\| x_i \|$ (see 2.16); in the present context they are norms on E since the relations $\| x_i \| = 0$ together imply $x = O$.

Continuity of a multilinear mapping

Let us recall that if (E_i) denotes a finite family of vector spaces, and f is a mapping of the product ΠE_i into another vector space F, then f is said to be *multilinear* if it is separately linear with respect to each of its variables. When the E_i and F are normed, the product of the E_i is also normed and one can seek to extend Proposition 4.3, characterizing the continuous linear mappings, to multilinear mappings.

6.1. Proposition. *Let* E_1, E_2, ..., E_n *and* F *be normed spaces and let* f *be a multilinear mapping of the product* E *of the* E_i *into* F; *then the following three assertions are equivalent*:

1. *f is continuous.*

2. *f is bounded on every bounded subset of* E.

3. *There exists a constant* $k \geqslant 0$ *such that, for every* $x = (x_i) \in E$,

$$\| f(x_1, x_2, ..., x_n) \| \leqslant k \| x_1 \| \cdot \| x_2 \| \cdots \| x_n \|.$$

PROOF.   For the norm on E we shall take $\| x \| = \sup \| x_i \|$.

$1 \Rightarrow 2$.   If f is continuous, its continuity at O implies the existence of a ball with center O in E on which $\| f(x) \| \leqslant 1$; by a homothetic transformation and from the relation $f(\lambda x) = \lambda^n f(x)$, we deduce that f is bounded on every ball with center O, hence also on every bounded subset of E.

$2 \Rightarrow 3$.   If f is bounded on every bounded subset of E, it is in particular bounded on the ball $\| x \| \leqslant 1$; we then put

$$\| f \| = \sup_{\| x \| \leqslant 1} \| f(x) \|.$$

For every $x = (x_i)$ such that $x_i \neq O$ for every i, the point $(\| x_i \|^{-1} x_i)$ belongs to the unit ball of E; therefore

$$\left\| f\left(\frac{x_1}{\| x_1 \|}, \frac{x_2}{\|x_2\|}, ..., \frac{x_n}{\| x_n \|} \right) \right\| \leqslant \| f \|,$$

from which $\| f(x_1, x_2, ..., x_n) \| \leqslant \| f \| \prod_i \| x_i \|$. When one of the x_i is O, this inequality still holds since both sides are then zero.

3 $\Rightarrow$ 1.   To simplify the notation, we shall carry out the proof only for $n = 2$. Suppose therefore that $\| f(x_1, x_2) \| \leqslant k \| x_1 \| \| x_2 \|$.

This relation clearly implies continuity at the point O; to prove continuity at a point (a_1, a_2), we put

$$x_1 = a_1 + u_1, \qquad x_2 = a_2 + u_2 .$$

Then

$$f(a_1 + u_1, a_2 + u_2) - f(a_1, a_2) = f(a_1, u_2) + f(u_1, a_2) + f(u_1, u_2),$$

from which, if $\| u_1 \| \leqslant \epsilon$ and $\| u_2 \| \leqslant \epsilon$,

$$\| f(x_1, x_2) - f(a_1, a_2) \| \leqslant k(\| a_1 \| \epsilon + \| a_2 \| \epsilon + \epsilon^2).$$

The term on the right tends to 0 with ϵ, which gives the desired continuity.

6.2. The normed space $\mathscr{L}(E_1, ..., E_n ; F)$

The continuous multilinear mappings of the product E of the E_i into F clearly form a vector space; we shall denote it by $\mathscr{L}(E_1, ..., E_n; F)$.

One can verify that

$$\| f \| = \sup_{\|x\| \leqslant 1} \| f(x) \| \qquad (\text{where } \| x \| = \sup \| x_i \|)$$

is a norm on this vector space, and that $\| f \|$ is the smallest number $k \geqslant 0$ satisfying the inequality of Proposition 6.1.

A proof modeled on that of Proposition 4.7 shows that when F is complete, the space $\mathscr{L}(E_1, ..., E_n; F)$ is also complete.

EXAMPLE.   Let E and E' denote a normed space and its topological dual, respectively. The mapping $(x, l) \to l(x)$ of E × E' into **K** is a bilinear form on E × E'; the inequality $| l(x) | \leqslant \| l \| \| x \|$ shows that this bilinear form is continuous and of norm $\leqslant 1$.

More generally, let E and F be normed spaces; the mapping $(x, l) \to l(x)$ of E × $\mathscr{L}(E, F)$ into F is bilinear and of norm $\leqslant 1$.

7. FINITE-DIMENSIONAL NORMED SPACES

We are already acquainted with a normed space of dimension n over **K**, namely $\mathbf{K}^n$ with the equivalent norms $\sup | x_i |$, $(\Sigma | x_i |^2)^{1/2}$, $\Sigma | x_i |$. We are going to see that this is the only one, up to isomorphism.

7.1. Lemma. *Every norm p on $\mathbf{K}^n$ is continuous.*

PROOF. Let $\{a_1, a_2, ..., a_n\}$ be the canonical basis of $\mathbf{K}^n$. For every point $x = (x_i)$ of $\mathbf{K}^n$ we have

$$p(x) = p\left(\sum x_i a_i\right) \leqslant \sum | x_i | p(a_i).$$

Therefore p is continuous at the point O; finally, the relation $| p(a + u) - p(a) | \leqslant p(u)$ shows that p is continuous at every point a.

7.2. Proposition. *All norms on a finite-dimensional vector space are equivalent.*

PROOF. Since every n-dimensional vector space over **K** is vectorially isomorphic to $\mathbf{K}^n$, it is sufficient to consider $\mathbf{K}^n$.

Let p_1 and p_2 be arbitrary norms on $\mathbf{K}^n$; by Lemma 7.1, they are continuous on $\mathbf{K}^n$, and since they do not vanish anywhere on the set $S = \{x : \Sigma | x_i | = 1\}$, the quotients $p_1 p_2^{-1}$ and $p_2 p_1^{-1}$ are defined and continuous on S. But the set S is bounded and closed in $\mathbf{K}^n$, hence compact; therefore these two quotients are bounded on S, and consequently on all of $\mathbf{K}^n$ by homogeneity.

7.3. Corollary. *For every n-dimensional normed space E and every basis $(b_1, b_2, ..., b_n)$ of E, the vectorial isomorphism $(x_i) \to \Sigma x_i b_i$ of $\mathbf{K}^n$ onto E is bicontinuous.*

One can say, more concisely, that every n-dimensional normed space is isomorphic to $\mathbf{K}^n$.

7.4. Corollary. *Every finite-dimensional subspace of a normed space E is complete, and hence closed in E.*

Indeed, since **K** is complete, so is $\mathbf{K}^n$ and therefore every finite-dimensional normed space, by Corollary 7.3.

7.5. Corollary. *Every multilinear mapping of a product of finite-dimensional normed spaces into an arbitrary topological vector space F is continuous.*

PROOF. To simplify the notation, we restrict ourselves to the case of a bilinear mapping f of a product $X \times Y$ into F. Corollary 7.3 shows that for X and Y we can take $\mathbf{K}^p$ and $\mathbf{K}^q$; if (a_i) and (b_j) denote the canonical bases of $\mathbf{K}^p$ and $\mathbf{K}^q$, respectively, then

$$f(x, y) = f\left(\sum x_i a_i, \sum y_j b_j\right) = \sum x_i y_j f(a_i, b_j).$$

For every i, j, the mapping $(x, y) \to x_i y_j$ is continuous; by the axioms of a TVS, the same is therefore true of f.

Topological characterization of finite-dimensional normed spaces

Since the field $\mathbf{K}$ is locally compact, the same is true of every space $\mathbf{K}^n$, hence also of every finite-dimensional normed space.

We are going to see that this statement has a converse, which is extremely important in the study of integral equations.

7.6. Theorem (of Frederic Riesz). *Every locally compact normed space is finite-dimensional.*

PROOF. Suppose the normed space E is locally compact. Then the origin O has a compact neighborhood V, and since the closed balls with center O and nonzero radius form a neighborhood base of O, one of these is contained in V, and is thus compact. By a homothetic transformation the closed unit ball B is thus compact.

The theorem will be proved if we show that the closed unit ball B of an infinite-dimensional normed space E is not compact. For this it suffices to show that B contains an infinite sequence (a_n) of points whose mutual distances are $> \frac{1}{2}$ (see Proposition 18.2, Chapter I).

Suppose the points a_i are defined for every $i \leqslant n$, and let F_n be the vector subspace of E spanned by these points. Since F_n is finite-dimensional, it is closed (Corollary 7.4) and there exists a point a of E such that $a \notin F_n$; therefore $d(a, F_n) \neq 0$, and there exists a point $b \in F_n$ such that $d(a, b) < 2\, d(a, F_n)$. This inequality is preserved by the translation $x \to (x - b)$ which leaves F_n invariant; in other words,

$$\| a - b \| = d(a - b), O) < 2\, d((a - b, F_n).$$

We put $a_{n+1} = \| a - b \|^{-1}(a - b)$; by a homothetic transformation with scale $\| a - b \|^{-1}$, this inequality becomes

$$1 = d(a_{n+1}, O) < 2\, d(a_{n+1}, F_n).$$

Thus $a_{n+1} \in B$, and the distance from a_{n+1} to F_n, and hence also to the a_i with index $i \leqslant n$, is $> \frac{1}{2}$. The desired sequence (a_n) can therefore be constructed recursively.

EXAMPLE. The normed space $\mathscr{C}([0, 1], \mathbf{K})$ is infinite-dimensional; therefore its closed unit ball is not compact.

An immediate verification of this fact consists in observing that the distance between any two monomials of the form t^{2^n} is $\geqslant \frac{1}{4}$.

III. SUMMABLE FAMILIES; SERIES; INFINITE PRODUCTS; NORMED ALGEBRAS

When one seeks to define the sum of an infinite family of real numbers, one is led to use a notion of limit, therefore also the topology of $\mathbf{R}$.

But once this topology is specified, the definition of the sum is still not unique. The first definition used, and which for a long time was the only one, assumed that the numbers to be added were arranged in a sequence a_0, a_1, ...; the convergence of this "series" is then defined in terms of the finite sums $s_n = a_0 + a_1 + \cdots + a_n$. When the sequence (s_n) converges to a number s, the series is said to converge and have sum s.

The choice of this definition was unavoidable when it was a question of the sums of infinite families having a natural order relation, such as the families (k^n), (n^{-2}), $((-1)^n n^{-1})$; it was then maintained by habit even when people began to consider arbitrary sequences (a_n), or "multiple series" for which the set of indices did not have a natural order.

But hardly any role was played in this definition by the algebraic properties of addition such as commutativity and associativity; thus, when these algebraic properties were better elucidated, and more general topological vector spaces began to be used, the need for a definition of the summability of a family $(a_i)_{i \in I}$ which was both valid in a more general setting and independent of an order on the index set I made itself felt.

We are going to study such a definition here.

8. SUMMABLE FAMILIES OF REAL NUMBERS

Let $(a_i)_{i \in I}$ be a finite or infinite family of real numbers; we denote by $\mathscr{F}$ the set, ordered by inclusion, of finite subsets of I, and for every $J \in \mathscr{F}$ we denote by A_J the finite sum $\sum_{i \in J} a_i$.

We shall say, in language which is still quite vague, that the given family is summable and has sum A, if A_J tends to A when J becomes larger and larger.

The first way of making this vague idea more precise consists in observing that since the ordered set $\mathscr{F}$ is an increasing directed set, the subsets of $\mathscr{F}$ of the form $\{J : J \supset J_0\}$ form a filter base $\mathscr{B}$ on $\mathscr{F}$. We then say that the family (a_i) has sum A if $A = \lim_{\mathscr{B}} A_J$.

But to avoid recourse to filter bases, we shall give a more direct equivalent definition of summability:

8.1. Definition. A FAMILY $(a_i)_{i \in I}$ OF REAL NUMBERS IS SAID TO BE SUMMABLE IF THERE EXISTS A REAL NUMBER A HAVING THE FOLLOWING PROPERTY:

FOR EVERY $\epsilon > 0$ THERE EXISTS A $J_0 \in \mathscr{F}$ SUCH THAT, FOR EVERY $J \in \mathscr{F}$ CONTAINING J_0,

$$| A - A_J | \leqslant \epsilon.$$

Let us show at once that if such a number A exists, it is unique. Indeed, let A and A′ be two such numbers; the relations

$$| A - A_J | \leqslant \epsilon \quad \text{for} \quad J_0 \subset J, \quad \text{and} \quad | A' - A_J | \leqslant \epsilon \quad \text{for} \quad J_0' \subset J$$

hold simultaneously if $J = J_0 \cup J_0'$; it follows that

$$| A - A' | \leqslant | A - A_J | + | A' - A_J | \leqslant 2\epsilon.$$

Since ϵ is arbitrary, $A = A'$.

Definition 8.1 can now be completed as follows:

THE NUMBER A WHOSE UNIQUENESS HAS JUST BEEN SHOWN IS CALLED THE SUM OF THE FAMILY $(a_i)_{i \in I}$, AND IS DENOTED BY $\sum_{i \in I} a_i$ OR $\sum_i a_i$ OR $\sum a_i$ WHEN NO CONFUSION OVER I IS POSSIBLE.

Families of positive numbers

Definition 8.1 will be usable only when we have a convenient criterion for summability; the study of families of positive numbers will give us such a criterion.

8.2. Proposition. *To say that a family $(a_i)_{i \in I}$ of numbers $\geqslant 0$ is summable is equivalent to saying that the set of finite sums A_K is bounded from above; we then have*

$$\sum_{i \in I} a_i = \sup_K A_K.$$

Proof. 1. Suppose the family (a_i) is summable; then with the notation of Definition 8.1 we have

$$|A - A_J| \leqslant \epsilon, \qquad \text{from which} \qquad A_J \leqslant A + \epsilon \quad \text{for every} \quad J \supset J_0.$$

Since the a_i are $\geqslant 0$, for every $K \in \mathcal{F}$ we have

$$A_K \leqslant A_{K \cup J_0} \leqslant A + \epsilon.$$

Therefore the set of numbers A_K is bounded from above by $A + \epsilon$, and hence by A since ϵ is arbitrary.

2. Conversely, suppose the set of A_K's is bounded from above, and let A be its supremum. By the definition of the supremum, for every $\epsilon > 0$ there exists a $J_0 \in \mathcal{F}$ such that

$$A - \epsilon \leqslant A_{J_0} \leqslant A.$$

For every $J \in \mathcal{F}$ such that $J_0 \subset J$ we therefore have

$$A - \epsilon \leqslant A_{J_0} \leqslant A_J \leqslant A, \qquad \text{hence} \qquad |A - A_J| \leqslant \epsilon.$$

This relation shows that the family (a_i) is summable and has sum A.

Example. Let $(\alpha_i)_{i \in I}$ be a family of pairwise disjoint open subintervals of the interval $[0, 1]$, and let a_i be the length of α_i. For every finite subset K of I we clearly have $A_K \leqslant 1$; therefore the family (a_i) is summable and has sum $\leqslant 1$.

8.3. Corollary. *Every subfamily of a summable family of numbers $\geqslant 0$ is summable.*

Indeed, if $I' \subset I$, the set of finite sums A_J such that $J \subset I$ contains the analogous set defined relative to I'; therefore if the first is bounded from above, so is the second.

8.4. Corollary (principle of comparison). *Let $(a_i)_{i \in I}$ and $(b_i)_{i \in I}$ be families of numbers $\geqslant 0$ with the same index set, and such that $a_i \leqslant b_i$ for every $i \in I$.*

If the family $(b_i)_{i \in I}$ is summable, so is the family $(a_i)_{i \in I}$, and the sums A and B satisfy the relation $A \leqslant B$.

Proof. Let B be the sum of the family (b_i); for every $J \in \mathcal{F}$ we have

$$A_J \leqslant B_J \leqslant B.$$

Therefore Proposition 8.2 shows that the family (a_i) is summable with sum $A \leqslant B$.

Note that these conclusions extend to the case where there is a constant $k \geqslant 0$ such that $a_i \leqslant kb_i$ for every i; we then have $A \leqslant kB$.

EXAMPLES. This comparison principle is a powerful tool which enables one, starting from given summable families, to find others.

8.5.   The most used basic families are those with index set **N** or **N***; they are thus sequences; we cite the most useful:

The geometric sequence (k^n), summable when $0 \leqslant k < 1$.

The sequence $(n^{-\alpha})$, summable when $\alpha > 1$.

A convenient procedure for constructing summable sequences (a_n) of numbers $\geqslant 0$ consists of starting with a decreasing numerical function f on **N** such that $\lim_{n \to \infty} f(n) = 0$, and putting

$$a_n = f(n) - f(n+1).$$

The relation $a_1 + a_2 + \cdots + a_n = f(1) - f(n+1) \leqslant f(1)$ shows that the family (a_n) is summable with sum $f(1)$.

For example, taking successively $f(n) = k^n$ and $f(n) = n^{-p}$ (where p is > 0), we obtain the summability of the sequences mentioned above.

The integration of decreasing functions defined on $[0, \infty)$ constitutes another procedure for constructing decreasing summable sequences; we shall examine this procedure in the study of integration under the heading "comparison of series and integrals."

8.6.   Let us recall two classical sufficient conditions for the summability of positive sequences, which are deduced by comparison with a sequence (k^n):

(a)   If $\lim \sup(a_{n+1}/a_n) < 1$, the sequence (a_n) is summable; indeed, there then exists a positive number $k < 1$ and an integer n_0 such that $a_{n+1}/a_n \leqslant k$ for $n \geqslant n_0$. We deduce from this that $a_{n_0+p} \leqslant a_{n_0} k^p$, which implies summability.

If $\lim \sup(a_{n+1}/a_n) \geqslant 1$, nothing can be concluded; for example, if $a_n = 2^{-n}$ or 3^{-n} according as n is even or odd, the limit superior above equals $+\infty$, yet the sequence (a_n) is summable.

(b)   If $\lim \sup(a_n)^{1/n} < 1$, the sequence is summable, since for all n sufficiently large

$$a_n < k^n \qquad \text{where} \quad k < 1.$$

If this limit superior equals 1, nothing can be concluded (consider the case where $a_n = n^{-\alpha}$); if it is > 1, then $\limsup a_n = +\infty$; hence the sequence is not summable.

8.7. The families whose index sets are $\mathbf{N}^2$, $\mathbf{N}^3$, or more generally $\mathbf{N}^n$, or a rather simple subset of $\mathbf{N}^n$ are often called (improperly, by the way, since there exists no natural order relation on these index sets) *double series, triple series, or n-uple series.*

Here again integration theory will enable us to establish the summability of many "multiple series."

For example, the *n*-uple series with general term $(p_1 + p_2 + \cdots + p_n)^{-\alpha}$ (where $p_i \in \mathbf{N}^*$) is summable if $\alpha > n$, and not summable if $\alpha \leqslant n$.

The double series with general term $(a^m + b^n)^{-1}$ (where $a, b > 1$) is summable.

Limit of families of positive numbers

8.8. Proposition. *Let $(a_i(\lambda))_{i \in I}$ be a summable family of positive numbers, depending on a parameter $\lambda \in L$, and let $\mathscr{B}$ be a filter base on L such that, for every $i \in I$, $a_i(\lambda)$ has a limit a_i along $\mathscr{B}$.*

If there exists a constant k such that $\sum_i a_i(\lambda) \leqslant k$ for every $\lambda \in L$, then the family (a_i) is summable, and $\sum_i a_i \leqslant k$.

PROOF. For every finite $J \subset I$ we have

$$\sum_{i \in J} a_i(\lambda) \leqslant k.$$

Holding J fixed and passing to the limit along $\mathscr{B}$ in this inequality, we obtain

$$\sum_{i \in J} a_i \leqslant k, \qquad \text{from which} \qquad \sum_{i \in I} a_i \leqslant k.$$

Z Here is an example showing that the sums $s_\lambda = \sum_i a_i(\lambda)$ need not converge (along $\mathscr{B}$) to $s = \sum_i a_i$.

We take $I = L = \mathbf{N}$ and put

$$a_i(n) = 0 \quad \text{if} \quad i \neq n; \qquad a_n(n) = 1.$$

One can verify that

$$a_i = \lim_{n \to \infty} a_i(n) = 0, \qquad s_n = 1 \quad \text{and} \quad s = 0;$$

hence

$$s \neq \lim_{n \to \infty} s_n.$$

A sufficient condition for the equality

$$s = \lim_{\mathscr{B}} s_\lambda$$

will be found in Problem 83.

Application to the space l_I^p

Let I be an arbitrary finite or infinite index set, and let p be a real number $\geqslant 1$.

As in Example 3.5, one can show that the subset of $\mathscr{F}(I, \mathbf{K})$ consisting of the families $(x_i)_{i \in I}$ of elements of $\mathbf{K}$ such that $\sum |x_i|^p < \infty$ is a vector subspace of $\mathscr{F}(I, \mathbf{K})$, and that $\|x\| = (\sum |x_i|^p)^{1/p}$ is a norm on this subspace.

We denote this vector space (real or complex) with this norm by l_I^p; when $I = \mathbf{N}$ we obtain the space l^p of Example 3.5.

8.9. Proposition. *For any* I, *the space l_I^p is complete.*

PROOF.   Let $(x(n))$ be a Cauchy sequence in l_I^p; for every $i \in I$, the relation

$$|x_i(r) - x_i(s)| \leqslant \|x(r) - x(s)\|$$

shows that the sequence of numbers $x_i(n)$ is a Cauchy sequence in $\mathbf{K}$; let its limit be x_i.

Since the Cauchy sequence $(x(n))$ is bounded in l_I^p, there exists a positive number k such that

$$\sum_i |x_i(n)|^p \leqslant k \qquad \text{for every } n.$$

Then Proposition 8.8 shows that $\sum_i |x_i|^p \leqslant k$; hence the point $x = (x_i)$ of $\mathscr{F}(I, \mathbf{K})$ belongs to l_I^p.

Finally, let us show that the point x is the limit in l_I^p of the sequence $(x(n))$. For every $\epsilon > 0$ there exists an integer $n(\epsilon)$ such that for all integers $r, s \geqslant n(\epsilon)$,

$$\sum_i |x_i(r) - x_i(s)|^p \leqslant \epsilon.$$

We hold r fixed and let s tend to ∞; Proposition 8.8 shows that

$$\sum_i |x_i(r) - x_i|^p \leqslant \epsilon.$$

In other words, $\| x(r) - x \|^p \leqslant \epsilon$ for every $r \geqslant n(\epsilon)$; therefore

$$x = \lim_{n \to \infty} x(n).$$

Families of real numbers

To study a family of real numbers, we are going to write it as the difference of two positive families.

8.10. Lemma. *Let $(a_i)_{i \in I}$ and $(b_i)_{i \in I}$ be summable families of real numbers with the same index set, with respective sums A and B.*

Then the family $(c_i)_{i \in I}$, where $c_i = a_i + b_i$, is summable with sum A + B.

PROOF.   Let $\epsilon > 0$; there exist corresponding J_0, $J_0' \in \mathscr{F}$ such that

$$| A - A_J | \leqslant \epsilon \quad \text{for} \quad J \supset J_0 \quad \text{and} \quad | B - B_J | \leqslant \epsilon \quad \text{for} \quad J \supset J_0'.$$

These inequalities hold simultaneously if $J \supset J_0 \cup J_0'$; hence

$$| A + B - (A_J + B_J)| \leqslant | A - A_J | + | B - B_J | \leqslant 2\epsilon$$

or, putting $C = A + B$,

$$| C - C_J | \leqslant 2\epsilon \quad \text{for every J such that} \quad J_0 \cup J_0' \subset J,$$

which shows that the family (c_i) is summable with sum C.

8.11. Proposition. *Let I be an index set. The collection of summable families of real numbers with index set I is a vector subspace of $\mathscr{F}(I, \mathbf{R})$, and the mapping $(a_i) \to \Sigma a_i$ is a linear functional on this space.*

This is immediate, from Lemma 8.10, if we observe that when the family (a_i) is summable with sum A, the family (λa_i) is summable with sum λA.

Since $\Sigma a_i \geqslant 0$ when each a_i is $\geqslant 0$, we also have $\Sigma a_i \leqslant \Sigma b_i$ when $a_i \leqslant b_i$ for every i.

REMARK.   It is sometimes useful to note that if I' is a subset of I such that $a_i = 0$ for every $i \notin I'$, the families $(a_i)_{i \in I}$ and $(a_i)_{i \in I'}$ are simultaneously summable (or not summable) and have equal sums.

8.12. Definition. A FAMILY (a_i) OF REAL NUMBERS IS SAID TO BE *ABSOLUTELY SUMMABLE* IF THE FAMILY $(| a_i |)$ OF THEIR ABSOLUTE VALUES IS SUMMABLE.

The word *absolutely* in this definition does not at all mean that the family (a_i) is summable in some absolute sense, which would in any case be meaningless; it refers simply to the fact that it is the *absolute value* of the a_i which enters in the definition.

8.13. Proposition. *Let (a_i) be a family of real numbers; then the following three statements are equivalent:*

1. *This family is absolutely summable.*
2. *This family is summable.*
3. *The set of finite sums A_K is bounded.*

PROOF. $1 \Rightarrow 2$. The members of each of the positive families (a_i^+) and (a_i^-) are bounded from above by the corresponding members of the family $(|a_i|)$; therefore if $(|a_i|)$ is summable, the comparison principle shows that the families (a_i^+) and (a_i^-) are summable. Hence, by Proposition 8.11, the family (a_i) which is their difference is also summable.

$2 \Rightarrow 3$. If the family (a_i) is summable, there exists $J_0 \in \mathscr{F}$ such that

$$|A - A_J| \leqslant 1 \qquad \text{for every finite} \quad J \supset J_0 .$$

But for every $K \in \mathscr{F}$ we have

$$|A_{K \cup J_0} - A_K| \leqslant \sum_{i \in J_0} |a_i| .$$

Therefore, comparing these inequalities for $J = K \cup J_0$ gives

$$|A - A_K| \leqslant 1 + \sum_{i \in J_0} |a_i| .$$

Thus, the set of numbers A_K is bounded.

$3 \Rightarrow 1$. The hypothesis implies the existence of two positive numbers k_1, k_2 such that $A_K \in [-k_1, k_2]$ for every $K \in \mathscr{F}$.

For every $K \in \mathscr{F}$, the sum of the $|a_i|$ such that $i \in K$ and $a_i \geqslant 0$ belongs to $[0, k_2]$, and the sum of the $|a_i|$ such that $i \in K$ and $a_i \leqslant 0$ belongs to $[0, k_1]$; therefore the sum of the $|a_i|$ such that $i \in K$ is $\leqslant k_1 + k_2$.

These sums are thus bounded from above; hence the family (a_i) is absolutely summable.

8.14. Corollary. *Every subfamily of a summable family of real numbers is summable.*

Indeed, the summability of the family $(a_i)_{i \in I}$ implies that of the family $(|a_i|)_{i \in I}$, hence that of the subfamily $(|a_i|)_{i \in I'}$, therefore, finally, that of the subfamily $(a_i)_{i \in I'}$.

Z The equivalence which has just been established between summability and absolute summability does not have an analogue in the theory of series; we recall for example that the alternating series with general term $(-1)^n n^{-1}$ is convergent although the series with general term n^{-1} is divergent.

We shall return later to the comparison of series and summable families.

9. SUMMABLE FAMILIES IN TOPOLOGICAL GROUPS AND NORMED SPACES

A number of the results of the preceding section rest solely on the existence of a group structure and a separated topology on **R**; thus, one might expect that the theory which we have expounded is valid in every commutative and separated topological group. We shall consider primarily the case of normed spaces, but it is interesting, in view of multipliable families, to give the definitions in the framework of topological groups.

We shall continue to use the notation $\mathscr{F}$, A_J introduced in the previous section.

9.1. Definition. LET G BE A SEPARATED COMMUTATIVE TOPOLOGICAL GROUP, WRITTEN ADDITIVELY, AND LET $(a_i)_{i \in I}$ BE A FAMILY OF ELEMENTS OF G.

THIS FAMILY IS SAID TO BE *SUMMABLE* IF THERE EXISTS AN ELEMENT A OF G HAVING THE FOLLOWING PROPERTY:

FOR EVERY NEIGHBORHOOD V OF O THERE EXISTS A $J_0 \in \mathscr{F}$ SUCH THAT

$$A - A_J \in V \quad \text{for every} \quad J \in \mathscr{F}, \quad J \supset J_0.$$

WHEN SUCH AN ELEMENT EXISTS, IT IS UNIQUE; IT IS CALLED THE *SUM* OF THE FAMILY AND DENOTED BY

$$\sum_{i \in I} a_i \quad \text{or} \quad \sum_i a_i \quad \text{or} \quad \sum a_i.$$

Let us prove that A is unique when it exists. It suffices to slightly modify the proof given following Definition 8.1.

For every neighborhood U of O there exists a symmetric neighborhood V of O such that $V + V \subset U$. We conclude from the relations $A - A_J \in V$ and $A' - A_J \in V$ that

$$A - A' \in V + V, \quad \text{hence} \quad A - A' \in U.$$

Thus the element $A - A'$ belongs to every neighborhood of O; since G is separated, $A - A' = O$ or $A = A'$.

REMARK 1.   When the group operation in G is written multiplicatively, it is preferable to say that the family (a_i) is *multipliable* and has product $A = \prod a_i$.

This is, for example, the case for the topological groups $\mathbf{R}^*$ and $\mathbf{C}^*$.

REMARK 2.   When I is finite, the family (a_i) is always summable and its sum is equal to the sum in the ordinary sense.

REMARK 3.   If I' denotes a subset of I such that $a_i = 0$ for every $i \notin I'$, the families $(a_i)_{i \in I}$ and $(a_i)_{i \in I'}$ are simultaneously summable (or not summable) and their sums are equal.

9.2. Proposition.   *Let $(a_i)_{i \in I}$ and $(b_i)_{i \in I}$ be summable families of elements of G with the same index set I, and let A and B be their sums.*

Then the family $(c_i)_{i \in I}$, where $c_i = a_i + b_i$, is summable with sum $A + B$.

The proof is an adaptation of that of Lemma 8.9.

9.3. Proposition.   *Let G and G' be commutative and separated topological groups, and let φ be a continuous representation of G in G'.*

If (a_i) is a summable family in G with sum A, the family (a_i'), where $a_i' = \varphi(a_i)$, is summable in G' with sum $A' = \varphi(A)$.

PROOF.   For every neighborhood V' of O in G', we put $V = \varphi^{-1}(V')$; the relation

$$A - A_J \in V \qquad \text{when} \quad J_0 \subset J$$

implies

$$\varphi(A) - \varphi(A_J) \in \varphi(V) \qquad \text{or} \qquad A' - A_J' \in V' \qquad \text{when} \quad J_0 \subset J.$$

In other words, the family (a_i') has sum A'.

Cauchy criterion

9.4. Definition.   A FAMILY (a_i) IN G IS SAID TO SATISFY THE C_{AUCHY} CRITERION IF FOR EVERY NEIGHBORHOOD V OF O THERE EXISTS A $J_0 \in \mathscr{F}$ SUCH THAT $A_K \in V$ FOR EVERY $K \in \mathscr{F}$ SUCH THAT $K \cap J_0 = \varnothing$.

In other words, after removing from the family a finite number of elements which are "too large," all the finite sums are small.

We now denote the set of numbers A_J for which $J_0 \subset J$ by $\mathscr{A}(J_0)$.

9.5. Proposition.   *To say that the family (a_i) satisfies the Cauchy criterion is equivalent to saying that for every neighborhood V of O there exists a $J_0 \in \mathscr{F}$ and a translate $a + V$ of V such that $\mathscr{A}(J_0) \subset a + V$.*

PROOF. 1. Suppose (a_i) satisfies the Cauchy criterion; every J containing J_0 is of the form $J_0 \cup K$, where $K \cap J_0 = \emptyset$; therefore $A_J = A_{J_0} + A_K$.

It follows from $A_K \in V$ that

$$A_J \in A_{J_0} + V, \qquad \text{hence} \qquad \mathscr{A}(J_0) \subset A_{J_0} + V.$$

2. Given V, there exists a symmetric neighborhood U of O such that $U + U \subset V$. If by hypothesis there exists a $J_0 \in \mathscr{F}$ and $a \in G$ such that $\mathscr{A}(J_0) \subset a + U$, then for every K with $K \cap J_0 = \emptyset$ we have

$$A_{J_0} \in a + U, \qquad A_{J_0} + A_K \in a + U, \qquad \text{from which} \qquad A_K \in U + U \subset V.$$

9.6. Corollary. *Every summable family satisfies the Cauchy criterion.*

Indeed, the condition $\mathscr{A}(J_0) \subset a + V$ holds on taking for a the sum of the family, and using Definition 9.1.

Z The converse of this corollary is in general false. But we shall see that it is true in complete normed spaces.

9.7. Proposition. *Every subfamily of a family satisfying the Cauchy criterion also satisfies it.*

Indeed, since the index sets of these families are I and I', with $I' \subset I$, it suffices in the statement of 9.4 to take, for the set J_0 relative to the subfamily, the set $I' \cap J_0$.

9.8. Proposition. *Let (a_i) be a family satisfying the Cauchy criterion. For every neighborhood V of O we have*

$$a_i \in V \quad \text{except for at most finitely many of the} \quad i.$$

To see this, it suffices to apply the Cauchy criterion to the sets K of the form $\{i\}$, where $i \notin J_0$.

9.9. Corollary. *If the group G is such that O has a countable neighborhood base, and if the family (a_i) satisfies the Cauchy criterion, then the set of indices i for which $a_i \neq O$ is finite or countable.*

Indeed, let (V_n) be a neighborhood base of O; for every n, the set I_n of indices i such that $a_i \notin V_n$ is finite. Since the set of i such that $a_i \neq O$ is simply the union of the I_n, this set is finite or countable.

Z This corollary might lead one to believe that the study of summable families in the usual groups, in particular in normed spaces, reduces to the study of families with countable index sets, that is, to the study of sequences (a_n).

This is not so for two reasons: On the one hand, the artificial introduction of an order on the set of indices introduces the risk of masking the commutativity and additivity properties of the sum; on the other hand, it can happen that one has to study *all* the summable families with a given nondenumerable index set I.

9.10. Commutativity

Since the definition of the summability of a family $(a_i)_{i \in I}$ does not involve any order structure on I, one can say, in a vague sense, that this notion is commutative. This assertion can be made precise in the following way: Let $(a_i)_{i \in I}$ and $(b_j)_{j \in I'}$ be two families of elements of G; if there exists a bijection φ of I to I' such that $b_{\varphi(i)} = a_i$ for every i, then the summability of one of these families implies that of the other, and their sums are equal.

Associativity

Associativity is deeper, and consists of the following proposition:

9.11. Proposition. *Let* $(I_\lambda)_{\lambda \in L}$ *be an arbitrary partition of an index set* I, *and let* $(a_i)_{i \in I}$ *be a family of elements of the group* G *indexed by* I.

If this family, as well as each of the subfamilies associated with the I_λ, *is summable, and if we denote their sums by* A *and* s_λ, *respectively, then the family* $(s_\lambda)_{\lambda \in L}$ *is summable and has sum* A.

PROOF. We borrow the notation $\mathscr{A}(J_0)$ used in Proposition 9.5; similarly, for every finite subset M_0 of L, let $\mathscr{L}(M_0)$ denote the set of finite sums $\Sigma_{\lambda \in M} s_\lambda$, where $M_0 \subset M$.

Given J_0, if we let M_0 be the finite set of those λ for which $J_0 \cap I_\lambda \neq \varnothing$, every sum $\Sigma_{\lambda \in M} s_\lambda$ for which $M_0 \subset M$ is the limit of sums A_J where $J_0 \subset J$; it follows that

$$\mathscr{L}(M_0) \subset \overline{\mathscr{A}(J_0)}, \qquad \text{from which} \qquad \overline{\mathscr{L}(M_0)} \subset \overline{\mathscr{A}(J_0)}.$$

For every neighborhood V of O, there exists a J_0 such that

$$\mathscr{A}(J_0) \subset A + V.$$

Therefore if V is closed, we also have

$$\overline{\mathscr{A}(J_0)} \subset A + V, \qquad \text{from which} \qquad \overline{\mathscr{L}(M_0)} \subset A + V.$$

Since the closed neighborhoods of O constitute a neighborhood base of O (see Problem 81), this relation shows that the family (s_λ) is summable with sum A.

EXAMPLE.   Let $(a_{p,q})$ be a summable double sequence of real numbers; every subfamily is then summable (Corollary 8.12), and

$$\sum_{p,q} a_{p,q} = \sum_p \Big(\sum_q a_{p,q}\Big) = \sum_q \Big(\sum_p a_{p,q}\Big).$$

Z It is not correct that if each of the subfamilies $(a_i)_{i \in I_\lambda}$ is summable and the family (s_λ) is summable, then $(a_i)_{i \in I}$ is always summable. To see this it suffices to take L infinite, with each of the subfamilies consisting of two elements, 1 and -1; then each s_λ equals 0. Hence the family (s_λ) is summable, but the family (a_i) is not.

On the other hand, here are two important cases in which this assertion is correct.

9.12.   L is finite. The family $(a_i)_{i \in I}$ is then the finite sum of the families $(a_i{}^\lambda)_{i \in I}$ defined as follows:

$$a_i{}^\lambda = a_i \quad \text{if} \quad i \in I_\lambda; \qquad a_i{}^\lambda = O \quad \text{if} \quad i \notin I_\lambda.$$

But if one of the two families $(a_i{}^\lambda)_{i \in I}$ and $(a_i)_{i \in I}$ is summable, the other is also, and they have the same sums; the desired result now follows from Proposition 9.2.

9.13.   The a_i are numbers $\geqslant 0$. We start by slightly extending the notion of the sum: By the sum of a family $(a_i)_{i \in I}$ of elements of $\bar{\mathbf{R}}_+ = [0, +\infty]$ we shall mean the supremum, finite or infinite, of the sums of all finite subfamilies of elements a_i .

Let then $(I_\lambda)_{\lambda \in L}$ be a partition of I; we shall show that for these generalized sums we again have

$$\sum_{i \in I} a_i = \sum_\lambda s_\lambda, \qquad \text{where} \qquad s_\lambda = \sum_{i \in I_\lambda} a_i .$$

First of all, $\Sigma_i\, a_i \geqslant$ (every finite sum of elements s_λ), by an obvious comparison principle; hence we obtain the desired relation with $\geqslant$ instead of $=$. The same relation, but with $\leqslant$ instead of $=$, follows from the fact that every finite sum of elements a_i is bounded from above by a finite sum of elements s_λ .

In particular, if each of the sums s_λ is finite and if $\Sigma_\lambda s_\lambda$ is finite, the same is true of $\Sigma_i\, a_i$ which, by Proposition 8.2, gives the desired result.

9.14. EXAMPLE. Let $(a_i)_{i \in I}$ and $(b_j)_{j \in J}$ be two summable families of real numbers; then the families $(|a_i|)_{i \in I}$ and $(|b_j|)_{j \in J}$ are summable. The family $(|a_i b_j|)$, whose index set is $I \times J$, can be partitioned into subfamilies indexed by the sets $i \times J$; but then, by Proposition 9.13,

$$\sum_{i,j} |a_i b_j| = \sum_i \left(\sum_j |a_i b_j| \right) = \sum_i \left(|a_i| \sum_j |b_j| \right)$$
$$= \left(\sum_i |a_i| \right) \left(\sum_j |b_j| \right).$$

Therefore the family $(a_i b_j)$ is absolutely summable, hence summable; by Proposition 9.11 we can write

$$\sum_{i,j} a_i b_j = \sum_i \left(\sum_j a_i b_j \right) = \sum_i \left(a_i \sum_j b_j \right) = \left(\sum_i a_i \right) \left(\sum_j b_j \right).$$

In short, the family $(a_i b_j)$, which is called the *product of the families* (a_i) and (b_j), is summable and its sum is the product of their sums.

Summability in normed spaces

The existence of a norm will enable us to rederive part of the results obtained in the case of **R**.

9.15. Theorem. *In a complete normed space* E, *every family of elements of* E *which satisfies the Cauchy criterion is summable.*

PROOF. Let $(a_i)_{i \in I}$ be a family of elements of E. It is immediate that the sets $\mathscr{A}(J_0)$ used in Proposition 9.5 form a filter base $\mathscr{B}$ on E; in addition this proposition shows that when the family (a_i) satisfies the Cauchy criterion, $\mathscr{B}$ is a Cauchy filter base (see Definition 20.7, Chapter I). Since E is complete, this filter base converges to a point $A \in E$ (see Proposition 20.8, Chapter I); therefore the family (a_i) is summable with sum A.

9.16. Corollary. *In a complete normed space, every subfamily of a summable family is summable.*

This is a consequence of the results 9.6, 9.7, and 9.15.

REMARK. If F denotes a vector subspace of a complete normed space E, with $\bar{F} = E$, and if (a_i) is a family of elements of F satisfying the Cauchy criterion, we have just seen that (a_i) is summable in E; but clearly if its sum does not belong to F, then (a_i) is not summable in F. This example shows the reason why a family can satisfy the Cauchy criterion without being summable.

Absolutely summable families in normed spaces

It is not always easy to recognize whether a family of elements of a normed space is summable. It is thus useful to have sufficient criteria for summability; such a criterion is furnished by the notion of absolute summability.

9.17. Definition. Let E be a normed space. A family (a_i) of elements of E is said to be *absolutely summable* if the family of their norms $\| a_i \|$ is summable.

This definition appears to depend upon the norm of E; in fact, it only depends on the topology of E, for if p and p' are equivalent norms on E, there exist constants k, $k' > 0$ such that $p' \leqslant kp$ and $p \leqslant k'p'$; thus if one of the families $(p(a_i))$, $(p'(a_i))$ is summable, the other is also.

9.18. Proposition. *In a complete normed space, every absolutely summable family is summable.*

Proof.   By Theorem 9.15, it suffices to show that if the family (a_i) is absolutely summable, it satisfies the Cauchy criterion.

But if the family $(\| a_i \|)$ is summable, it satisfies the Cauchy criterion; therefore for every $\epsilon > 0$ there exists a $J_0 \in \mathscr{F}$ such that

$$\sum_{i \in K} \| a_i \| \leqslant \epsilon \qquad \text{for every} \qquad K \in \mathscr{F}, \quad K \cap J_0 = \varnothing.$$

But

$$\| A_K \| = \left\| \sum_{i \in K} a_i \right\| \leqslant \sum_{i \in K} \| a_i \|, \qquad \text{from which} \qquad \| A_K \| \leqslant \epsilon.$$

Therefore the family (a_i) satisfies the Cauchy criterion.

Z It is essential to note that in a normed space, a family can be summable without being absolutely summable; here are two examples.

EXAMPLE 1.   Let (f_n) be the sequence of elements of $\mathscr{C}([0, 1], \mathbf{R})$ defined by

$$f_n(t) = t \sin^2 \frac{\pi}{t} \qquad \text{on} \qquad \left[\frac{1}{n+1}, \frac{1}{n} \right]; \qquad f_n(t) = 0 \quad \text{off this interval.}$$

Then

$$\| f_n \| \geqslant f_n \left(\frac{1}{n + \frac{1}{2}} \right) = \frac{2}{2n + 1};$$

thus the family (f_n) is not absolutely summable; but it is summable and its sum is the function f defined by

$$f(0) = 0; \quad f(t) = t \sin^2 \frac{\pi}{t} \quad \text{if} \quad t \neq 0.$$

EXAMPLE 2. Let a_n be the vector in the normed space l^2 all of whose coordinates are zero, except for the nth, which equals n^{-1}. The family (a_n) is not absolutely summable since $\| a_n \| = n^{-1}$; but this family is summable, and its sum is the vector

$$x = (1, 2^{-1}, ..., n^{-1}, ...).$$

These two examples are simply special cases of the following general result:

In every infinite-dimensional normed space, there exist summable sequences which are not absolutely summable (see Problem 84).

We are going to see that the situation is simpler in finite-dimensional spaces.

9.19. Proposition. *In a finite-dimensional space, summability and absolute summability are equivalent.*

PROOF. Every finite-dimensional normed space over **K** is a finite-dimensional normed space over **R**; on the other hand, Corollary 7.3 permits us to assume that the latter space is $\mathbf{R}^n$, with the norm

$$\| x \| = \sum | x_p |.$$

Since $\mathbf{R}^n$ is complete, every absolutely summable family in $\mathbf{R}^n$ is summable. Conversely, if the family (a_i) is summable in $\mathbf{R}^n$, Proposition 9.3 shows that for every $p \leqslant n$, the family (a_i^p) of the pth coordinates of the a_i is summable; therefore the family $(| a_i^p |)$ is summable. Since $\| a_i \| = \Sigma_p | a_i^p |$, the family $(\| a_i \|)$, which is the sum of n summable families, is summable.

9.20. Corollary. *For every family of complex numbers, summability and absolute summability are equivalent.*

Multilinear mappings of summable families

We are going to extend the result obtained in 9.14 concerning the product of two families of real numbers.

9.21. Proposition. *Let* E *and* F *be normed spaces, and let* f *be a continuous bilinear mapping of* E × F *into a complete normed space* G.

Let $(a_i)_{i \in I}$ $((b_j)_{j \in J})$ *be a summable family of elements of* E (F) *with sum* A (B). *When these two families are* **absolutely summable,** *then the family* $(f(a_i, b_j))$ *is absolutely summable, and has sum* f(A, B).

PROOF. Since f is continuous, there exists (see Proposition 6.1) a constant k such that

$$\| f(x, y) \| \leqslant k \, \| x \| \, \| y \| \qquad \text{for all} \quad x, y.$$

Therefore

$$\| f(a_i, b_j) \| \leqslant k \, \| a_i \| \, \| b_j \|;$$

but since the families $(\| a_i \|)$ and $(\| b_j \|)$ are summable, the family of products $\| a_i \| \, \| b_j \|$ is summable (see 9.14). Therefore the family $(f(a_i, b_j))$ is absolutely summable, and since G is complete, it is summable.

We now observe that for every $a \in E$ we have $\sum_j f(a, b_j) = f(a, B)$, since the mapping $y \to f(a, y)$ is linear and continuous (see Proposition 9.3); similarly for the $f(a_i, b)$.

Therefore, by the associativity of the sum we have

$$\sum_{i,j} f(a_i, b_j) = \sum_i \left(\sum_j f(a_i, b_j) \right) = \sum_i f(a_i, B) = f(A, B).$$

9.22. Corollary. *If* (a_i) *and* (b_j) *are two summable families of complex numbers with respective sums* A *and* B, *the family* $(a_i b_j)$ *of products is summable with sum* AB.

Indeed, the mapping $(x, y) \to xy$ of **C** × **C** into **C** is bilinear and continuous.

REMARK   1.   Proposition 9.21 evidently extends to every continuous multilinear mapping.

REMARK   2.   In the statement of Proposition 9.21, the hypothesis that the families (a_i) and (b_j) are absolutely summable is essential; however, the assumption that G is complete can be omitted, for it suffices to observe that if G is not complete, we can assume it to be imbedded in a complete normed space G′ (see Problem 48).

10. SERIES; COMPARISON OF SERIES AND SUMMABLE FAMILIES

10.1. Definition.   LET $(a_n)_{n \in N}$ BE A SEQUENCE OF ELEMENTS OF A SEPARATED COMMUTATIVE TOPOLOGICAL GROUP G.

THE *SERIES* DEFINED BY THE SEQUENCE (a_n) IS THE PAIR CONSISTING OF THE TWO SEQUENCES (a_n) AND (s_n), WHERE s_n IS THE PARTIAL SUM $\sum_{i \leqslant n} a_i$.

THIS SERIES IS SAID TO *CONVERGE* IF THE SEQUENCE (s_n) IS CONVERGENT; ITS LIMIT s (WHICH IS UNIQUE, AS G IS SEPARATED) IS CALLED THE *SUM* OF THE SERIES AND IS DENOTED BY $\sum_0^\infty a_n$ OR SIMPLY $\sum a_n$.

WHEN THE SERIES DOES NOT CONVERGE, IT IS SAID TO *DIVERGE*.

REMARK 1. It is convenient to denote the series defined by the sequence (a_n) by the symbol $a_0 + a_1 + \cdots + a_n \ldots$; this notation is *a priori* meaningless, but it is rather suggestive.

One also says, more simply, "the series with general term a_n" or "the series (a_n)."

REMARK 2. Sometimes the index set **N** is replaced by **N***; more generally, one can replace **N** by a sequence of indices with an order isomorphic to that of **N**.

REMARK 3. If the operation in G is written multiplicatively, the term "series" is replaced by "infinite product," and the limit of the partial products $p_n = \prod_0^n a_i$ is denoted by $\prod_0^\infty a_i$.

REMARK 4. When the a_n are real numbers, one also says that the series (a_n) converges in $\bar{\mathbf{R}}$ and has sum $+ \infty$ (or $- \infty$) if $\lim s_n = + \infty$ (or $- \infty$).

Let us point out, without giving either statements or proofs, that Propositions 9.2 and 9.3 have immediate analogues for series.

Cauchy criterion

10.2. Definition. A *SERIES* WITH GENERAL TERM a_n IN G IS SAID TO SATISFY THE *CAUCHY CRITERION* IF THE SEQUENCE (s_n) OF PARTIAL SUMS IS A CAUCHY SEQUENCE IN G; IN OTHER WORDS, IF FOR EVERY NEIGHBORHOOD V OF O THERE EXISTS AN INTEGER n_0 SUCH THAT THE RELATIONS $n_0 \leqslant p \leqslant q$ IMPLY

$$s_q - s_p \in V, \quad \text{i.e.,} \quad (a_{p+1} + a_{p+2} + \cdots + a_q) \in V.$$

When G is a normed space, it is more convenient to replace the neighborhood V in this statement by a number $\epsilon > 0$, and the condition $s_q - s_p \in V$ by $\| s_q - s_p \| \leqslant \epsilon$.

10.3. Proposition. 1. *Every convergent series satisfies the Cauchy criterion.*

2.   *Conversely, when* G *is a complete normed space, every series satisfying the Cauchy criterion is convergent.*

This is immediate, since the convergence of a series (a_n) is defined in terms of the convergence of the sequence (s_n).

10.4. Proposition. *For every series satisfying the Cauchy criterion (thus, in particular, for every convergent series), the sequence* (a_n) *tends to* O.

Indeed, with the notation of Definition 10.2, we have

$$a_{n+1} = s_{n+1} - s_n \in V \qquad \text{for every} \quad n \geqslant n_0 \, .$$

Z Let us recall the well-known fact that the converse of this proposition is false, even in **R**. For example, the series with general term $a_n = n^{-1}$ does not satisfy the Cauchy criterion since $s_{2p} - s_p \geqslant \frac{1}{2}$ for every p; nevertheless $\lim a_n = 0$.

Commutativity and associativity

We first study *associativity*, which is easier to study than commutativity. If one does not change the order of the elements a_n of a series, the only grouping of terms which is possible consists of grouping them in segments of the form $(a_{p+1} + a_{p+2} + \cdots + a_q)$; we can then state:

10.5. Proposition. *Let* (a_n) *be a sequence of elements of* G, *and let* (α_n) *be a strictly increasing sequence of integers* $\geqslant 0$; *we put* $b_n = \Sigma a_i$, *where the summation is over those i satisfying* $\alpha_{n-1} \leqslant i < \alpha_n$.
If the series (a_n) *satisfies the Cauchy criterion, so does the series* (b_n). *If the first converges, so does the second, and their sums are equal.*

Indeed, the sequence of partial sums of the second series is a subsequence of the sequence of partial sums of the first series.

Z It can happen that the second series converges and the first series does not; for example, if $a_n = (-1)^n$ and $b_n = a_{2n} + a_{2n+1}$.

10.6. Definition. A SERIES (a_n) IS SAID TO BE *COMMUTATIVELY CONVERGENT** IF THE SERIES $(a_{\pi(n)})$ IS CONVERGENT FOR EVERY PERMUTATION π OF **N**.

Observe that this definition does not require *a priori* that the series (a_n) and $(a_{\pi(n)})$ have the same sum.

---

* An equivalent terminology is *unconditionally convergent.*

10.7. Theorem. *To say that a series (a_n) is commutatively convergent is equivalent to saying that the family (a_n) is summable.*

The sum of the family (a_n) is then equal to the sum of each of the series $(a_{\pi(n)})$.

PROOF. 1. Suppose the family (a_n) is summable, and let A be its sum. For every neighborhood V of O there exists a finite subset J_0 of **N** such that $A - A_J \in V$ for every finite $J \supset J_0$.

If n_0 is the largest element of J_0, the segment $[0, p]$ of **N** contains J_0 for every $p \geqslant n_0$, hence $A - s_p \in V$; in other words, the series (a_n) has sum A. This argument is clearly applicable to each of the series $(a_{\pi(n)})$.

2. Suppose, on the contrary, that the family (a_n) is not summable. Then there exists a neighborhood V of O such that for every finite $J \subset \mathbf{N}$ there exists a finite $K(J) \subset \mathbf{N} \div J$ for which $A_{K(J)} \notin V$.

Put $J_0 = \varnothing$, and $J_{n+1} = J_n \cup K(J_n)$ for $n \geqslant 0$. The sets $K(J_n)$ are finite subsets of **N** which are pairwise disjoint, and for each of them

$$A_{K(J_n)} \notin V.$$

One can easily construct a permutation π of **N** such that in the sequence $(a_{\pi(n)})$ the elements a_n for which $n \in K(J_p)$ (for given p) are consecutive.

We now put $b_n = a_{\pi(n)}$; the series (b_n) does not satisfy the Cauchy criterion because it contains an infinite number of disjoint "segments" $(b_{p+1}, ..., b_q)$ each of whose sum lies outside V.

Therefore the series (a_n) is not commutatively convergent.

REMARK. In fact the proof shows more: It shows that if the family (a_n) does not satisfy the Cauchy criterion, there exists a series $(a_{\pi(n)})$ which does not satisfy it either.

Absolutely convergent series in normed spaces

10.8. Definition. LET E BE A NORMED SPACE; A SERIES (a_n) IN E IS SAID TO BE *ABSOLUTELY CONVERGENT* IF THE SERIES WITH GENERAL TERM $\| a_n \|$ IS CONVERGENT.

This definition leads us to the study of series with positive terms.

10.9. Lemma. *Let (a_n) be a sequence of positive numbers; the following three statements are equivalent:*

1. *The series (a_n) is convergent.*
2. *The set of sums s_n is bounded from above.*
3. *The family (a_n) is summable.*

PROOF. 1 ⇒ 2.   For, the sequence (s_n) is increasing; thus if $\lim s_n = s$, we have $s_n \leqslant s$ for every n.

2 ⇒ 3. For, every sum A_K is bounded from above by a sum $A_{[0,n]} = s_n$; thus if $s_n \leqslant k$, the sums A_K are bounded from above, which implies the summability of the family (a_n).

3 ⇒ 1. For by Theorem 10.7, summability implies the convergence of the series (and even commutative convergence).

10.10. Corollary. *To say that a series (a_n) in a normed space is absolutely convergent is equivalent to saying that the family (a_n) is absolutely summable.*

10.11. Corollary. *In a complete normed space, every absolutely convergent series is commutatively convergent.*

This last corollary follows from 9.18, 10.7, and 10.10.

10.12. Proposition (case of finite-dimensional spaces). *Let (a_n) be a sequence of elements of a finite-dimensional normed space.*
  The following statements are equivalent:

1.   *The series (a_n) is commutatively convergent.*
2.   *The series (a_n) is absolutely convergent.*
3.   *The family (a_n) is summable.*
4.   *The family (a_n) is absolutely summable.*

This is a consequence of 9.19, 10.10, and 10.11.
  This proposition applies in particular to series of complex numbers.

10.13. Conditionally convergent series. The alternating harmonic series with general term $(-1)^n n^{-1}$ is an example of a convergent series which is not commutatively convergent; such a series is sometimes said to be *conditionally convergent*. This is a rather evocative terminology which should not however be abused: For example, if a series (a_n) is conditionally convergent, so is the series $(-a_n)$, but the sum of these two series is commutatively convergent, hence not conditionally convergent. Similarly there do not exist, properly speaking, criteria for conditional convergence; there exist only criteria (sufficient) for convergence in which one is not concerned with knowing whether or not the series (a_n) is commutatively convergent.

The most useful criteria of this type are furnished by a simple inequality due to Abel.

10.14. Lemma. *Let (a_n) be a sequence of elements of a normed space* E, *and let (λ_n) be a decreasing sequence of positive numbers; we put*

$$k_n = \sup_{p \geqslant 0} \| a_n + a_{n+1} + \cdots + a_{n+p} \|.$$

Then for every n, p we have

$$\| \lambda_n a_n + \lambda_{n+1} a_{n+1} + \cdots + \lambda_{n+p} a_{n+p} \| \leqslant \lambda_n k_n .$$

PROOF. Put $b_{n,p} = a_n + a_{n+1} + \cdots + a_{n+p}$; by a simple transformation called *Abel's transformation* (similar to integration by parts) one can write

$$\| \lambda_n a_n + \cdots + \lambda_{n+p} a_{n+p} \|$$
$$= \| \lambda_n b_{n,0} + \lambda_{n+1}(b_{n,1} - b_{n,0}) + \cdots + \lambda_{n+p}(b_{n,p} - b_{n,p-1}) \|$$
$$= \|(\lambda_n - \lambda_{n+1})b_{n,0} + \cdots + (\lambda_{n+p-1} - \lambda_{n+p})b_{n,p-1} + \lambda_{n+p}b_{n,p} \|$$
$$\leqslant k_n((\lambda_n - \lambda_{n+1}) + \cdots + (\lambda_{n+p-1} - \lambda_{n+p}) + \lambda_{n+p}) = \lambda_n k_n .$$

It follows from this lemma that if the sequence $(\lambda_n k_n)$ tends to 0, the series $(\lambda_n a_n)$ satisfies the Cauchy criterion. Hence, using the fact that the sequence (λ_n) is decreasing, we obtain two cases where the series $(\lambda_n a_n)$ will converge:

10.15. Proposition (Abel's rule). *Let (a_n) be a sequence of elements of a complete normed space* E, *and let (λ_n) be a decreasing sequence of positive numbers.*

In each of the following two cases, the series $(\lambda_n a_n)$ is convergent:

(a)　*The series (a_n) is convergent.*

(b)　*The set of sums $s_n = a_0 + a_1 + \cdots + a_n$ is bounded in* E, *and* $\lim_{n \to \infty} \lambda_n = 0$.

PROOF. Since E is complete it suffices, by Lemma 10.14, to verify that the sequence $(\lambda_n k_n)$ tends to 0.

In the first case, the convergence of the series (a_n) implies $\lim_{n \to \infty} k_n = 0$; but $\lambda_n \leqslant \lambda_0$, from which $\lambda_n k_n \leqslant \lambda_0 k_n$, and the result follows.

In the second case, the relation $a_n + a_{n+1} + \cdots + a_{n+p} = s_{n+p} - s_{n-1}$ shows that the set of $b_{n,p}$ is bounded; therefore there exists a number $k \geqslant 0$ such that $k_n \leqslant k$. We therefore have $\lambda_n k_n \leqslant \lambda_n k$, from which $\lim_{n \to \infty} \lambda_n k_n = 0$.

10.16. EXAMPLES. Let us call a series of real numbers whose general term can be written as $\lambda_n a_n$, where $a_n = (-1)^n$ and $\lambda_n \geqslant 0$ (or $\lambda_n \leqslant 0$, but a change of sign throughout leads back to the preceding case) an *alternating series*.

The condition $\| s_n \| \leqslant k$ is satisfied since $s_n = 0$ or 1. Therefore if λ_n *decreases* to 0, the alternating series with general term $(-1)^n \lambda_n$ is convergent.

10.17. Let us take for a_n the complex number k^n, where $| k | = 1$ and $k \neq 1$. The relation $s_n = (1 - k^{n+1})/(1 - k)$ shows that

$$| s_n | \leqslant 2 | 1 - k |^{-1}.$$

Therefore, with the preceding notation, the series $(\lambda_n k^n)$ is convergent when (λ_n) is a decreasing positive sequence with limit 0.

The series of real (imaginary) parts also converges; in other words, if we put $k = e^{it}$, the real series with general term $\lambda_n \cos nt$ ($\lambda_n \sin nt$) converges for every $t \not\equiv 0 \mod 2\pi$.

10.18. Method of study of a numerical series. The central idea consists in studying the behavior of the general term a_n; if it does not tend to 0, the series diverges; if it tends to 0, one tries to determine whether the series of absolute values $| a_n |$ converges.

To do this, if $| a_n |$ is given by a complicated expression, one tries to bound $| a_n |$ from above by the general term of a positive series which is easier to study; for example, if $a_n = n^{-2} \cos n$, we have $| a_n | \leqslant n^{-2}$, which implies absolute convergence. If $| a_n |$ is given by a simple and regular algorithm, one can try to apply the criteria using $\lim \sup$ of $| a_{n+1} |/| a_n |$ or of $| a_n |^{1/n}$ (see 8.6). But the truly general rule consists in studying the rapidity of convergence of $| a_n |$ to 0.

If the series $(| a_n |)$ diverges, one can try to apply Abel's rule; it is in theory always applicable (see Problems 107 and 108), but apart from the cases pointed out in 10.16 and 10.17, the cases where it is of service are rather rare.

Finally, it should not be forgotten that the convergence of a series (a_n) is simply the convergence of the sequence (s_n). For example, in the study of the expansion of functions in series, when one has the identity

$$f(t) = a_0(t) + a_1(t) + \cdots + a_n(t) + r_n(t),$$

and when, for a given t, $\lim_{n \to \infty} r_n(t) = 0$, the series with general term $a_n(t)$ converges and has sum $f(t)$.

11. SERIES AND SUMMABLE FAMILIES OF FUNCTIONS

We are going to study here series and summable families whose elements depend on a parameter; in other words, series and summable families of functions; we shall give only the statements of the results for summable families; a simple adaptation will give the corresponding results for series.

11.1. Definition. LET X BE AN ARBITRARY SET; LET G BE A SEPARATED COMMUTATIVE TOPOLOGICAL GROUP, AND LET $(a_i)_{i \in I}$ BE A FAMILY OF MAPPINGS OF X INTO G.

WE SAY THAT THE FAMILY $(a_i(x))$ IS *UNIFORMLY SUMMABLE* ON X IF IT IS SUMMABLE (WITH SUM $s(x)$) FOR EVERY $x \in X$, AND IF THE FINITE PARTIAL SUMS $s_J = \Sigma_{i \in J} a_i$ CONVERGE UNIFORMLY TO s, THAT IS, IF FOR EVERY NEIGHBORHOOD V OF O THERE EXISTS A FINITE $J_0 \subset I$ SUCH THAT FOR EVERY FINITE J CONTAINING J_0, AND FOR EVERY $x \in X$,

$$s(x) - s_J(x) \in V.$$

For series $(a_n(x))$, uniform convergence is expressed by the uniform convergence of the sequence $s_n = a_0 + a_1 + \cdots + a_n$ to s.

11.2. Proposition. *If the family* $(a_i(x))$ *is summable for every* $x \in X$, *the following statements are equivalent*:

1. *The family* $(a_i(x))$ *is uniformly summable on* X.

2. (*Uniform Cauchy criterion*). *For every neighborhood* V *of* O, *there exists a finite* $J_0 \subset I$ *such that* $s_K(x) \in V$ *for every finite* K *disjoint from* J_0 *and every* $x \in X$.

PROOF. $1 \Rightarrow 2$. Let U be a symmetric neighborhood of O such that $U + U \subset V$. By hypothesis there exists a finite $J_0 \subset I$ such that, for every finite K disjoint from J_0 and every $x \in X$,

$$s(x) - s_{J_0}(x) \in U; \qquad s(x) - s_{J_0 \cup K}(x) \in U;$$

hence

$$s_K(x) \in U + U \subset V.$$

$2 \Rightarrow 1$. The hypothesis implies that for every neighborhood V of O there exists a finite $J_0 \subset I$ such that for any finite J and J' containing J_0, and for every $x \in X$,

$$s_{J'}(x) - s_J(x) \in V.$$

Let us assume V closed and fix J; for every $x \in X$, $s(x)$ is the limit of the sums $s_{J'}(x)$; we therefore have

$$s(x) - s_J(x) \in V.$$

Since the closed V form a neighborhood base of O, we have proved the uniform summability of the family $(a_i(x))$.

REMARK. When G is a normed space, the condition $s_K(x) \in V$ can, if preferable, be expressed in the form $\| s_K(x) \| \leqslant \epsilon$.

11.3. Corollary. *Let (a_i) be a family of mappings of a set X into a complete normed space E.*

In order that the family $(a_i(x))$ be uniformly summable on X, it is necessary and sufficient that it satisfy the uniform Cauchy criterion.

PROOF. If the family is uniformly summable, by Proposition 11.2 it satisfies the uniform Cauchy criterion. Conversely, if this criterion is satisfied, the family $(a_i(x))$ is summable for every x since E is complete (see Theorem 9.15); therefore by 11.2 it is uniformly summable.

11.4. Proposition. *Let (a_i) be a family of mappings of a topological space X into a normed space E.*

If each a_i is continuous and if the family (a_i) is uniformly summable, then its sum is continuous.

Indeed, for every $\epsilon > 0$ there exists a finite $J_0 \subset I$ such that

$$\| s(x) - s_{J_0}(x) \| \leqslant \epsilon$$

for every $x \in X$. Therefore s is the uniform limit of functions s_{J_0}; since the s_{J_0} are continuous, so is s.

Normal convergence

It is not always easy to prove the uniform summability of a family of functions; it is well to have available convenient sufficient conditions for this. Here is one such condition which is nothing but absolute summability in the space $\mathscr{B}(X, E)$.

11.5. Definition. LET $(a_i)_{i \in I}$ BE A FAMILY OF MAPPINGS OF A SET X INTO A NORMED SPACE; THIS FAMILY IS SAID TO BE *NORMWISE SUMMABLE* IN X IF THERE EXISTS A SUMMABLE FAMILY $(k_i)_{i \in I}$ OF NUMBERS $\geqslant 0$ SUCH THAT $\| a_i(x) \| \leqslant k_i$ FOR EVERY $i \in I$ AND $x \in X$.

This condition can also be expressed, more concisely, by the condition

$$\sum_i \| a_i \| < \infty, \qquad \text{where} \quad \| a_i \| = \sup_{x \in X} \| a_i(x) \|.$$

Note that the word "normwise" in this definition is chosen to remind one of the use of the "norm" of uniform convergence.

11.6. Proposition. *Every normwise summable family of mappings of a set* X *into a* **complete** *normed space is uniformly summable.*

PROOF. The inequality

$$\left\| \sum_{i \in K} a_i(x) \right\| \leqslant \sum_{i \in K} k_i$$

shows, since the family (k_i) is summable, that the family (a_i) satisfies the uniform Cauchy criterion, which by Corollary 11.3 implies uniform summability.

Comparison of the various modes of convergence

11.7. With every family (a_i) of mappings of a set X into a normed space E are associated the notions of pointwise, uniform, absolute, and normwise summability, with similar distinctions for the convergence of series.

The relations among these various modes of summability or convergence are a source of confusion for the beginner; we are therefore going to dwell a bit on these relations.

We shall examine here only the case of series; and to eliminate difficulties of another order which exist when E is not complete, we shall assume that E *is complete*.

The propositions established above lead to the following diagram:

$$\begin{array}{ccc} & \rightharpoonup \quad \text{absolute conv.} \quad \rightharpoondown & \\ \text{normwise conv.} & & \text{pointwise conv.} \\ & \rightharpoondown \quad \text{uniform conv.} \quad \rightharpoonup & \end{array}$$

It clearly follows that normwise convergence implies pointwise convergence, but we shall see from several examples that there exist no implications other than the five just written down, even when the functions in question are continuous numerical functions on [0, 1].

11.8. Absolute convergence (for every x) does not imply uniform convergence.

Indeed, put

$$a_n(x) = (x^n - x^{n+1});$$

the series $(a_n(x))$ is positive and converges for every x, and therefore converges absolutely. But

$$s(x) = 1 \quad \text{if} \quad x \neq 1, \quad \text{and} \quad s(x) = 0 \quad \text{if} \quad x = 1.$$

Since the sums s_n are continuous, the limit s would be continuous if the convergence were uniform; since s is not continuous, the convergence is not uniform.

11.9. Conversely, uniform convergence does not imply absolute convergence.

Indeed, put

$$a_n(x) = (-1)^n n^{-1} \quad \text{for every} \quad x \in [0, 1] \quad \text{and every} \quad n \geqslant 1.$$

The series $(a_n(x))$ converges uniformly, but does not converge absolutely for any x.

11.10. Finally, we shall show that uniform convergence and absolute convergence together do not imply normwise convergence: It suffices to take the series (f_n) used in Example 1 which follows Proposition 9.18.

11.11. Application. Let α and β be nonzero complex numbers whose quotient is not real, and let P be the subset of **C** consisting of the complex numbers of the form

$$w_{p,q} = p\alpha + q\beta, \quad \text{where} \quad p, q \in \mathbf{Z};$$

this is a closed additive subgroup of **C**, each of whose points is isolated.

Let $a_{p,q}$ denote the function defined on $\mathbf{C} \doteq \mathrm{P}$ by

$$a_{0,0}(z) = z^{-2}; \quad a_{p,q} = (z - w_{p,q})^{-2} - w_{p,q}^{-2} \quad \text{if} \quad (p, q) \neq (0, 0).$$

We shall show that for every compact set K in **C**, the family obtained from the family $(a_{p,q})$ by removing a suitable finite subfamily is uniformly summable on K.

Indeed, let $\rho > 0$; we discard from $(a_{p,q})$ those terms $a_{p,q}$ such that $|w_{p,q}| \leqslant 2\rho$.

If $|w| > 2\rho$, and if $|z| \leqslant \rho$, then

$$\left| \frac{1}{(z-w)^2} - \frac{1}{w^2} \right| = \left| \frac{z(2w-z)}{w^2(z-w)^2} \right| \leqslant |\rho| \frac{3|w|}{|w|^2 |\frac{1}{2}w|^2} = \frac{12\rho}{|w|^3}.$$

But the family of numbers $|w_{p,q}|^{-3}$ (where $(p, q) \neq (0, 0)$) is summable; indeed, we observe that $|w_{p,q}| \geqslant k(|p| + |q|)$ where k is a number > 0 (use the fact that $|x\alpha + y\beta|$ and $|x| + |y|$ are two norms on **C**). Therefore

$$\sum |w_{p,q}|^{-3} \leqslant \sum k^{-3}(|p| + |q|)^{-3} \leqslant 4k^{-3} \sum_{p,q \geqslant 0} (p+q)^{-3}.$$

$$\vdots$$

Since the family of numbers $(p + q)^{-3}$, where $p, q \in \mathbf{N}$ and $(p, q) \neq (0, 0)$, is summable (see 8.7), the family of numbers $| w_{p,q} |^{-3}$ is summable.

Thus the family $(a_{p,q})$, after the removal of a finite number of terms, is normwise convergent on the disk $| z | < \rho$; since the $a_{p,q}$ under consideration are continuous on this disk (and even holomorphic*), their sum is continuous (and even holomorphic) on this disk.

The sum f of all the $a_{p,q}$ is therefore holomorphic in $\mathbf{C} \doteq P$, and more precisely it is meromorphic* in $\mathbf{C}$, with P the set of poles, and the singular part of f at the pole $w_{p,q}$ is $(z - w_{p,q})^{-2}$.

This function f plays an important role in the theory of doubly periodic meromorphic functions.

12. MULTIPLIABLE FAMILIES AND INFINITE PRODUCTS OF COMPLEX NUMBERS

Summable families and series in a separated and commutative topological group have been defined in Sections 9 and 10; and we remarked that when the group operation is written multiplicatively, they are referred to as multipliable families and infinite products.

This is the case, in particular, when the group G is the multiplicative group $\mathbf{C}^*$ of nonzero complex numbers, taken with the topology induced by that of $\mathbf{C}$.

Since the theory which was developed for general groups G applies to $\mathbf{C}^*$, these general results have immediate counterparts in $\mathbf{C}^*$. Nevertheless, the fact that the essential applications of multipliable families of complex numbers will be in the theory of holomorphic functions leads us to slightly modify the definition of multipliable families and infinite products by no longer excluding the value 0 as a possible product. This extension will in addition simplify the discussion by permitting us to use the fact that $\mathbf{C}$ is a complete metric space.

Let $(a_i)_{i \in I}$ be a family of elements of $\mathbf{C}$; we shall use the notations $\mathscr{F}$ and $\mathscr{B}$ which appear in Definition 8.1, and for every $J \in \mathscr{F}$ we shall write p_J for the finite product $\prod_{i \in J} a_i$.

12.1. Definition. A FAMILY $(a_i)_{i \in I}$ OF ELEMENTS OF $\mathbf{C}$ IS SAID TO BE MULTIPLIABLE IN $\mathbf{C}$, WITH PRODUCT p, IF FOR EVERY $\epsilon > 0$ THERE EXISTS $J_0 \in \mathscr{F}$ SUCH THAT $| p - p_J | \leqslant \epsilon$ FOR EVERY $J \in \mathscr{F}$ CONTAINING J_0.

THE PRODUCT p IS WRITTEN AS $\prod_{i \in I} a_i$, OR $\prod_i a_i$, OR $\prod a_i$.

IF IN ADDITION $p \neq 0$, THE FAMILY $(a_i)_{i \in I}$ IS SAID TO BE MULTIPLIABLE IN $\mathbf{C}^*$.

---

* This allusion to holomorphic and meromorphic functions is intended for students who have had a course in the theory of functions of a complex variable.

In other words, the family (a_i) is multipliable with product p if the p_J converge to p along the filter base $\mathscr{B}$.

The uniqueness of p follows from the fact that the topology of **C** is separated.

We note that if $p \neq 0$, then $a_i \neq 0$ for every i; Definition 12.1 then coincides with the definition of multipliability in the topological group **C*** (whence the terminology adopted in 12.1).

We can similarly define the convergence of an infinite product with general term a_n (where $n \in \mathbf{N}$ or $\mathbf{N}^*$) by the convergence of the sequence of partial products $p_n = \prod_{k \leqslant n} a_k$ to p.

12.2. Definition. A FAMILY $(a_i)_{i \in I}$ OF ELEMENTS OF **C** IS SAID TO SATISFY THE *CAUCHY CRITERION* (FOR *MULTIPLICATION*) IF FOR EVERY $\epsilon > 0$ THERE EXISTS $J_0 \in \mathscr{F}$ SUCH THAT $|1 - p_K| \leqslant \epsilon$ FOR EVERY $K \in \mathscr{F}$ DISJOINT FROM J_0.

We remark that when all the a_i are $\neq 0$, this criterion is identical with that of 9.4 for the multiplicative group **C***.

When a family (a_i) satisfies the Cauchy criterion, for every $\epsilon > 0$ the number of i such that $|1 - a_i| > \epsilon$ is finite; in particular, $a_i = 0$ for only a finite number of indices i.

It is immediate that every subfamily of a family satisfying the Cauchy criterion also satisfies it.

12.3. Lemma. *When a family (a_i) satisfies the Cauchy criterion, the set of finite products p_J is bounded in* **C**.

PROOF. With the notation of Definition 12.2, every $J \in \mathscr{F}$ can be written as $J = J_0' \cup K$, where $J_0' \subset J_0$ and $K \cap J_0 = \varnothing$. Put $h = \sup|p_{J_0'}|$ where $J_0' \subset J_0$; since J_0 is finite, there are finitely many J_0', and so $h < \infty$.

We therefore have

$$|p_J| = |p_{J_0'}| \, |p_K| \leqslant h(1 + \epsilon).$$

12.4. Proposition. *Let (a_i) be a family of elements of* **C**.

1. *If this family is multipliable in* **C***, it satisfies the Cauchy criterion (for multiplication).*

2. *Conversely, if it satisfies the Cauchy criterion, it is multipliable in* **C**; *if in addition $a_i \neq 0$ for every i, it is multipliable in* **C***.

PROOF. 1. If the family (a_i) is multipliable in **C***, the general theory of Section 9 is applicable; therefore Corollary 9.6 shows that (a_i) satisfies the Cauchy criterion.

2. Put $k = \sup |p_J|$ (where $J \in \mathscr{F}$); Lemma 12.3 shows that $k < \infty$. Now put for every $J_0 \in \mathscr{F}$,

$$\epsilon(J_0) = \sup_{J_0 \subset J} |1 - p_{J-J_0}|.$$

Then for every $J \in \mathscr{F}$ containing J_0 we have, with $K = J \dot- J_0$,

$$|p_{J_0} - p_J| = |p_{J_0}(1 - p_K)| \leqslant k\epsilon(J_0).$$

Therefore the set $\mathscr{A}(J_0)$ of p_J such that $J_0 \subset J$ has diameter in $\mathbf{C}$ not greater than $2k\epsilon(J_0)$. But the Cauchy criterion implies that $\epsilon(J_0)$ tends to 0 along the filter base $\mathscr{B}$; therefore the filter base consisting of the $\mathscr{A}(J_0)$ is a Cauchy filter base in $\mathbf{C}$. Since $\mathbf{C}$ is complete, this filter base converges to a point p of $\mathbf{C}$. Therefore the family (a_i) is multipliable with product p.

If one of the a_i equals 0, the family (a_i) is multipliable with product 0.

If no one of the a_i equals 0, the relation $p_{J_0 \cup K} = p_{J_0} p_K$ (for $J_0 \cap K = \emptyset$) shows that if we take $\epsilon < \frac{1}{2}$ (and if J_0 and K have the meaning adopted in 12.1 and 12.2), then

$$|p_J| \geqslant \tfrac{1}{2}|p_{J_0}| \neq 0.$$

Therefore, since p is the limit of the p_J,

$$|p| \geqslant \tfrac{1}{2}|p_{J_0}|, \quad \text{or} \quad p \neq 0.$$

Z A multipliable family which has product 0 does not always satisfy the Cauchy criterion. Example: Every infinite family such that $|a_i| < \frac{1}{2}$ for every i.

12.5. Corollary. *Every subfamily of a family which is multipliable in $\mathbf{C}^*$ is multipliable in $\mathbf{C}^*$.*

Indeed, if (a_i) is multipliable in $\mathbf{C}^*$, it satisfies the Cauchy criterion, as does therefore every subfamily. Hence every subfamily is multipliable in $\mathbf{C}$, and indeed in $\mathbf{C}^*$ since no a_i equals 0.

Relation between the multipliability of $(1 - u_i)$ and the summability of (u_i)

The fact that for every family (a_i) multipliable in $\mathbf{C}^*$, all the a_i, with the exception of a finite number, are ϵ-close to 1, leads us to put $a_i = 1 + u_i$.

Not only is this form suggestive, but it leads to the following theorem, which forms a bridge between the notions of multipliability and summability.

12.6. Theorem. *Let* $(1 + u_i)$ *be a family of elements of* **C**.

1. *If the family* (u_i) *is summable in* **C**, *the family* $(1 + u_i)$ *is multipliable in* **C**; *if in addition* $1 + u_i \neq 0$ *for every i, its product is in* **C***.

2. *If the family* $(1 + u_i)$ *is multipliable in* **C***, *the family* (u_i) *is summable in* **C**.

Proof. We put, for every $z \in$ **C**,

$$f(z) = e^z = \sum_0^\infty z^n/n! \ .$$

The elementary theory of holomorphic functions enables one to establish the following properties, which we shall assume here (see also Problem 144):

(a) The function f (which is called the "exponential") is a continuous representation of the additive group **C** in the multiplicative group **C***.

(b) If we put $V = \{z : |z| \leqslant \frac{1}{2}\}$, the set $W = f(V)$ is a closed neighborhood of 1, and the restriction of f to V is a homeomorphism of V with $f(V)$.

We shall also use the following relation, whose verification is elementary:

$$\tfrac{1}{2} |\alpha| \leqslant |f(\alpha) - 1| \leqslant 2\alpha \qquad \text{for every} \quad \alpha \in V.$$

Taking account of Corollary 9.20, this relation proves the following property:

(c) For every family (α_i) of elements of V, the summability of (α_i) and that of $(f(\alpha_i) - 1)$ are equivalent.

1. Suppose all the $1 + u_i$ belong to W, and denote by α_i the element of V such that $f(\alpha_i) = 1 + u_i$; property (c) shows that if the family (u_i) is summable, so is the family (α_i). But then, since f is a continuous representation of **C** into **C***, Proposition 9.3 shows that the family of numbers $f(\alpha_i) = 1 + u_i$ is multipliable and that its product is $\neq 0$.

When the u_i form an arbitrary summable family, all the u_i with the exception of a finite number belong to the neighborhood $-1 + W$ of 0; therefore, by what we have just seen, the family of the corresponding $1 + u_i$ is multipliable and its product is $\neq 0$. Thus the original family is multipliable and its product is $\neq 0$ if all the numbers $1 + u_i$ are $\neq 0$.

2. Conversely, let $(1 + u_i)_{i \in I}$ be a family, multipliable in **C***, such that all the finite products p_J belong to W; if p is its product, we then have $p \in W$ since W is closed.

Let α_i be the point of V such that $f(\alpha_i) = 1 + u_i$; let s be the point of V such that $f(s) = p$, and put $s_J = \Sigma_{i \in J} \alpha_i$ for every $J \in \mathscr{F}$.

Property (a) shows that $f(s_J) = p_J$; hence by property (b), the convergence of the p_J to p implies the convergence of the s_J to s. Therefore the family (α_i) is summable with sum s. Finally, property (c) shows that the family of numbers $u_i = f(\alpha_i) - 1$ is summable.

Now suppose that $(1 + u_i)$ is an arbitrary family, multipliable in $\mathbf{C}^*$. It therefore satisfies the Cauchy criterion (see Proposition 12.4); therefore after the removal of a finite number of terms, the remaining family will have all its partial products in W. We have just seen that the corresponding family of u_i is then summable, from which follows the summability of the initial family (u_i).

Commutatively convergent infinite products

Theorem 10.7 shows that in the topological group $\mathbf{C}^*$, to say that an infinite product with general term a_n is commutatively convergent is equivalent to saying that the family (a_n) is multipliable. We are going to extend this result to products in $\mathbf{C}$.

12.7. Proposition. *Let (a_n) be a sequence of elements of $\mathbf{C}$.*

To say that the infinite product of the a_n is commutatively convergent is equivalent to saying that the family (a_n) is multipliable in $\mathbf{C}$. The product of (a_n) is then equal to each of the infinite products $\prod a_{\pi(n)}$.

PROOF. 1. If the family (a_n) is multipliable in $\mathbf{C}$ with product p, the same argument as was used in Theorem 10.7 shows that each of the infinite products $\prod a_{\pi(n)}$ converges to p.

2. Suppose, on the other hand, that the family (a_n) is not multipliable in $\mathbf{C}$; this clearly implies that $a_n \neq 0$ for every n. Then there are two possible cases:

(a) The set of partial products p_J is not bounded; an argument analogous to that used for Theorem 10.7 enables us to construct a permutation π of $\mathbf{N}$ such that the infinite product $\prod a_{\pi(n)}$ diverges.

(b) The set of partial products p_J is bounded. Then let k be the supremum of the set $(| p_J |)$.

The point 0 cannot be an adherent point of the set of p_J, as otherwise there would exist, for every $\epsilon > 0$, a $J_0 \in \mathscr{F}$ such that $| p_{J_0} | \leqslant \epsilon$, and we would have $| p_J | \leqslant k\epsilon$ for every $J \in \mathscr{F}$ containing J_0; therefore the family (a_n) would be multipliable with product 0.

But, since (a_n) is not multipliable in $\mathbf{C}^*$, by Theorem 10.7 there exists a permutation π of $\mathbf{N}$ such that the infinite product $\prod a_{\pi(n)}$

diverges in $\mathbf{C}^*$; nor can it converge to 0 since 0 is not an adherent point of the set of p_J. Therefore this infinite product diverges in $\mathbf{C}$.

12.8. Corollary. *Let $(1 + u_n)$ be a sequence of elements of $\mathbf{C}^*$.*
The following statements are equivalent:

1. *The series with general term $| u_n |$ is convergent.*

2. *The infinite product with general term $1 + u_n$ is commutatively convergent and its product (unique by 12.7) is $\neq 0$.*

This is a consequence of the statements 12.6, 12.7, and 10.12.

When the sequence $(1 + u_n)$ satisfies one of these equivalent conditions, the infinite product of the numbers $1 + u_n$ is said to be *absolutely convergent*, or *commutatively convergent*.

Conditionally convergent infinite products

Just as for conditionally convergent series, we shall say that an infinite product with general term $1 + u_n$ is conditionally convergent if it is convergent without being commutatively convergent.

One might think, in analogy with Theorem 12.6, that the conditional convergence of the infinite product of the numbers $1 + u_n$ is equivalent to the conditional convergence of the series (u_n); we shall see that this equivalence is approximately fulfilled when the u_n are real, but that this is not so when they are complex.

12.9. Proposition. *Let (u_n) be a sequence of **real** numbers with limit 0, and such that $1 + u_n \neq 0$ for every n.*

1. *If the series (u_n) is convergent, the product of the $1 + u_n$ converges to a number $p \in \mathbf{R}$; $p \neq 0$ if $\Sigma u_n^2 < \infty$, and $p = 0$ if $\Sigma u_n^2 = \infty$.*

2. *Conversely, if the product of the $1 + u_n$ converges to a number $p \neq 0$, the series (u_n) converges if $\Sigma u_n^2 < \infty$, and has sum $+ \infty$ if $\Sigma u_n^2 = \infty$.*

PROOF. We can assume, after discarding a finite number of terms, that $1 + u_n > 0$ for every n. We are then led to use the isomorphism $x \to \log x$ of the multiplicative group $\mathbf{R}_+^*$ onto the additive group $\mathbf{R}$. If we put $\alpha_n = \log(1 + u_n)$, the convergence of the product of the $1 + u_n$ to p is equivalent to the convergence of the series (α_n) to $\log p$. But

$$\alpha_n = \log(1 + u_n) = u_n - \tfrac{1}{2} u_n^2 (1 + \epsilon_n), \qquad \text{where } \lim_{n \to \infty} \epsilon_n = 0.$$

Since the series (u_n^2) is positive, this relation shows that when $\Sigma u_n^2 < \infty$, the convergence of one of the series (u_n), (α_n) implies that of the other.

When the series (u_n) converges and $\Sigma u_n{}^2 = \infty$, then $\Sigma \alpha_n = -\infty$; therefore $p = 0$.

Conversely, when the series (α_n) converges and $\Sigma u_n{}^2 = \infty$, we have $\Sigma u_n = \infty$.

REMARK.   When $p = 0$, which is equivalent to $\Sigma \alpha_n = -\infty$, the situation is more complex; it can happen that the series (u_n) converges, diverges to $+\infty$ or to $-\infty$, or diverges in the most complete sense.

12.10.   General case.   The preceding proof has already shown how the logarithm function comes in; we are going to use it again when the u_n are complex.

Let $1 + u_n$ be the general term of an infinite product, with $\lim u_n = 0$. With the notation used in connection with Theorem 12.6, we have $1 + u_n \in W$ for every sufficiently large n; therefore $1 + u_n$ is of the form $\exp \alpha_n$, where $\alpha_n \in V$. Thus if we denote the inverse f^{-1} of f in W by log, then

$$\alpha_n = \log(1 + u_n),$$

and we can assert that *the convergence of the infinite product of the $1 + u_n$ in $\mathbf{C}^*$ is equivalent to the convergence of the series with general term* $\alpha_n = \log(1 + u_n)$.

The elementary theory of holomorphic functions shows that

$$\alpha = \log(1 + u) = u - \frac{u^2}{2} + \cdots + \frac{(-1)^{n+1}u^n}{n} + \cdots \qquad \text{for} \quad 1 + u \in W .$$

In practice it is this expansion in an infinite series which allows one to conclude whether or not an infinite product converges.

EXAMPLE 1.   If the series $(|u_n|^2)$ converges, the relation

$$\alpha = \log(1 + u) = u - \frac{u^2}{2}(1 + \epsilon(u)), \qquad \text{where} \quad \lim_{u \to 0} \epsilon(u) = 0,$$

shows that the series (u_n) and (α_n) converge or diverge simultaneously.

EXAMPLE 2.   Here, on the other hand, is an example showing that if the series $(u_n{}^2)$ is not absolutely convergent, the series (u_n) can converge without the product of the $1 + u_n$ converging in $\mathbf{C}$, or even in $\mathbf{C}$ taken with a point at infinity.

We put $u_n = (-1)^n n^{-1/2}$ or $i(-1)^n n^{-1/2}$ according as the integer part of $\log n$ is even or odd.

One can verify that the series (u_n) is convergent and that the series $(u_n{}^3)$ is absolutely convergent, and, finally, that the series $(u_n{}^2)$ diverges and that the sequence of its partial sums s_n has as adherent points all the points of a closed interval (not reducing to a single point of **R**). Then it follows from the relation

$$\alpha = \log(1 + u) = u - \frac{u^2}{2} + \frac{u^3}{3}(1 + \epsilon(u)), \qquad \text{where } \lim_{u \to 0} \epsilon(u) = 0,$$

that the sequence of partial products $\prod_1^n (1 + u_p)$ has as its adherent points in **C** the points of a bounded interval belonging to a line passing through 0.

Products and multipliable families of functions

Definition 11.1 for the uniform summability of a family of functions with values in a group G is immediately applicable, together with its consequences, to the case where G is the group **C***.

We are now going to study a sufficient condition for uniform multipliability by formulating it in such a way as to include applications with values in **C** rather than in **C*** only.

12.11. Definition. LET X BE AN ARBITRARY SET, AND LET $(u_i)_{i \in I}$ BE A FAMILY OF MAPPINGS OF X INTO **C**.

THE FAMILY OF FUNCTIONS $1 + u_i$ IS SAID TO BE *NORMWISE MULTI-PLIABLE* IF ALL THE FUNCTIONS u_i ARE BOUNDED AND IF THE FAMILY (u_i) IS NORMWISE SUMMABLE (THAT IS, PUTTING $\| u_i \| = \sup_x | u_i(x)|$, THE FAMILY $(\| u_i \|)$ IS SUMMABLE).

12.12. Proposition. *Let* $(1 + u_i)_{i \in I}$ *be a normwise multipliable family of mappings of a set* X *into* **C**.

1.   *For every* $x \in X$ *the family* $(1 + u_i(x))$ *is multipliable in* **C**, *and its product* $p(x)$ *is zero only if one of the* $1 + u_i(x)$ *is zero.*

2.   *The product* p *is the uniform limit on* X *of the finite products* p_J *(along the filter base* $\mathcal{B}$ *associated with* I).

PROOF.   1.   The first statement is a direct result of Theorem 12.6.

2.   Put $k_i = \| u_i \|$; by hypothesis the family (k_i) is summable, hence the family $(1 + k_i)$ is multipliable; let k be its product.

For every $J \in \mathscr{F}$ and every $x \in X$ we have

$$| p_J(x)| \leqslant \prod_{i \in J} (1 + k_i) \leqslant k.$$

On the other hand, for every $\epsilon > 0$ there exists $J_0 \in \mathscr{F}$ such that, for every $K \in \mathscr{F}$ disjoint from J_0,

$$\prod_{i \in K} (1 + k_i) - 1 \leqslant \epsilon, \qquad \text{from which} \qquad \left| \prod_{i \in K} (1 + u_i(x)) - 1 \right| \leqslant \epsilon.$$

This relation implies, by passing to the limit, that for every $J \in \mathscr{F}$ containing J_0,

$$\left| \prod_{i \notin J} (1 + u_i(x)) - 1 \right| \leqslant \epsilon.$$

But we also have

$$p - p_J = p_J(p_{I-J} - 1);$$

therefore $|p(x) - p_J(x)| \leqslant k\epsilon$ for every $J \in \mathscr{F}$ containing J_0, from which follows the uniform convergence of the p_J to p.

12.13.   Corollary.   *If $(1 + u_i)_{i \in I}$ is a normwise multipliable family of continuous mappings of a topological space X into $\mathbf{C}$, the product p of this family is bounded and continuous, and the set of its zeros is the union of the zeros of the factors.*

EXAMPLE.   Let a_n be the mapping of $\mathbf{C}$ into $\mathbf{C}$ defined by

$$a_0(z) = z; \qquad a_n(z) = 1 - z^2/n^2 \qquad \text{for every} \quad n > 0.$$

On each disk $\{z : |z| < \rho\}$ we have $|n^{-2}z^2| \leqslant n^{-2}\rho^2$; therefore the family (a_n) is normwise multipliable on each of these disks. Its product p is the uniform limit on each of these disks of finite products of the a_n, therefore of polynomials in z. Therefore p is a holomorphic function on $\mathbf{C}$; the set of its zeros is $\mathbf{Z}$, and each of these zeros is simple.

13. NORMED ALGEBRAS

Let us recall that an *algebra* over the field $\mathbf{K}$ is a ring A together with a rule for associating, with every $(\lambda, x) \in \mathbf{K} \times A$, an element λx of A in such a way that:

1. A is a vector space over $\mathbf{K}$ when taken with this rule.

2. $\lambda(xy) = (\lambda x)y = x(\lambda y)$.

The algebra A is said to be commutative when the multiplication in A is commutative.

We are now going to study algebras over **K** which have a norm compatible with the multiplication in A, in a sense which we are going to specify.

13.1. Definition. An algebra A over the field **K** is called a *normed algebra* over **K** if it has a norm (on A considered as a vector space) such that

$$\| xy \| \leqslant \| x \| \| y \| \qquad \text{for all} \quad x, y \in A.$$

A normed algebra A is said to be *complete* (or is called a *Banach algebra*) if the normed vector space A is complete.

Examples of normed algebras

13.2. **C** taken with the norm $\| x \| = | x |$ is a Banach algebra.

13.3. The algebra $\mathcal{M}^{(n)}$ of nth order square matrices (x_{ij}) over **K** is a normed algebra for the norm $\| M \| = \Sigma_{i,j} | x_{ij} |$, where the x_{ij} are the elements of the matrix M.

It is easily verified that this norm is compatible with multiplication. This algebra is complete since the dimension of the vector space $\mathcal{M}^{(n)}$ is finite (in fact n^2).

13.4. Let E be a normed vector space; the vector space $\mathcal{L}(E)$ of endomorphisms of E (that is, continuous linear mappings of E into E) becomes an algebra when it is provided with the product $f \circ g$ defined by $f \circ g(x) = f(g(x))$.

The norm which we have taken on $\mathcal{L}(E)$ (Proposition 4.6) satisfies the relation

$$\| f \circ g \| \leqslant \| f \| \| g \|.$$

Therefore $\mathcal{L}(E)$, taken with this norm, is a normed algebra. When E is complete, this algebra is complete (see Proposition 4.7).

13.5. The vector space $\mathcal{B}(X, \mathbf{C})$ of bounded mappings of a set X into **C** is an algebra under the ordinary multiplication defined by

$$fg(x) = f(x)g(x).$$

The norm of uniform convergence on this space satisfies the condition $\| fg \| \leqslant \| f \| \| g \|$.
This normed algebra is complete.

13.6.   When X is a topological space, the subset of $\mathcal{B}(X, \mathbf{C})$ consisting of the continuous functions is a subalgebra of $\mathcal{B}(X, \mathbf{C})$; it is closed in the latter, and hence complete.

With every subset Y of X one can associate the subset of $\mathcal{B}(X, \mathbf{C})$ consisting of the continuous functions which vanish on Y; this is a complete subalgebra of $\mathcal{B}(X, \mathbf{C})$.

13.7.   The vector space $\mathcal{D}^0(\mathbf{R}, \mathbf{R})$ of continuous numerical functions with compact support can be taken as an algebra with the ordinary product (defined by $fg(x) = f(x)g(x)$). But it can also be taken as an algebra in another way, thanks to the *convolution product* $f * g$ defined by

$$f * g(x) = \int_{\mathbf{R}} f(x - t)g(t) \, dt.$$

One can verify that $f * g$ belongs to $\mathcal{D}^0(\mathbf{R}, \mathbf{R})$, that the convolution product is associative and commutative, and that the mapping $(f, g) \to f * g$ is bilinear.

If we put

$$\|f\| = \int_{\mathbf{R}} |f(t)| \, dt,$$

the vector space $\mathcal{D}^0(\mathbf{R}, \mathbf{R})$ becomes a normed space, which is, incidentally, incomplete; let us verify that this norm is compatible with the convolution product, that is, that $\|f * g\| \leqslant \|f\| \|g\|$:

$$\|f * g\| \leqslant \int_{\mathbf{R}^2} |f(x - t)g(t)| \, dt \, dx = \int_{\mathbf{R}^2} |f(u)g(v)| \, du \, dv = \|f\| \|g\|.$$

13.8.   Here is a similar example, in which $\mathbf{R}$ is replaced by $\mathbf{Z}$ and the Lebesgue measure on $\mathbf{R}$ is replaced by the measure m on $\mathbf{Z}$ for which $m(X)$ = number of points of X (for every finite $X \subset \mathbf{Z}$):

Let A be the vector space of mappings $a : n \to a_n$ of $\mathbf{Z}$ into $\mathbf{R}$ such that $\Sigma |a_n| < \infty$; if we put $\|a\| = \Sigma |a_n|$, A becomes a normed space, which is complete by Proposition 9.24.

For every $a, b \in A$ we define the convolution product $c = a * b$ by the relation

$$c_n = \sum_{i+j=n} a_i b_j .$$

Since the families (a_i) and (b_j) are absolutely summable, the same is true of the family of products $a_i b_j$, and therefore of each of its subfamilies. This shows, on the one hand, that c_n is well defined for every n, and, on the other hand, that

$$\sum_n |c_n| \leqslant \left(\sum |a_n|\right)\left(\sum |b_n|\right).$$

In other words, $a * b$ is indeed an element of A, and $\| a * b \| \leqslant \| a \| \| b \|$. Finally, the convolution product is associative (and commutative), and the mapping $(a, b) \to a * b$ is bilinear. We have therefore defined the structure of a complete normed algebra on A.

This algebra A contains, as a closed subalgebra, the space l^1 of summable families (a_n) such that $a_n = 0$ for every $n < 0$.

13.9. Let $\varDelta$ be the closed disk $\{z : | z | \leqslant 1\}$ of **C**, and let $\mathscr{H}(\varDelta)$ be the subspace of $\mathscr{C}(\varDelta, \mathbf{C})$ consisting of the functions which are holomorphic in the interior of $\varDelta$. This is an important subalgebra of the Banach algebra $\mathscr{C}(\varDelta, \mathbf{C})$; the fact that every uniform limit of holomorphic functions is holomorphic implies that this algebra is closed in $\mathscr{C}(\varDelta, \mathbf{C})$ and therefore complete.

13.10. The vector space $\mathscr{C}^1([0, 1], \mathbf{R})$ of numerical functions on $[0, 1]$ which have a continuous first derivative is an algebra when taken with the ordinary product.

An elementary calculation shows that the norm

$$\| f \| = \sup_x | f(x) | + \sup_x | f'(x) |$$

(for which this space is complete) is compatible with the product defined on this algebra.

13.11. REMARK. Every normed algebra over **C** is also a normed algebra over **R**; these two algebras are simultaneously complete or incomplete.

13.12. REMARK. (a) The relation $\| xy \| \leqslant \| x \| \| y \|$ implies, by induction, $\| x^n \| \leqslant \| x \|^n$.

(b) Since multiplication in A is continuous, the mapping $x \to xx = x^2$ of A into A is continuous; more generally, an induction argument shows that the mapping $x \to x^n$ is continuous for every integer $n \geqslant 1$.

13.13. REMARK. Let A be a normed vector space, and suppose that A is provided with a multiplication which makes A an algebra. It is not necessarily a normed algebra; but if the multiplication is continuous, that is, if the mapping $(x, y) \to xy$ of $A \times A$ into A is continuous, it follows from Proposition 6.1 that there exists a constant $k > 0$ such that

$$\| xy \| \leqslant k \| x \| \| y \|.$$

If we put $p(x) = k \| x \|$, then p is a norm on A which is equivalent to the original norm, and which moreover satisfies

$$p(xy) = k \| xy \| \leqslant k^2 \| x \| \| y \| = p(x)p(y).$$

Therefore the new norm is compatible with multiplication.

For example, if in the algebra $\mathscr{M}^{(n)}$ of square matrices of order n we put $\| M \| = \sup_{i,j} | x_{ij} |$, the norm obtained is not compatible with multiplication, but its product by n is.

Norm of the unit

13.14.　Recall that the *unit* of an algebra A is any element e of A such that

$$ex = xe = x$$

for every $x \in A$.

If one such element e exists, it is unique; but such an element need not exist. One can determine, in the preceding examples, those cases in which a unit exists.

When a normed algebra A has a unit e, the relation $e = ee$ implies $\| e \| \leqslant \| e \|^2$, from which $\| e \| \geqslant 1$. In most of the preceding examples, $\| e \| = 1$; nevertheless it can happen, as in Example 13.3, that $\| e \| \neq 1$. But we shall see that one can then replace the norm on A by an equivalent (in the sense of the equivalence of norms on a vector space) norm p which is still compatible with multiplication, and such that $p(e) = 1$.

For every $a \in A$, let $\bar{a}$ denote the linear mapping $x \to ax$ of A into A; $\bar{a}$ is an element of $\mathscr{L}(A)$ since $\| ax \| \leqslant \| a \| \| x \|$, and the mapping $a \to \bar{a}$ of A into $\mathscr{L}(A)$ is linear; therefore if we put $p(a) = \| \bar{a} \|$, p is a seminorm on A.

The relation $\| ax \| \leqslant \| a \| \| x \|$ shows that

$$p(a) = \| \bar{a} \| \leqslant \| a \|;$$

but on the other hand, since $\bar{a}(e) = ae$, we have

$$p(a) \geqslant \| e \|^{-1} \| ae \| = \| e \|^{-1} \| a \|,$$

from which

$$\| e \|^{-1} \| a \| \leqslant p(a) \leqslant \| a \|.$$

This relation shows that p is a norm on A which is equivalent to the original norm. The algebra A taken with this norm is isomorphic to the subalgebra of $\mathscr{L}(A)$ consisting of the elements $\bar{a}$; therefore $p(ab) \leqslant p(a)p(b)$, and $p(e) = 1$.

We note, finally, that there can exist, on a given algebra, several equivalent norms which are compatible with multiplication and such that $\| e \| = 1$; for example, if E denotes a finite-dimensional vector space, the norm which we have taken on the algebra $A = \mathscr{L}(E)$ satisfies the required conditions, and it varies with the norm chosen on E.

Product of two absolutely summable families

13.15. Proposition. *If $(a_i)_{i \in I}$ and $(b_j)_{j \in J}$ are two absolutely summable families of elements of a Banach algebra, with respective sums α and β, the family of products $(a_i b_j)$ is also absolutely summable, and has sum $\alpha\beta$.*

This result, which generalizes Corollary 9.22, follows as does the latter from Proposition 9.21, since the mapping $(x, y) \to xy$ of $A \times A$ into A is on the one hand bilinear, and on the other hand continuous since $\| xy \| \leqslant \| x \| \| y \|$.

Power series in a Banach algebra

13.16. One can add and multiply in an algebra A over **K**; thus, with every formal polynomial P(X) with coefficients in **K** one can associate the mapping $x \to P(x)$ of A into A. If A is a normed algebra, one can carry out passage to the limit, and therefore one can expect to be able to define the sum of a power series with coefficients in **K** (and even with coefficients in A when A is commutative).

If $a_0 + a_1 X + \cdots + a_n X^n + \cdots$ is a formal series in X, with coefficients in **K**, we shall define the *radius of convergence* of this formal series as the element ρ of $\bar{\mathbf{R}}_+$ defined by

$$1/\rho = \varlimsup_{n \to \infty} | a_n |^{1/n}.$$

This definition is justified by the well-known fact that if x denotes an element of **K**, the series $(a_n x^n)$ converges when $| x | < \rho$, and diverges when $| x | > \rho$.

We are going to rederive various of these conclusions for Banach algebras. All the algebras with which we shall be concerned from now on will be assumed to have units, denoted by e, and we will identify the element λ of **K** with the element λe of A.

13.17. Proposition. *Let A be a Banach algebra over* **K**, *and let* $(a_n X^n)$ *be a formal power series (over* **K**), *with radius of convergence* $\rho > 0$.

For every positive number $r < \rho$, *the series* $(a_n x^n)$ *is convergent and normwise convergent in the ball* $\{x : \| x \| \leqslant r\}$. *Its sum* $f(x)$ *is continuous on the open ball* $\{x : \| x \| < \rho\}$.

PROOF. Let r' be any number such that $r < r' < \rho$. For every n sufficiently large,

$$| a_n |^{1/n} \leqslant 1/r';$$

therefore if $\| x \| \leqslant r$, we have

$$\| a_n x^n \| \leqslant | a_n | r^n \leqslant (r/r')^n.$$

Since the geometric series with general term $(r/r')^n$ is convergent, the series $(a_n x^n)$ is normwise convergent in the ball $\{x : \| x \| \leqslant r\}$, and since A is complete, the series is convergent.

Each of the terms $a_n x^n$ of the series is continuous; therefore the normwise convergence implies that the sum f of this series is continuous in each open ball $\{x : \| x \| < r\}$, hence also in the open ball

$$\{x : \| x \| < \rho\}.$$

13.18. REMARK. Contrary to the situation in the classical case where A is the field **C** itself, we cannot assert that when $\| x \| > \rho$, the series $(a_n x^n)$ diverges; this is essentially tied up with the fact that one can have $\| x^n \| < \| x \|^n$, while in **C** one has $\| x^n \| = \| x \|^n$.

For example, if there exists a $u \neq 0$ such that $u^n = 0$ for every $n \geqslant 2$ (which, in particular, can happen in the algebra $\mathscr{M}^{(2)}$ of square matrices of order 2), the series $(a_n x^n)$ clearly converges when $x = ku$, even when $\| ku \| > \rho$.

13.19. Proposition. *Let* $(a_n X^n)$ *and* $(b_n X^n)$ *be two formal power series in* X, *with radii of convergence* α *and* β, *and let* $(c_n X^n)$ *be their formal product (defined by* $c_n = \Sigma_{p+q=n}\, a_p b_q$).

If A is a Banach algebra, the series $(c_n x^n)$ *is absolutely convergent for every* $x \in A$ *such that* $\| x \| < \inf(\alpha, \beta)$, *and the sums* A(x), B(x), C(x) *of these series satisfy the relation*

$$C(x) = A(x)B(x) = B(x)A(x).$$

PROOF. If $\| x \| < \alpha$ and β, each of the series $(a_n x^n)$ and $(b_n x^n)$ is absolutely convergent; therefore (see Proposition 13.15) the family

of products $a_p b_q x^{p+q}$ is absolutely summable and its sum is equal to
$A(x)B(x)$; since $a_p b_q x^{p+q} = b_q a_p x^{q+p}$, this sum is also equal to $B(x)A(x)$.
The associativity of the sum then permits us to group the set of terms
$a_p b_q x^{p+q}$ of degree $p + q = n$, whose sum is simply $c_n x^n$, which is the
desired result.

13.20.   Corollary.   *Let* A *be a Banach algebra. For every* $x \in A$ *such that*
$\| x \| < 1$, *the element* $e - x$ *is invertible and its inverse is the element*
$e + x + \cdots + x^n + \cdots$.

Indeed, let us take for the series $(a_n X^n)$ the polynomial $1 - X$, and
for the series $(b_n X^n)$ the series $1 + X + \cdots + X^n + \cdots$; the formal
product of these two series is the constant 1.

On the other hand, $\alpha = + \infty$ and $\beta = 1$; hence the corollary follows
from Proposition 13.19.

The exponential on a Banach algebra

The formal series $(X^n/n!)$ has radius of convergence $+ \infty$. Therefore
if A is a Banach algebra, the series $(x^n/n!)$ is absolutely convergent on
all of A; its sum is denoted by $\exp x$ or e^x, and the mapping $x \to \exp x$
is called the *exponential*; it is continuous.

13.21. Proposition.   *If* x *and* y *are any two* **permutable** *elements of* A,
then

$$\exp(x + y) = (\exp x)(\exp y) = (\exp y)(\exp x).$$

PROOF.   Since the families $(x^p/p!)$ and $(y^q/q!)$ are absolutely summable,
the same is true of the family $(x^p y^q/p!q!)$, and its sum is $(\exp x)(\exp y)$;
since $x^p y^q = y^q x^p$, this sum is also equal to $(\exp y)(\exp x)$.

Moreover, the commutativity of x and y implies, for every $n \geqslant 0$,

$$\sum_{p+q=n} \frac{x^p y^q}{p!q!} = \frac{1}{n!} \sum_{p+q=n} \frac{(p+q)!}{p!q!} x^p y^q = \frac{(x+y)^n}{n!}.$$

The associativity of the sum of the $x^p y^q/p!q!$ thus allows us to write

$$(\exp x)(\exp y) = \sum_n \frac{(x+y)^n}{n!} = \exp(x + y).$$

13.22.   Corollary.   *For every* $x \in A$ *and for all* $\lambda, \mu \in$ **K**, *we have*

$$\exp((\lambda + \mu)x) = (\exp \lambda x)(\exp \mu x).$$

13.23. Corollary. *For every* $x \in A$, $\exp x$ *is invertible and its inverse is* $\exp(-x)$.

The group of invertible elements of a Banach algebra

As in every ring, the set of invertible elements of an algebra A forms a group G under multiplication, whose identity element is the unit in A.

When A is a Banach algebra, the structure of G can be further specified.

13.24. Proposition. *Let* A *be a Banach algebra.*

1. *The group* G *of invertible elements of* A *is an open set in* A.

2. *The topology on* G *induced by that of* A *is compatible with the group structure of* G.

PROOF. 1. By Corollary 13.20, G contains the open ball V with center e and radius 1. Now for every $a \in G$, the mapping $x \to ax$ is a homeomorphism of A with itself; therefore aV is an open set containing a. But all the elements of aV are invertible, hence $aV \subset G$. Thus G is the union of the open sets aV, and is therefore open.

2. Multiplication is continuous in A; it therefore remains to show that the mapping $x \to x^{-1}$ is continuous in G.

Corollary 13.20 shows that this mapping is continuous at the point $x = e$; to show its continuity at every point $a \in G$, we write x^{-1} in the form $x^{-1} = a^{-1}v$, where $v = u^{-1}$ and $u = xa^{-1}$. The mapping $x \to u$ is continuous and $u(a) = e$; the mapping $u \to v$ is continuous at $u = e$, and the mapping $v \to a^{-1}v$ is continuous; therefore the mapping $x \to x^{-1}$ is continuous at the point $x = a$.

EXAMPLE. Let E be a complete normed space; then the algebra $\mathscr{L}(E)$ is complete. Therefore the set of invertible elements of $\mathscr{L}(E)$ is open. We have thus rederived a result pointed out during the study of the stability of isomorphisms of E onto itself.

IV. HILBERT SPACES

The first normed vector spaces which came to the attention of mathematicians, apart from the Euclidean spaces $\mathbf{R}^n$, were those whose norm resembles the Euclidean norm of $\mathbf{R}^n$. These are the Hilbert spaces, named after the man who gave the first examples of these spaces and obtained important applications of them to Analysis.

The first mathematicians who used these spaces appreciated above all the ease of calculation and the great analogy between the geometry of these spaces and that of the finite-dimensional Euclidean spaces. But interest in these spaces has not diminished, and at present they are still the spaces most used in functional analysis and theoretical physics.

14. DEFINITION AND ELEMENTARY PROPERTIES OF PREHILBERT SPACES

Hermitean forms

14.1. The Euclidean norm of $\mathbf{R}^3$ is related to the traditional scalar product $(x \mid y) = \Sigma x_i y_i$ by the equality $\| x \|^2 = (x \mid x)$. If one wishes to introduce analogous notions in $\mathbf{C}^3$ by putting $(x \mid y) = \Sigma x_i y_i$, one runs into two difficulties: On the one hand, there exist $x \neq O$ in $\mathbf{C}^3$ for which $(x \mid x) = 0$; and on the other hand, $(x \mid x)$ is not positive. Therefore the bilinear form $(x \mid y)$ on $\mathbf{C}^3$ cannot be used to define a norm on $\mathbf{C}^3$.

But if we observe that the classical norm of $\mathbf{C}$ has a square which can be written as $\| x \|^2 = x\bar{x}$, it becomes natural to define a norm on $\mathbf{C}^3$ by putting $\| x \|^2 = \Sigma x_i \bar{x}_i$; if we agree to call the function $(x \mid y) = \Sigma x_i \bar{y}_i$ the scalar product on $\mathbf{C}^3$, we obtain the convenient relation $\| x \|^2 = (x \mid x)$.

The new scalar product $(x \mid y)$ is still linear with respect to x, but it is conjugate-linear with respect to y (a mapping f of one vector space into another is said to be *conjugate-linear* if it is additive and if $f(\lambda x) = \bar{\lambda} f(x)$ for every $\lambda \in \mathbf{K}$).

We are going to systematically study such scalar products.

14.2. Definition. LET E BE A VECTOR SPACE OVER K. BY A *HERMITEAN FORM* ON E IS MEANT A MAPPING φ OF E $\times$ E INTO **K** SUCH THAT:

1. FOR EVERY $y \in$ E, THE MAPPING $x \rightarrow \varphi(x, y)$ IS A LINEAR FUNCTIONAL ON E;

2. FOR ALL $x, y \in$ E WE HAVE $\varphi(y, x) = \overline{\varphi(x, y)}$.

Condition 2 is called *Hermitean symmetry*; it implies that $\varphi(x, x)$ is real; when $\mathbf{K} = \mathbf{R}$, it is simply ordinary symmetry.

Properties 1 and 2 imply

$$\varphi(x, y_1 + y_2) = \overline{\varphi(y_1 + y_2, x)} = \overline{\varphi(y_1, x)} + \overline{\varphi(y_2, x)}$$
$$= \varphi(x, y_1) + \varphi(x, y_2);$$

$$\varphi(x, \lambda y) = \overline{\varphi(\lambda y, x)} = \bar{\lambda} \, \overline{\varphi(y, x)} = \bar{\lambda} \, \varphi(x, y).$$

Thus φ is conjugate-linear with respect to y.

EXAMPLE 1. We are going to determine every Hermitean form on an n-dimensional space E over **K**: Let (a_i) be a basis of E, and let (x_i), (y_i) denote the coordinates of two points x, y of E with respect to this basis.

If φ is a Hermitean form on E, then

$$\varphi(x, y) = \varphi\left(\sum x_i a_i, \sum y_i a_i\right) = \sum x_i \bar{y}_j \, \varphi(a_i, a_j).$$

If we put $\alpha_{ij} = \varphi(a_i, a_j)$, the Hermitean symmetry of φ implies $\alpha_{ij} = \overline{\alpha_{ji}}$. Conversely, for every system of n^2 complex numbers α_{ij} such that $\alpha_{ij} = \overline{\alpha_{ji}}$, the function $\varphi(x, y) = \sum \alpha_{ij} x_i \bar{y}_j$ is a Hermitean form on E.

EXAMPLE 2. Let E be the vector space $\mathscr{C}^1([0, 1], \mathbf{K})$ and let α and β be continuous *real-valued* functions on $[0, 1]$.

For every $x, y \in$ E we put

$$\varphi(x, y) = \int_0^1 \left(\alpha(t)x(t)\overline{y(t)} + \beta(t)x'(t)\overline{y'(t)}\right) dt.$$

The function φ is clearly linear with respect to x and is Hermitean symmetric; therefore φ is a Hermitean form on E.

14.3. Definition. A HERMITEAN FORM φ ON E IS SAID TO BE *POSITIVE* IF $\varphi(x, x) \geqslant 0$ FOR EVERY $x \in$ E; IT IS SAID TO BE *POSITIVE DEFINITE* OR *POSITIVE AND NONDEGENERATE* IF MOREOVER $\varphi(x, x) > 0$ FOR EVERY $x \neq O$.

It is evident that every linear combination with positive coefficients of positive Hermitean forms is itself positive and Hermitean.

EXAMPLES. In Example 1 above, if $\alpha_{ij} = 0$ when $i \neq j$, and $\alpha_{ii} \geqslant 0$ for every i, the form φ is positive. If in addition $\alpha_{ii} > 0$ for every i, it is positive definite.

In Example 2, if $\alpha \geqslant 0$ and $\beta \geqslant 0$, the form φ is positive. If in addition $\alpha > 0$ it is positive definite; on the other hand, if $\alpha = 0$ and $\beta > 0$, it is degenerate.

14.4. Proposition. *Let φ be a positive Hermitean form on E.*

1. *For all $x, y \in$ E we have*

$$|\varphi(x, y)|^2 \leqslant \varphi(x, x)\,\varphi(y, y) \qquad \text{(Cauchy–Schwartz inequality)}.$$

If φ is positive definite, the equality holds only when x and y are linearly dependent.

2.   *The mapping $x \rightarrow (\varphi(x, x))^{1/2}$ is a seminorm on E; it is a norm when φ is positive definite.*

PROOF.   1.   We shall make use of the fact that $\varphi(\lambda x + y, \lambda x + y) \geqslant 0$ for every $\lambda \in \mathbf{K}$; then

$$f(\lambda) = \varphi(\lambda x + y, \lambda x + y) = a\lambda\bar{\lambda} + b\lambda + \bar{b}\bar{\lambda} + c \geqslant 0, \tag{1}$$

where we have put

$$a = \varphi(x, x), \qquad b = \varphi(x, y), \qquad c = \varphi(y, y).$$

If $a = c = 0$, then setting $\lambda = -\bar{b}$ in (1), we obtain

$$-2b\bar{b} \geqslant 0,$$

from which $b = 0$; therefore $| b |^2 = ac$.

If for example $a \neq 0$, then setting $\lambda = -\bar{b}a^{-1}$ in (1), we obtain

$$\frac{ac - b\bar{b}}{a} \geqslant 0,$$

which yields the desired relation since $a > 0$.

Now suppose that the form φ is positive definite; the relation $f(\lambda) = 0$ implies $\lambda x + y = \mathrm{O}$. Now if $| b |^2 = ac$ and $a \neq 0$, the preceding calculation shows that for $\lambda = -\bar{b}a^{-1}$ we have $f(\lambda) = 0$, which implies $\lambda x + y = \mathrm{O}$; if $c \neq 0$ we have a similar relation $x + \mu y = \mathrm{O}$, while if $a = c = 0$, then $x = y = \mathrm{O}$.

Conversely, when x and y are linearly dependent, it is immediate that $| b |^2 = ac$.

2.   Put $p(x) = (\varphi(x, x))^{1/2}$; the relation $p(x + y) \leqslant p(x) + p(y)$ can be written, after squaring both sides, as

$$\varphi(x + y, x + y) \leqslant \varphi(x, x) + \varphi(y, y) + 2(\varphi(x, x)\, \varphi(y, y))^{1/2}$$

or

$$2\mathscr{R}\, \varphi(x, y) = \varphi(x, y) + \overline{\varphi(x, y)} \leqslant 2(\varphi(x, x)\, \varphi(y, y))^{1/2},$$

which follows from the Cauchy-Schwartz inequality.

Moreover, the relation $\varphi(\lambda x, \lambda x) = |\lambda|^2 \varphi(x, x)$ shows that

$$p(\lambda x) = |\lambda| p(x);$$

therefore p is a seminorm. It is a norm when $p^2(x) = \varphi(x, x)$ vanishes only for $x = O$, that is, when φ is positive definite.

14.5. *Definition.* A VECTOR SPACE E, TOGETHER WITH A POSITIVE DEFINITE HERMITIAN FORM φ DEFINED ON E AND THE NORM ASSOCIATED WITH φ BY THE RELATION $\| x \|^2 = \varphi(x, x)$, IS CALLED A *PREHILBERT SPACE*.

THE PREHILBERT SPACE E IS CALLED A *HILBERT SPACE* WHEN THE NORMED SPACE E IS COMPLETE.

In general $\varphi(x, y)$ is denoted by $(x \mid y)$, and $(x \mid y)$ is called the *scalar product* of x and y; in the course of a calculation we shall often simplify the notation by writing xy for $(x \mid y)$ and x^2 for $(x \mid x)$.

If F is a vector subspace of E, the trace on F of the scalar product on E is a scalar product on F.

14.6. REMARK. If E is a prehilbert space over **C**, the scalar product $(x \mid y)$ takes nonreal values as well as real values (unless E consists of the point O); therefore $(x \mid y)$ is not a scalar product on E regarded as a vector space over **R**. On the other hand, it is clear that $\mathscr{R}(x \mid y)$ is symmetric in x and y, and linear with respect to x when E is regarded as a vector space over **R**. Moreover $(x \mid x) = \mathscr{R}(x \mid x)$; therefore $\mathscr{R}(x \mid y)$ is a scalar product on the real space E, and the norms associated with $(x \mid y)$ and $\mathscr{R}(x \mid y)$ are identical.

We shall have occasion at times to use the scalar product $\mathscr{R}(x \mid y)$, which we shall call the *real scalar product associated with* $(x \mid y)$, or more simply the real scalar product of E.

Examples of prehilbert spaces

14.7. The vector space $E = \mathscr{C}([0, 1], \mathbf{R})$ taken with the scalar product defined by

$$(x \mid y) = \int_0^1 x(t) y(t) \, dt$$

is a real prehilbert space; we show that it is incomplete.

Put $x_n(t) = \inf(n, t^{-1/3})$; then

$$\| x_n - x_{n+p} \|^2 = \int_0^1 (x_n(t) - x_{n+p}(t))^2 \, dt \leqslant \int_0^{\epsilon_n} t^{-2/3} \, dt,$$

where $\epsilon_n = 1/n^3$.

Since $\| x_n - x_{n+p} \|$ tends to 0 as $n \to \infty$, the sequence (x_n) is a Cauchy sequence in E. But it does not converge, as for every $x \in$ E we have

$$\| x - x_n \|^2 \geqslant \int_{\epsilon_n}^1 (x(t) - x_n(t))^2 \, dt = \int_{\epsilon_n}^1 (x(t) - t^{-1/3})^2 \, dt.$$

Therefore

$$\liminf_{n \to \infty} \| x - x_n \|^2 \geqslant \int_0^1 (x(t) - t^{-1/3})^2 \, dt.$$

But since the function $t^{-1/3}$ is not bounded on $(0, 1]$, there exists a compact interval on which $(x(t) - t^{-1/3})^2 > 0$; therefore the integral of this function is > 0, and the sequence (x_n) cannot have x as a limit.

In fact, the actual limit of the sequence (x_n) would be the function $t^{-1/3}$, which belongs to a Hilbert space containing E, namely the space of square summable functions on $[0, 1]$, which we shall study with the theory of integration.

14.8. We are going to see that the complete normed space l_I^2 defined earlier (see 8.9) is a Hilbert space; to show this, it suffices to prove that its norm is associated with a scalar product.

But for all $x, y \in l_I^2$, the inequality $2 \sum | x_i \bar{y}_i | \leqslant \sum (| x_i |^2 + | y_i |^2)$ shows that the family $(x_i \bar{y}_i)$ is summable.

We then put $(x \mid y) = \sum x_i \bar{y}_i$; this is evidently a positive Hermitean form on l_I^2, and the relation $(x \mid x) = \sum | x_i |^2$ shows that the seminorm associated with this form is simply the norm on l_I^2.

The importance of the spaces l_I^2 stems from the simple form of the expression defining their scalar product and from the fact, which we will establish later (see 16.13), that every Hilbert space is isomorphic to a space l_I^2. When $I = \{1, 2, ..., n\}$, l_I^2 is simply the space $\mathbf{K}^n$, taken with the Euclidean norm if $\mathbf{K} = \mathbf{R}$, and the Hermitean norm if $\mathbf{K} = \mathbf{C}$; when $I = \mathbf{N}$, l_I^2 is simply the Hilbert space l^2.

14.9. Useful inequalities and identities. 1. With the simplified notation introduced in 14.5, the Cauchy-Schwartz inequality is written as

$$| xy |^2 \leqslant x^2 y^2 \qquad \text{or} \qquad | xy | \leqslant \| x \| \| y \|.$$

From this inequality and the inequality $2ab \leqslant a^2 + b^2$ (where $a, b \in \mathbf{R}$) follows also

$$2| xy | \leqslant x^2 + y^2. \tag{1}$$

Finally, we note the inequality

$$(x + y)^2 \leqslant 2(x^2 + y^2),$$

which is equivalent to the relation $0 \leqslant (x - y)^2$.

2.   From the relations

$$(x + y)^2 = x^2 + y^2 + xy + yx \qquad \text{and} \qquad (x - y)^2 = x^2 + y^2 - xy - yx$$

we obtain by addition the following important identity, which involves only the norm:

$$\| x + y \|^2 + \| x - y \|^2 = 2\| x \|^2 + 2\| y \|^2. \tag{2}$$

This result is sometimes expressed by the statement that for any parallelogram the sum of the squares of the diagonals equals the sum of the squares of the sides.

3.   Expanding $(x + y)^2$ and $(x - y)^2$, we obtain by subtraction

$$2(xy + yx) = \| x + y \|^2 - \| x - y \|^2. \tag{3}$$

When $\mathbf{K} = \mathbf{R}$, then $xy = yx$, from which

$$4xy = \| x + y \|^2 - \| x - y \|^2.$$

When $\mathbf{K} = \mathbf{C}$, replacing y by iy in (3) yields

$$2(xy - yx) = i(\| x + iy \|^2 - \| x - iy \|^2) \tag{3'}$$

from which, on adding (3) and (3'), we obtain

$$4xy = \| x + y \|^2 - \| x - y \|^2 + i(\| x + iy \|^2 - \| x - iy \|^2). \tag{4}$$

This relation shows that the scalar product of a prehilbert space is determined by its norm.

14.10. Isomorphism of two prehilbert spaces.   Let E and F be prehilbert spaces over the same field $\mathbf{K}$. By an *isomorphism of* E *onto* F is meant a vectorial isomorphism f of E onto F which preserves the scalar product, in the sense that

$$(f(x) \mid f(y)) = (x \mid y) \qquad \text{for all} \quad x, y \in E.$$

Then this isomorphism also preserves the norm; therefore E and F are simultaneously complete or incomplete.

Conversely, if f is a vectorial isomorphism which preserves the norm, then by identity (4) of 14.9 f also preserves the scalar product.

Orthogonal vectors

14.11. Definition. Two ELEMENTS x AND y OF A PREHILBERT SPACE E ARE SAID TO BE ORTHOGONAL IF THEIR SCALAR PRODUCT $(x \mid y)$ IS ZERO.

Two SUBSETS X AND Y OF E ARE SAID TO BE ORTHOGONAL IF EVERY ELEMENT OF X IS ORTHOGONAL TO EVERY ELEMENT OF Y; THIS RELATION IS WRITTEN X $\perp$ Y.

If $(x \mid y) = 0$, then $(y \mid x) = \overline{(x \mid y)} = 0$; thus the relation of orthogonality is symmetric.

Since the relation $(x \mid x) = 0$ implies $x = O$, the only vector which is orthogonal to itself is O; this vector is also orthogonal to every $x \in$ E.

It follows, for example, that the relation of orthogonality between vector subspaces of E is symmetric, and that the only common point of two orthogonal subspaces is the point O. Therefore the sum of the dimensions of two orthogonal subspaces in $\mathbf{K}^n$ is $\leqslant n$; thus two planes in $\mathbf{R}^3$ are never orthogonal (although they can be in the weaker sense used in elementary geometry).

More generally, two AFFINE VARIETIES X AND Y IN E ARE SAID TO BE ORTHOGONAL IF THE VECTOR SUBSPACES IN E WHICH ARE PARALLEL TO X AND Y, RESPECTIVELY, ARE ORTHOGONAL.

14.12. Proposition (Pythagorean theorem). *Let x and y be vectors in a prehilbert space over* **K**.

If x and y are orthogonal, then $\| x + y \|^2 = \| x \|^2 + \| y \|^2$. *When* **K** $=$ **R**, *the converse is true*.

PROOF. The relation $(x + y)^2 = x^2 + y^2 + xy + yx$ shows that if $xy = 0$, which implies $yx = 0$, then $(x + y)^2 = x^2 + y^2$.

Conversely, this last relation implies $xy + yx = 0$; if **K** $=$ **R**, we have in addition $xy = yx$, hence $2xy = 0$, or $xy = 0$.

Z On the other hand, if **K** $=$ **C** the relation $(x + y)^2 = x^2 + y^2$ implies only that $2\mathscr{R}(xy) = xy + yx = 0$, from which follows the orthogonality of x and y relative to the *real* scalar product of E.

For example, in **C** regarded as a vector space over **C**, there exists no pair of orthogonal nonzero vectors; still, we have

$$\| x + y \|^2 = \| x \|^2 + \| y \|^2$$

whenever the vectors $x = x_1 + ix_2, y = y_1 + iy_2$ satisfy the relation

$$\mathscr{R}(xy) = x_1 y_1 + x_2 y_2 = 0.$$

14.13. Lemma. *In every prehilbert space* E, *the mapping* $(x, y) \to (x \mid y)$ *of* E × E *into* **R** *is continuous.*

PROOF.   Since we have **K** = **R** or **C**, $(x \mid y)$ is always a bilinear form on E regarded as a vector space over **R**. The inequality $\mid (x \mid y) \mid \leqslant \parallel x \parallel \parallel y \parallel$ therefore shows, by Proposition 6.1, that this function is continuous on E × E.

14.14. Proposition. *The set of vectors of* E *orthogonal to a given vector* $a \neq O$ *is a closed hyperplane.*

PROOF.   The set in question is the set of zeros of the linear functional $f : x \to (x \mid a)$, and is therefore a hyperplane. On the other hand, f is continuous by Lemma 14.13; therefore the hyperplane $f^{-1}(0)$ is closed.

14.15. Corollary. *The set* X^0 *of vectors in* E *orthogonal to a set* $X \subset E$ *is a closed vector subspace of* E (*possibly the set* {O}).

This is immediate since every intersection of closed vector subspaces of E is itself a closed vector subspace.

It is evident that $X \subset Y$ implies $X^0 \supset Y^0$; therefore if we denote the set $(X^0)^0$ by X^{00}, we also have $X^{00} \subset Y^{00}$.

We also observe that $X \subset X^{00}$ since $X \perp X^0$.

14.16. Median hyperplane of two points.   Let E be a prehilbert space over **R**, and let a, b be distinct points of E. The set X of points $x \in E$ which are equidistant from a and b is defined by the relation

$$(a - x)^2 = (b - x)^2, \qquad \text{or} \qquad x(b - a) = \tfrac{1}{2}(b^2 - a^2).$$

If we put $x = y + \tfrac{1}{2}(b + a)$, this relation becomes $y(b - a) = 0$. Therefore the set in question is the affine hyperplane orthogonal to $b - a$ and passing through the midpoint of the segment joining a and b.

When E is a prehilbert space over **C**, we can reduce the problem to the preceding case by taking E with its real scalar product; the real hyperplane X then contains the complex affine hyperplane orthogonal to $b - a$ and passing through the midpoint of the segment joining a and b, but is not identical with it.

Angle between two nonnull vectors

It is proved in elementary geometry that if x and y are nonnull vectors in $\mathbf{R}^2$, then

$$(x \mid y) = \parallel x \parallel \parallel y \parallel \cos \theta,$$

where θ denotes the angle between the halflines passing from the origin O through x and y, respectively.

Now if E is a real prehilbert space, the Cauchy-Schwartz inequality shows that if x and y are nonnull vectors in E, then

$$-1 \leqslant \frac{(x \mid y)}{\| x \| \| y \|} \leqslant 1.$$

On the other hand, the theory of the cosine function, defined as the sum of the series with general term $(-1)^n t^{2n}/(2n)!$, shows that for every $k \in [-1, 1]$ there exists a single real number $\theta \in [0, \pi]$ such that $\cos \theta = k$; we are thus led to the following definition:

14.17. Definition. BY THE *ANGLE* BETWEEN TWO NONNULL VECTORS x, y OF A REAL PREHILBERT SPACE E IS MEANT THE REAL NUMBER θ DEFINED BY THE RELATIONS

$$0 \leqslant \theta \leqslant \pi; \qquad (x \mid y) = \| x \| \| y \| \cos \theta.$$

To say that θ is an acute (right, obtuse) angle is equivalent to saying that $(x \mid y) > 0 \ (= 0, \ < 0)$.

Proposition 14.4 shows that $| \cos \theta | = 1$ only when x and y are linearly dependent; when $y = \lambda x$ with $\lambda > 0$, $\theta = 0$; when $y = \lambda x$ with $\lambda < 0$, $\theta = \pi$.

In a prehilbert space over **C**, the only way of introducing the notion of angle is to go back to the real case by using the real scalar product $\mathscr{R}(x \mid y)$; in other words, we shall put

$$\mathscr{R}(x \mid y) = \| x \| \| y \| \cos \theta.$$

By means of this definition we can write, for all $x, y \neq 0$,

$$\| x + y \|^2 = \| x \|^2 + \| y \|^2 + 2\| x \| \| y \| \cos \theta.$$

Z In using angles in a *complex* prehilbert space, it should not be forgotten that the condition $\theta = \pi/2$ does not imply the orthogonality of x and y.

15. ORTHOGONAL PROJECTION. STUDY OF THE DUAL

One is often led, both in theoretical research and applied mathematics, to problems of the following kind:

Let E be a normed space, X a subset of E, and x a point of E; to find a point x' of X which best approximates x, in other words, whose distance from x is equal to the distance $d(x, \mathrm{X})$ from x to X.

Such a point x' will be called the *projection* of x on X.

When X is compact, this problem has at least one solution (see Chapter I, Proposition 17.4); otherwise it may have no solution.

The following theorem answers the question when X is a complete convex subset of a prehilbert space.

15.1. Theorem. *Let* E *be a prehilbert space over* **K**, *and let* X *be a complete convex subset of* E.

1. *Every point* $x \in$ E *has a unique projection* x' *(which we shall sometimes denote by* $P_X(x)$*) on* X.

2. *The projection* x' *of* x *is characterized by the condition*

$$\mathscr{R}((x - x') \mid (u - x')) \leqslant 0 \qquad \text{for every} \quad u \in X.$$

3. For all $x, y \in$ E with projections x', y' on X, we have

$$\| x' - y' \| \leqslant \| x - y \|.$$

PROOF. 1. Put $d = d(x, X)$; for every $\epsilon > 0$ let B_ϵ denote the closed ball with center x and radius $d + \epsilon$, and put $P_\epsilon = X \cap B_\epsilon$. The set of projections of x on X is simply the intersection of the P_ϵ; it is a question of showing that this intersection contains a unique point.

Every P_ϵ is nonempty, and since X and B_ϵ are convex, P_ϵ is convex; hence for all $a, b \in P_\epsilon$ the midpoint of the segment joining a and b belongs to P_ϵ. But the identity (2) of 14.9 allows us to write

$$\| x - a \|^2 + \| x - b \|^2 = 2\| x - m \|^2 + \tfrac{1}{2}\| a - b \|^2.$$

Since $\| x - a \|$, $\| x - b \|$, and $\| x - m \|$ lie between d and $d + \epsilon$, we thus have

$$\| a - b \|^2 \leqslant 2(2(d + \epsilon)^2 - 2d^2) = 4\epsilon(2d + \epsilon).$$

This inequality gives an upper bound for the diameter of P_ϵ; we see that this diameter tends to 0 with ϵ.

On the other hand, P_ϵ is an increasing function of ϵ, hence the intersection of the P_ϵ is equal to the intersection of the decreasing sequence (P_{ϵ_n}), where $\epsilon_n = n^{-1}$; but the P_{ϵ_n} are closed in X which is assumed complete. Therefore Proposition 20.6 of Chapter I shows that the intersection of the P_{ϵ_n} contains exactly one point.

2. To simplify the calculations, we reduce the problem to the case $x' = O$ by a translation. For every $u \in X$, and every $\lambda \in (0, 1]$, we have $\lambda u \in X$; therefore if O is the projection of x on X,

$$\| x \|^2 \leqslant \| x - \lambda u \|^2 \qquad \text{or} \qquad 2\mathscr{R}(x \mid u) \leqslant \lambda \| u \|^2.$$

Since λ is arbitrarily small, we have $\mathscr{R}(x \mid u) \leqslant 0$; this is just the desired relation when we take $x' = O$.

Conversely, if $\mathscr{R}(x \mid u) \leqslant 0$ for every $u \in X$, then

$$\| x - u \|^2 = (x - u)^2 = x^2 - 2\mathscr{R}(x \mid u) + u^2 \geqslant x^2 = \| x \|^2;$$

thus O is the projection of x on X.

3. Put $x - y = (x - x') + (x' - y') + (y' - y) = (x' - y') + u$. Then

$$(x - y)^2 = (x' - y')^2 + u^2 + 2\mathscr{R}(u \mid (x' - y')).$$

But

$$u(x' - y') = -(x - x')(y' - x') - (y - y')(x' - y').$$

By the second part of the theorem, the real part of the right side is $\geqslant 0$; therefore $(x - y)^2 \geqslant (x' - y')^2$.

This inequality can be expressed by the statement that the mapping P_X of E onto X is of Lipschitz class with ratio 1.

REMARK. Part 2 of the theorem can be expressed in terms of angles; indeed, the relation $\mathscr{R}((x - x') \mid (u - x')) \leqslant 0$ asserts, when $x \neq x'$ and $u \neq x'$, that the angle between the vectors $x - x'$ and $u - x'$ is $\geqslant \pi/2$.

15.2. Corollary. *Let* X *be a complete convex cone in a prehilbert space* E. *If* x' *denotes the projection of a point* x *on* X, *then*

$$\| x \|^2 = \| x' \|^2 + \| x - x' \|^2 \qquad \text{and} \qquad \mathscr{R}(x \mid x') = (x' \mid x').$$

PROOF. Each of these relations is equivalent to the relation $\mathscr{R}(x' \mid x - x') = 0$, which we are going to prove.

Since X is a cone, we have $\lambda x' \in X$ for every $\lambda > 0$; we can therefore put $u = \lambda x'$ in the inequality of part 2 of Theorem 15.1. According as $\lambda < 1$ or $\lambda > 1$, we obtain

$$\mathscr{R}(x - x' \mid x') \geqslant 0 \qquad \text{or} \qquad \mathscr{R}(x - x' \mid x') \leqslant 0,$$

from which the desired equality follows.

15.3. Corollary. *Let* X *be a complete vector subspace of a prehilbert space* E, *and let* $x \in E$.

The projection x' of x on X is the only point of X such that $x - x'$ is orthogonal to X.

PROOF. We reduce the proof by translation to the case where $x' = O$ (which leaves X invariant).

1. If O is the projection of x on X, then $\mathscr{R}(x \mid u) \leqslant 0$ for every $u \in X$. If v is any point of X, the points $-v$, iv, $-iv$ also belong to X; therefore the relation $\mathscr{R}(x \mid u) \leqslant 0$ is satisfied when $u = v$, $-v$, iv, or $-iv$. It follows that the real part and the imaginary part of $(x \mid v)$ are zero, whence $(x \mid v) = 0$.

2. Conversely, if $(x \mid v) = 0$ for every $v \in X$, we have

$$\| x - v \|^2 = \| x \|^2 + \| v \|^2 \geqslant \| x \|^2;$$

hence O is the projection of x on X.

15.4. Corollary (Transitivity of projections). *Let E be a prehilbert space, F a complete vector subspace of E, X a convex subset of F, x a point of E and x' its projection on F.*

If x' has a projection x'' on X, then x'' is also the projection of x on X, and conversely.

PROOF. Since $x - x'$ is orthogonal to F, for every $y \in X$ we have

$$\| x - y \|^2 = \| x - x' \|^2 + \| x' - y \|^2.$$

Therefore the functions $\| x - y \|$ and $\| x' - y \|$ of the variable y attain their minimum values simultaneously on X, which proves the corollary.

15.5. REMARK. Corollary 15.4 extends by translation to the case where F is a complete affine variety of E.

Therefore if F_1, F_2, ..., F_n is a finite decreasing sequence of complete affine varieties of E, if x' denotes the projection of x on F_1, and if x_p is defined recursively as the projection of x_{p-1} on F_p, the point x_n coincides with the projection of x on F_n. This is an extension of a classical result of elementary geometry in $\mathbf{R}^3$.

Z The statement of 15.4 is not correct if the subspace F of E is replaced by an arbitrary complete convex subset of E.

Orthogonal subspaces

15.6. Proposition. *Let X be a complete vector subspace of a prehilbert space E.*

1.   *The mapping* P_X *of* E *onto* X *is a continuous linear mapping of norm* 1 (*if* X $\neq$ {O});

2.   *The kernel* $P_X^{-1}(O)$ *of this mapping is the subspace* X^0 *orthogonal to* X, *and* $X^{00} = X$;

3.   E *is the direct sum of* X *and* X^0, *and for every* $x \in X$ *we have*

$$\| x \|^2 = \| P_X(x) \|^2 + \| P_{X^0}(x) \|^2.$$

PROOF.   1.   For all $x, y \in E$ and for every $u \in X$ we have, by Corollary 15.3,

$$(x - x')u = 0 \qquad \text{and} \qquad (y - y)u = 0.$$

Hence for all $\lambda, \mu \in \mathbf{K}$,

$$((\lambda x + \mu y) - (\lambda x' + \mu y'))u = 0.$$

By 15.3, $\lambda x' + \mu y'$ is thus the projection of $\lambda x + \mu y$ on X; in other words, $P_X(\lambda x + \mu y) = \lambda P_X(x) + \mu P_X(y)$, which shows the linearity of P_X.

The relation $\| x \|^2 = \| x' \|^2 + \| x - x' \|^2$ shows that P_X is norm decreasing; on the other hand, the restriction of P_X to X is the identity operator; therefore if X $\neq$ {O}, $\| P_X \| = 1$.

2.   To say that $P_X(x) = O$ is equivalent to saying that $x - O$ is orthogonal to X (by 15.3); therefore $P_X^{-1}(O) = X^0$.

For every x orthogonal to X^0, we have simultaneously

$$x'(x - x') = 0 \qquad \text{and} \qquad x(x - x') = 0,$$

from which $(x - x')^2 = 0$. Hence $x = x'$; in other words, $x \in X$.

This shows that $X^{00} \subset X$; but we already had the opposite inclusion, hence $X^{00} = X$.

3.   The relation $x = x' + (x - x')$, where $x - x' \in X^0$, shows that $E = X + X^0$; since the only element common to X and X^0 is O, E is indeed the direct sum of X and X^0.

Finally, the relation $\| x \|^2 = \| P_X(x) \|^2 + \| P_{X^0}(x) \|^2$ follows at once from $x = x' + (x - x')$.

15.7. Corollary.   *For every vector subspace* X *of a Hilbert space* E, X^{00} *is the closure of* X.

PROOF.   Since X^{00} is closed and $X \subset X^{00}$, we also have $\bar{X} \subset X^{00}$; on the other hand, the relation $X \subset \bar{X}$ implies $X^{00} \subset (\bar{X})^{00} = \bar{X}$, which yields the desired equality.

The dual of a Hilbert space

We have seen in 4.8 that the topological dual $E' = \mathscr{L}(E, \mathbf{K})$ of a normed space E is a complete normed space. We are going to see that when E is a Hilbert space, the normed spaces E and E' are isomorphic under a remarkable conjugate-linear isomorphism. This is one of the properties which explains the important role of Hilbert spaces.

15.8. Proposition. *Let* E *be a Hilbert space and* E' *its topological dual.*

1. *For every* $a \in E$ *the linear functional* $\varphi_a : x \to (x \mid a)$ *has norm* $\| a \|$.

2. *The mapping* $a \to \varphi_a$ *of* E *into* E' *is a conjugate-linear isomorphism of the normed spaces* E *and* E'.

PROOF. 1. The Cauchy-Schwartz inequality shows that $\| \varphi_a \| \leqslant \| a \|$; on the other hand, for $a \neq O$, if $x = \| a \|^{-1}a$, then $(x \mid a) = \| a \|$, hence $\| \varphi_a \| \geqslant \| a \|$; in short, $\| \varphi_a \| = \| a \|$.

2. The mapping $a \to \varphi_a$ of E into E' is conjugate-linear, that is,

$$\varphi_{a+b} = \varphi_a + \varphi_b \; ; \qquad \varphi_{\lambda a} = \bar{\lambda}\varphi_a \; ;$$

this is a consequence of the fact that $(x \mid a)$ is conjugate-linear with respect to a.

On the other hand, the mapping φ is norm preserving, therefore injective. It remains for us to show that it is surjective, that is, every $u \in E'$ is of the form φ_a.

If $u = O$, this is obvious, with $a = O$. If $u \neq O$, let X be the hyperplane $u^{-1}(0)$; since $E = X + X^0$ and since $X \neq E$, there exists $b \in X^0$, $b \neq O$. The two linear functionals u and φ_b vanish on the hyperplane X and are not identically zero, hence are proportional; therefore there exists a scalar λ such that $u(x) = \lambda(x \mid b)$ for every x. In other words, $u = \varphi_a$ where $a = \bar{\lambda}b$.

When $\mathbf{K} = \mathbf{R}$, φ is evidently an isomorphism in the ordinary sense.

EXAMPLE 1. Let us take $\mathbf{C}^n$ with the canonical scalar product

$$(x \mid y) = \sum x_i \bar{y}_i \; .$$

Every linear functional u on $\mathbf{C}^n$ is of the form $u(x) = \sum \alpha_i x_i$, that is, $u(x) = (x \mid a)$, where a is the point with coordinates $\bar{\alpha}_i$.

EXAMPLE 2. Proposition 15.8 shows that every continuous linear functional on the Hilbert space l_1^2 can be written in a unique way in the form $x \to \sum x_i \bar{a}_i$, where $\sum |a_i|^2 < \infty$.

15.9. REMARK. Proposition 15.8 cannot be extended to any incomplete prehilbert space E since E′, being complete, cannot be isomorphic to an incomplete space E.

For example, let E be the subspace of l^2 consisting of the sequences (x_n) (where $n \geqslant 1$) such that $x_n = 0$ except for a finite number of indices. Let a be the point of l^2 with coordinates $a_n = n^{-1}$; the linear functional on E defined by

$$x \to (x \mid a) = \sum n^{-1} x_n$$

is continuous, but clearly cannot be written in the form $(x \mid b)$, where $b \in E$.

Weak topology on a Hilbert space

In Example 3.11 we defined the weak topology of a topological vector space E. When E is a Hilbert space, for every $x \in E$ such that $x \neq O$ there exists a linear functional $u \in E'$ such that $u(x) \neq 0$ (for example $u = \varphi_x$); therefore the weak topology of E is separated.

From Proposition 15.8 and the convergence criterion stated in 3.11, we have the following criterion:

15.10. Proposition. *Let* E *be a Hilbert space,* x_0 *a point of* E, *and* $\mathscr{B}$ *a filter base on* E.

To say that x_0 *is the weak limit of* $\mathscr{B}$ *is equivalent to saying that for every* $a \in E$,

$$(x_0 \mid a) = \lim_{\mathscr{B}}(x \mid a).$$

Z Let us call the topology on E associated with the norm the *strong topology.*

Since each of the linear functionals $x \to (x \mid a)$ is continuous, the strong convergence of $\mathscr{B}$ to x_0 implies the weak convergence of $\mathscr{B}$ to x_0. It follows that if $\mathscr{B}$ converges weakly to x_0, $\mathscr{B}$ cannot converge strongly to any point $x_0' \neq x_0$; but it can happen that $\mathscr{B}$ does not converge strongly to x_0. Here is an example in l^2:

Let u_n be the point of l^2 all of whose coordinates are zero except for that with index n, which equals 1. For every $a \in l^2$, the sequence $((u_n \mid a))$ tends to 0; therefore the sequence (u_n) tends weakly to O. But this sequence does not converge strongly to O since $\| u_n \| = 1$ for every n.

15.11. Proposition. *Let* E *be a Hilbert space,* x_0 *a point of* E *and* $\mathscr{B}$ *a filter base on* E; *the following statements are equivalent:*

1. $$x_0 = \underset{\mathscr{B}}{\text{strong limit}}\, x.$$

2. $$x_0 = \underset{\mathscr{B}}{\text{weak limit}}\, x \quad and \quad \|\, x_0\,\| = \underset{\mathscr{B}}{\lim}\, \|\, x\,\|.$$

PROOF. The implication $1 \Rightarrow 2$ is obvious; let us prove the converse. The hypothesis implies that x_0^2 is the limit of xx_0 (hence also of $x_0 x$) and of x^2. Thus $x_0^2 + x^2$ and $x_0 x + xx_0$ have limit $2x_0^2$; we therefore have

$$\underset{\mathscr{B}}{\lim}(x_0 - x)^2 = \underset{\mathscr{B}}{\lim}(x_0^2 + x^2 - (x_0 x + xx_0)) = 0.$$

In other words, $\mathscr{B}$ converges strongly to x_0.

16. ORTHOGONAL SYSTEMS

The convenience of rectangular coordinate systems in the Euclidean spaces $\mathbf{R}^n$ impels us to ask whether one cannot use analogous systems in prehilbert spaces; in fact, the total orthogonal systems will play this role.

16.1. Definition. LET E BE A PREHILBERT SPACE. BY AN *ORTHOGONAL SYSTEM* (OR FAMILY) IN E WE MEAN A FAMILY $(a_i)_{i \in I}$ OF ELEMENTS OF E WHICH ARE NONZERO AND PAIRWISE ORTHOGONAL.

AN ORTHOGONAL SYSTEM (a_i) IS CALLED AN *ORTHONORMAL SYSTEM* IF THE NORM OF EVERY a_i EQUALS 1.

An orthonormal system (a_i) is thus characterized by the relations

$$(a_i \mid a_j) = 0 \quad \text{if} \quad i \neq j, \quad \text{and} \quad = 1 \quad \text{if} \quad i = j.$$

It is immediate that if (a_i) is an orthogonal system, the system $(\|\, a_i\,\|^{-1} a_i)$ is orthonormal.

Every orthogonal system is linearly independent; indeed, if $\Sigma_{i \in J} \lambda_i a_i = O$, where J is a finite subset of I, then

$$\left(\sum \lambda_i a_i\right)^2 = \sum |\lambda_i|^2 a_i^2 = 0,$$

which implies $\lambda_i = 0$ for every $i \in J$.

16.2. Definition. LET (a_i) BE AN ORTHONORMAL SYSTEM IN E. FOR EVERY $x \in E$, THE SCALAR PRODUCT $\xi_i = (x \mid a_i)$ IS CALLED THE ith *COORDINATE* OF x WITH RESPECT TO THE SYSTEM (a_i).

The coordinate ξ_i of x therefore depends only on the element a_i and not on the other elements of the system.

16.3. Proposition. *Let* E *be a prehilbert space. For every orthonormal system* (a_i) *in* E *and for every* $x \in$ E, *the family* $(|\xi_i|^2)$ *is summable, and*

$$\sum_i |\xi_i|^2 \leqslant \|x\|^2 \qquad (Bessel's\ inequality).$$

PROOF.   It is a question of proving that for every finite subset J of I,

$$\sum_{i \in J} |\xi_i|^2 \leqslant \|x\|^2.$$

But taking into account that $(\xi_i a_i \mid x) = (x \mid \xi_i a_i) = |\xi_i|^2$, we have

$$0 \leqslant \left(x - \sum_{i \in J} \xi_i a_i\right)^2 = x^2 - \sum_{i \in J} |\xi_i|^2,$$

which gives the desired relation.

We are now going to characterize the orthonormal systems for which the sum of the $|\xi_i|^2$ is equal to $\|x\|^2$.

Recall that a family (a_i) of elements of E is said to be *total* if the vector subspace of E which it generates is everywhere dense on E, or equivalently if every element of E is the limit of linear combinations of elements a_i.

16.4. Theorem. *Let* E *be a prehilbert space, and let* (a_i) *be an orthonormal system in* E. *The following statements are equivalent*:

1. *For all* x, $y \in$ E, *the family* $(\xi_i \bar{\eta}_i)$ *is summable with sum* $(x \mid y)$ *(where* ξ_i *and* η_i *are the* ith *coordinates of* x *and* y, *respectively).*

2. *For every* $x \in$ E *we have* $\|x\|^2 = \Sigma |\xi_i|^2$ *(Parseval relation).*

3. *For every* $x \in$ E, *the family* $(\xi_i a_i)$ *is summable with sum* x.

4. *The family* (a_i) *is total in* E.

PROOF.   1 $\Rightarrow$ 2.   Indeed, (2) is a special case of (1).

2 $\Rightarrow$ 3.   Since the sum of the family $(|\xi_i|^2)$ is $\|x\|^2$, for every $\epsilon > 0$ there exists a finite subset J_0 of I such that

$$\|x\|^2 - \sum_{i \in J} |\xi_i|^2 \leqslant \epsilon^2$$

for every finite subset J of I containing J_0. Hence

$$\left(x - \sum_{i\in J} \xi_i a_i\right)^2 = \|x\|^2 - \sum_{i\in J} |\xi_i|^2 \leqslant \epsilon^2, \quad \text{from which} \quad \left\|x - \sum_{i\in J} \xi_i a_i\right\| \leqslant \epsilon,$$

which proves the desired property.

3 $\Rightarrow$ 4.   Since $x = \sum \xi_i a_i$ for every $x \in E$, every x is the limit of finite sums of elements $\xi_i a_i$; therefore the family (a_i) is total.

4 $\Rightarrow$ 1.   Let $x \in E$ and $\epsilon > 0$; by hypothesis there exists a finite linear combination $y = \sum_{i\in J} \alpha_i a_i$ such that $\|x - y\| \leqslant \epsilon$. Therefore *a fortiori* the projection x' of x on the space generated by the finite family $(a_i)_{i\in J}$ satisfies the relation $\|x - x'\| \leqslant \epsilon$; but the vector $(x - \sum_{i\in J} \xi_i a_i)$ is orthogonal to each of the a_i (where $i \in J$), hence $x' = \sum_{i\in J} \xi_i a_i$.

We therefore have

$$0 \leqslant \left(x - \sum_{i\in J} \xi_i a_i\right)^2 = x^2 - \sum_{i\in J} |\xi_i|^2 \leqslant \epsilon^2.$$

This inequality holds for every ϵ; therefore, taking into account Bessel's inequality, we obtain

$$\|x\|^2 = \sum_i |\xi_i|^2 = \sum_i \xi_i \bar{\xi}_i. \tag{1}$$

If now x and y are arbitrary elements of E, with coordinates (ξ_i) and (η_i), the summability of the $|\xi_i|^2$ and the $|\eta_i|^2$ implies the summability of the $\xi_i \bar{\eta}_i$ and the $\bar{\xi}_i \eta_i$; this allows us to use relation (1) to express all the squares in the identity

$$4xy = (x + y)^2 - (x - y)^2 + i((x + iy)^2 - (x - iy)^2)$$

as functions of the ξ_i and η_i. We thus obtain the desired identity $xy = \sum \xi_i \bar{\eta}_i$.

16.5. Definition.   Every orthonormal system in a prehilbert space E which satisfies one of the assertions of Theorem 16.4 is called an *orthonormal basis* of E.

16.6.   Extension of the formulas to an orthogonal basis.   It often happens that the family (a_i) which appears naturally in a theory is not an orthonormal basis, but there exist scalars $\lambda_i \neq 0$ such that the family of the $b_i = \lambda_i a_i$ is an orthonormal basis.

We shall call such a family (a_i) an *orthogonal basis* of E. To say that a family (a_i) is of this type is clearly equivalent to saying that it is orthogonal and total.

The relations

$$x = \sum \xi_i b_i \quad \text{and} \quad \| x \|^2 = \sum | \xi_i |^2, \quad \text{where} \quad \xi_i = (x \mid b_i),$$

then become

$$x = \sum \alpha_i a_i \quad \text{and} \quad \| x \|^2 = \sum \| a_i \|^2 | \alpha_i |^2, \quad \text{where} \quad \alpha_i = \frac{(x \mid a_i)}{\| a_i \|^2}.$$

The scalar α_i is called the ith *Fourier coefficient* of x with respect to the basis (a_i); more generally, the scalars $\alpha_i = (x \mid a_i)/\| a_i \|^2$, where (a_i) is an orthogonal system, total or not, are called the Fourier coefficients of x with respect to (a_i).

In actual fact these formulas can be rederived without introducing the b_i; one writes formally

$$x = \sum \alpha_i a_i, \quad \text{from which} \quad x^2 = \left(\sum \alpha_i a_i \right)^2 \quad \text{and} \quad xa_i = \left(\sum \alpha_i a_i \right) a_i.$$

The formal expansion of these two relations gives the equations written above.

Z It is essential to note that by Proposition 16.13, an "orthonormal (or orthogonal) basis" of a Hilbert space E is an algebraic basis of E only when E is finite dimensional (see also Problem 195).

Characterization of orthonormal bases in a Hilbert space

16.7. Definition. Let E be a prehilbert space. An orthonormal system $(a_i)_{i \in I}$ in E is said to be *maximal* if every orthonormal system containing it is identical with it.

This condition is equivalent to saying that every vector x which is orthogonal to all the a_i is zero; in other words, the condition $((x \mid a_i) = 0$ for every $i \in I)$ implies $(x = O)$, or equivalently, the only vector x all of whose coordinates are zero is $x = O$.

16.8. Proposition. *When E is complete, the four equivalent assertions in Theorem 16.4 are equivalent to the following*:

5.   *The orthonormal system (a_i) is maximal.*

Proof.   1.   If the system (a_i) satisfies assertion 3, the relation

$x = \Sigma\,\xi_i a_i$ shows that if all the ξ_i vanish, then $x = O$; hence the system is maximal.

2. Conversely, suppose the system (a_i) is maximal; let L be the vector subspace generated by the a_i. If we had $\overline{L} \neq E$, Proposition 15.6 would show the existence of a vector $x \neq O$ orthogonal to $\overline{L}$ and hence to each of the a_i, which is impossible since (a_i) is maximal.

Therefore $\overline{L} = E$; in other words, the system (a_i) is total.

Z Proposition 16.8 does not extend to incomplete prehilbert spaces (see Problems 197–199); this does not mean, however, that such a space cannot have an orthonormal basis.

Existence of orthonormal bases

The four assertions in Theorem 16.4 show the usefulness of orthonormal bases for the representation of elements of a prehilbert space E. It is therefore important to know conditions which are sufficient for the existence of such a basis.

We are going to show, by different methods, that such a basis exists in complete spaces E and in separable spaces E.

16.9. Lemma.   *Every orthonormal system in a prehilbert space E is contained in a maximal orthonormal system.*

PROOF.   Let us first recall that an ordered set A is said to be *inductive* if every totally ordered subset of A has an upper bound which belongs to A; let us also recall the statement of Zorn's lemma (which is equivalent to the axiom of choice):

"In an inductive ordered set A, every element of A has an upper bound which is a maximal element of A."

To apply Zorn's lemma, it will be convenient here to consider an orthonormal system in E as a subset of E (rather than an indexed subset of E).

If we order the set A of orthonormal systems s in E by inclusion, A becomes an inductive set. Indeed, let S be a totally ordered subset of A; the union $\hat{S}$ of the $s \in S$ is an orthonormal system, for if a_1 and a_2 are elements of $\hat{S}$ belonging, respectively, to s_1 and s_2 (where $s_1 \subset s_2$ for example), a_1 and a_2 belong to s_2 and are therefore orthogonal. Thus $\hat{S}$ is an element of A which is an upper bound for every $s \in S$; hence we have shown that A is inductive, from which the lemma follows.

16.10. Proposition.   *Every Hilbert space E has an orthonormal basis.*

Proof. Lemma 16.9 shows that E contains a maximal orthonormal system, and by Proposition 16.8 this system is an orthonormal basis.

More generally, it follows from 16.8 and 16.9 that every finite or infinite orthonormal system in a Hilbert space is contained in an orthonormal basis.

16.11. Lemma. *Let* E *be a prehilbert space, and let* $(a_0, a_1, ...)$ *be a finite or infinite sequence of linearly independent vectors in* E; *for every n, let* L_n *be the subspace of* E *generated by* $a_0, a_1, ..., a_n$.

If we put $b_0 = a_0$ *and* $b_{n+1} = a_{n+1} - P_{L_n}(a_{n+1})$, *then the sequence* (b_n) *is an orthogonal system, and for every n the vectors* $b_0, b_1, ..., b_n$ *generate* L_n .

Proof. Using induction, let us assume that $(b_0, b_1, ..., b_n)$ is an orthogonal system which generates L_n .

The relation $b_{n+1} = a_{n+1} - P_{L_n}(a_{n+1})$ shows that $b_{n+1} \neq O$ since a_{n+1} does not belong to L_n , and b_{n+1} is orthogonal to L_n by Corollary 15.3. Therefore $(b_0, b_1, ..., b_{n+1})$ is an orthogonal system, and since $a_{n+1} = b_{n+1} +$ a vector in L_n , this system generates the same subspace as does $(a_0, a_1, ..., a_{n+1})$.

The orthogonal sequence (b_n) is called the *orthogonal system obtained from the sequence* (a_n) *by the Gram-Schmidt orthogonalization procedure.*

In practice, the sequence (b_n) is determined as follows: Assuming the b_i to be known for all $i \leqslant n$, we put

$$b_{n+1} = a_{n+1} + \sum_1^n \lambda_i b_i .$$

For every $i \leqslant n$ we therefore have

$$0 = (a_{n+1} \mid b_i) + \lambda_i(b_i \mid b_i), \qquad \text{which determines the } \lambda_i .$$

Finally, if we put $b_n' = \| b_n \|^{-1} b_n$, the sequence (b_n') is clearly orthonormal.

16.12. Proposition. *Every separable prehilbert space* E (*that is, containing an everywhere dense countable subset*) *has an orthonormal basis which is finite or countable.*

Proof. By hypothesis there exists a countable subset D of E such that $\overline{D} = E$. Let us arrange the points of D in a sequence (α_n) and denote by (α_{i_n}) the subsequence consisting of the elements α_i which are not linear combinations of elements α_j with index $j < i$. By construction the α_{i_n} are linearly independent, and a simple induction argument shows that every α_i is a linear combination of elements α_{i_n}; hence the sequence (α_{i_n}) is total in E.

The sequence obtained from (α_{i_n}) by the Gram-Schmidt orthogonalization procedure is total since it generates the same vector space as does the sequence (α_{i_n}); hence it is an orthogonal basis of E, and an orthonormal basis is at once obtained from it.

The assertions of 16.11 and 16.12 are of great importance for the representation of functions; the study of Fourier series and orthogonal polynomials will furnish an illustration of this.

Isomorphism of Hilbert spaces

16.13. Proposition. *Let* E *be a prehilbert space with an orthonormal basis* $(a_i)_{i \in I}$. *If for every* $x \in$ E *we denote by* ξ_i *the* ith *coordinate of* x *with respect to this basis, then the mapping* $f : x \to (\xi_i)$ *of* E *into* l_I^2 *is an isomorphism of* E *onto an everywhere dense vector subspace of* l_I^2. *When* E *is complete, the mapping* f *is an isomorphism of* E *onto* l_I^2.

PROOF. Theorem 16.4 shows that for every $x \in$ E, $\|x\|^2 = \Sigma \, |\xi_i|^2$; therefore (ξ_i) is a point of l_I^2 and the mapping f, which is clearly linear, is norm preserving. Hence by 14.10, f is an isomorphism of E onto $f($E$)$.

Since $f($E$)$ evidently contains the canonical basis of l_I^2, which is total in l_I^2, $f($E$)$ is everywhere dense on l_I^2.

In particular, if E is complete, so is $f($E$)$; therefore $f($E$)$ is both everywhere dense and closed in l_I^2; in other words, $f($E$) = l_I^2$.

16.14. Corollary. *Let* E *be a Hilbert space, and let* $(a_i)_{i \in I}$ *be an orthonormal basis of* E. *For every family* $(\xi_i)_{i \in I}$ *of elements of* **K** *such that* $\Sigma |\xi_i|^2 < \infty$, *there exists a point* $x \in$ E *having* (ξ_i) *for its coordinates with respect to the given basis.*

This result, which follows directly from 16.13, constitutes a converse to statement 2 of Theorem 16.4.

16.15. Corollary. *Let* E *be a separable prehilbert space. If* E *has finite dimension* n, E *is isomorphic to* **K**^{n}.

If E *is infinite-dimensional,* E *is isomorphic to an everywhere dense vector subspace of* l^2, *and to* l^2 *itself if* E *is complete.*

This is an immediate consequence of 16.12 and 16.13.

16.16. Proposition. 1. *All orthonormal bases of a Hilbert space* E *have the same cardinality (called the* geometric dimension *of* E).

2. *To say that two Hilbert spaces are isomorphic is equivalent to saying that they have the same geometric dimension.*

PROOF. 1. If E has finite dimension n, every orthonormal basis of E is an algebraic basis; hence its cardinal number is n.

Suppose therefore that E is infinite-dimensional, and let $(a_i)_{i \in I}$ and $(b_j)_{j \in J}$ be two orthonormal bases of E.

The set A of finite linear combinations with rational coefficients (rational complex if $\mathbf{K} = \mathbf{C}$) of the a_i is everywhere dense on E; since I is infinite and $\mathbf{Q}$ is countable, the cardinals $\bar{A}$ and $\bar{I}$ of A and I are equal (use the fact, which we shall accept here, that for every integer p, I and I^p have the same cardinality).

But the open balls B_j of E with center b_j and radius $\frac{1}{2}$ are pairwise disjoint; hence, since each B_j contains at least one point of A, we have $\bar{J} \leqslant \bar{A} = \bar{I}$. Similarly $\bar{I} \leqslant \bar{J}$; hence $\bar{I} = \bar{J}$.

2. Every isomorphism of two Hilbert spaces carries every orthonormal basis of one into an orthonormal basis of the other; therefore two such spaces have the same geometric dimension.

Conversely, if two Hilbert spaces E and F have the same geometric dimension, they have orthonormal bases which can be indexed by the same set I. By Proposition 16.13, E and F are each isomorphic to l_I^2; hence they are isomorphic.

16.17. REMARK. The most used Hilbert spaces are those whose geometric dimension is $\aleph_0$. The only space of this type which we have encountered up to now is l^2; we shall see another important concrete example in the theory of integration.

17. FOURIER SERIES AND ORTHOGONAL POLYNOMIALS

Fourier series

Let E be the vector space of continuous mappings of $\mathbf{R}$ into $\mathbf{C}$ with period 2π.

For every $x, y \in E$ we put

$$(x \mid y) = \int_0^{2\pi} x(t)\overline{y(t)} \, dt = \int_\alpha^{\alpha+2\pi} x(t)\overline{y(t)} \, dt.$$

This positive Hermitean form is a scalar product on E, as the relation $(x \mid x) = 0$ implies $x(t) = 0$ for every $t \in [0, 2\pi]$ since x is continuous, hence also $x(t) = 0$ for every $t \in \mathbf{R}$ since x has period 2π.

The space E taken with this scalar product is a prehilbert space, but it is not complete (see Example 14.7), and it is only by using the Lebesgue integral that we shall later be able to substitute for E the space of square summable functions with period 2π, which is complete.

For every $n \in \mathbf{Z}$, let us denote by a_n the function $t \to e^{int}$, which clearly belongs to E.

17.1. Proposition. 1. *The family of functions e^{int} is an orthogonal basis of* E.

2. *For every $x \in$ E we have*

$$(x \mid x) = 2\pi \sum \mid \alpha_n \mid^2, \qquad where \qquad \alpha_n = (x \mid a_n)/2\pi.$$

3. *The family of functions $\alpha_n e^{int}$ is summable in* E *and has sum x.*

PROOF. We have

$$(a_p \mid a_q) = \int_0^{2\pi} e^{i(p-q)t}\, dt = 0 \qquad (\text{if } p \neq q),$$

$$\text{or} \qquad = 2\pi \qquad (\text{if } p = q);$$

therefore (a_n) is an orthogonal family.

On the other hand, by application no. 2, Chapter II, p. 149, every function $x \in$ E is the uniform limit of linear combinations of the a_n; but the relation

$$\int_0^{2\pi} \mid f(t)\mid^2 dt \leqslant 2\pi(\sup \mid f(t)\mid)^2$$

shows that uniform convergence implies convergence in the norm of E. It follows that the family (a_n) is total in E; therefore it is an orthogonal basis of E.

Assertions 2 and 3 then follow from Theorem 16.4 and the formulas of 16.6.

17.2. REMARK. It is sometimes convenient, particularly when the functions x which one wishes to study are real valued, to replace the family of functions e^{int} by the family of functions $\cos nt$ (where $n \geqslant 0$) and $\sin nt$ (where $n \geqslant 1$); an elementary calculation shows that this family is also orthogonal.

On the other hand, it is total in E since the family (e^{int}) is total and the relation $e^{int} = \cos nt + i \sin nt$ shows that each e^{int} is a linear combination of $\cos nt$ and $\sin nt$; therefore the family of these latter functions is an orthogonal basis of E.

If we denote the elements $\cos nt$ and $\sin nt$ of E by c_n and s_n, respectively, the Fourier coefficients v_n and σ_n of a function $x \in$ E are given by the relations

$$v_0 = (x \mid c_0)/2\pi; \qquad v_n = (x \mid c_n)/\pi; \qquad \sigma_n = (x \mid s_n)/\pi \qquad \text{for} \quad n \geqslant 1.$$

The Parseval relation here assumes the form

$$(x \mid x) = 2\pi \mid v_0 \mid^2 + \pi \sum_1^\infty (\mid v_n \mid^2 + \mid \sigma_n \mid^2).$$

Z Proposition 17.1 shows that for every function $x \in E$, the sequence of functions

$$x_n(t) = \sum_{-n}^n \alpha_p e^{ipt}$$

converges to x in quadratic mean. But it says nothing concerning pointwise convergence or uniform convergence.

We shall return to these questions during the study of integration. Let us simply note here that if the sequence of functions x_n converges uniformly to a function x', then $x' = x$; indeed, the sequence (x_n) will then also converge to x' in the sense of convergence in E, and since it can have only one limit, we have $x' = x$.

17.3. Orthogonal polynomials. Let I be a closed interval, bounded or not, of **R**, and let p be a continuous numerical function which is > 0 on the interior of I, and such that

$$\int_I \mid t \mid^n p(t) \, dt < \infty$$

for every integer $n \geqslant 0$. We shall call such a function a *weight on* I.

Let E_p be the subset of $\mathscr{C}(I, \mathbf{K})$ consisting of the functions x such that

$$\int_I \mid x(t)\mid^2 p(t) \, dt < \infty.$$

The relations $\mid x + y \mid^2 \leqslant 2 \mid x \mid^2 + 2 \mid y \mid^2$ and $2 \mid xy \mid \leqslant \mid x \mid^2 + \mid y \mid^2$ show that E_p is a vector space and that the function

$$(x \mid y) = \int_I x(t)\overline{y(t)}p(t) \, dt$$

is a positive Hermitean form on E_p.

Since in addition p is continuous, and > 0 on the interior of I, the relation $(x \mid x) = 0$ implies $x(t) = 0$ for every $t \in I$, hence $x = O$. In other words, $(x \mid y)$ is a scalar product on E_p which makes E_p a prehilbert space.

The assumptions on p imply that every monomial t^n is an element of E_p; moreover, the t^n are linearly independent since every polynomial which is identically zero on I has vanishing coefficients. We can therefore apply the Gram-Schmidt orthogonalization procedure to the sequence (t^n).

Put $a_n(t) = t^n$; the recursion relations

$$P_0 = a_0 ; \qquad P_n = a_n - \text{(projection of } a_n \text{ on } L_{n-1})$$

show that P_n is a polynomial of degree n with real coefficients, and whose term of highest degree is t^n.

The P_n are called the *orthogonal polynomials associated with the weight p on* I.

One is sometimes led, in certain questions, to replace the P_n by the proportional polynomials $p_n = \lambda_n P_n$, where λ_n is a nonzero scalar (for example, it is sometimes assumed that p_n takes the value 1 at one of the end points of I); but in what follows, we shall only consider the P_n.

17.4. Classical examples.

1. $I = [-1, 1]$ and $p(t) = (1 - t)^\alpha (1 + t)^\beta$ (where α, $\beta > -1$).

The corresponding polynomials P_n are called the *Jacobi polynomials*. For $\alpha = \beta = 0$ (hence $p(t) = 1$) these are the *Legendre polynomials*. For $\alpha = \beta = -\frac{1}{2}$ these are the *Chebyshev polynomials*.

2. $I = [0, \infty)$ and $p(t) = e^{-t}$.

The polynomials P_n are then called the *Laguerre polynomials*.

3. $I = (-\infty, +\infty)$ and $p(t) = \exp(-t^2)$.

The polynomials P_n are then called the *Hermite polynomials*.

17.5. Proposition.   *When the interval* I *is compact, the sequence* (P_n) *of polynomials associated with the weight p on* I *is an orthogonal basis of the prehilbert space* E_p.

PROOF.   Every continuous function on I is the uniform limit of polynomials (see application no. 1, Chapter II, p. 149), hence of linear combinations of the P_n. Therefore the sequence (P_n) is total in E_p (same proof as for Proposition 17.1); since this sequence is moreover orthogonal, it is an orthogonal basis of E_p.

Z 1.   When the interval I is unbounded, there exist weights p on I for which the sequence (P_n) is not an orthogonal basis of E_p. But one can prove that the Laguerre and Hermite polynomials do form orthogonal bases of the respective spaces E_p (see Problem 205).

2.   Just as for Fourier series, the series with general term $\alpha_n P_n(t)$ associated with an element $x \in E_p$ does not always converge uniformly, or even pointwise, to the function $x(t)$; but if it converges uniformly, it is necessarily to $x(t)$.

General properties of sequences of orthogonal polynomials

We are going to show that the sequence (P_n) of orthogonal polynomials associated with a weight p on an interval I has various interesting properties independent of the weight chosen; we shall use for this the following two obvious remarks:

17.6.   For every n, the polynomial P_n is orthogonal to all polynomials Q of degree $< n$, since such a Q is a linear combination of the P_i with $i < n$.

17.7.   For every n, $P_n - tP_{n-1}$ is a polynomial of degree $< n$, hence

$$(tP_{n-1} \mid P_n) = (P_n \mid P_n).$$

17.8.   The definition of the scalar product of E_p shows that for every x, y, $z \in E_p$ we have

$$(xy \mid z) = (xy\bar{z} \mid 1) = (x \mid \bar{y}z).$$

17.9. Proposition.   *The roots of each of the polynomials P_n are real and distinct, and lie in the interior of* I.

PROOF.   The orthogonality of P_n and P_0 implies that

$$\int_I P_n(t)p(t)\,dt = 0.$$

Therefore P_n changes sign at one interior point at least of I. More generally, let $(t_1, t_2, ..., t_r)$, where $t_i < t_{i+1}$, be the sequence of roots of P_n interior to I at which P_n changes sign. We want to show that $r = n$; but since obviously $r \leqslant n$, it suffices to rule out the case $r < n$. If we put $Q(t) = (t - t_1)(t - t_2) \cdots (t - t_r)$, the polynomial $P_n Q$ has a fixed sign on I, which implies $(P_n \mid Q) \neq 0$; Remark 17.6 shows that this is incompatible with the inequality $r < n$.

17.10. Proposition   (Recursion relation).   *There exist two sequences of real numbers* λ_n, μ_n, *with* $\mu_n > 0$, *such that*

$$P_n = (t + \lambda_n)P_{n-1} - \mu_n P_{n-2} \qquad \text{for every } n \geqslant 2.$$

PROOF. Since $P_n - tP_{n-1}$ is of degree $\leqslant (n-1)$, we can write

$$P_n - tP_{n-1} = \sum_{i \leqslant n-1} c_i P_i .$$

We therefore have, for every $i \leqslant n-1$,

$$-(tP_{n-1} \mid P_i) = c_i(P_i \mid P_i). \tag{1}$$

But by Remark 17.8, $(tP_{n-1} \mid P_i) = (P_{n-1} \mid tP_i)$; therefore if $i+1 < n-1$, that is, $i < n-2$, this scalar product is zero, hence $c_i = 0$ except for $i = n-2$ and $n-1$.

For $i = n-2$, Remark 17.7 shows that

$$-(P_{n-1} \mid P_{n-1}) = c_{n-2}(P_{n-2} \mid P_{n-2}).$$

Thus $c_{n-2} < 0$; for $i = n-1$, relation (1) shows only that c_{n-1} is real.

REMARK. The recursion relation for the polynomials $p_n = \lambda_n P_n$ clearly has a similar form, although less simple:

$$p_n = (u_n t + v_n)p_{n-1} + w_n p_{n-2} .$$

PROBLEMS

NOTE. The rather difficult problems are marked by an asterisk.

GENERAL TOPOLOGICAL VECTOR SPACES

1. Let E be a topological vector space, and let X, Y $\subset$ E; prove the following properties:

(a) If X is open, so is X + Y.

(b) If X and Y are compact, and if E is separated, then X + Y is compact.

Show by an example constructed in $\mathbf{R}^2$ that X and Y can be closed without X + Y being closed.

2. Let $\mathscr{C}(\mathbf{R}, \mathbf{R})$ be the space of continuous functions on $\mathbf{R}$, taken with the topology of uniform convergence defined by the ecart

$$d(f, g) = \sup |f(x) - g(x)|.$$

Show that this topology is not compatible with the vector space structure of $\mathscr{C}(\mathbf{R}, \mathbf{R})$, although it is compatible with its additive group structure.

*3. For every number $\epsilon > 0$, and every $x \in \mathscr{C}([0, 1], \mathbf{R})$, we shall say that ϵ is associated with x if the set of points $t \in [0, 1]$ such that $| x(t) | \geqslant \epsilon$ can be covered by a finite family of intervals, the sum of whose lengths is $\leqslant \epsilon$; we then put

$$p(x) = \text{infimum of the set of all } \epsilon \text{ associated with } x.$$

(a) Show that p is not a norm on $\mathscr{C}([0, 1], \mathbf{R})$ but that nevertheless $p(x) = p(-x)$ and $p(x + y) \leqslant p(x) + p(y)$; deduce from this that if we put $d(x, y) = p(x - y)$, d is a metric on this space.

(b) Show that for every ball B with center O and radius $\rho > 0$ associated with this metric, the convex envelope of B is the entire space.

(c) Show that the topology associated with this metric is compatible with the vector space structure of $\mathscr{C}([0, 1], \mathbf{R})$, but is not locally convex.

(d) Show that the only continuous linear functional on this space is the linear functional O.

4. For every number $\epsilon > 0$ and every $x \in \mathscr{C}([0, 1], \mathbf{R})$, we shall say that ϵ is associated with x if the set of points $t \in [0, 1]$ such that $| x(t) | \geqslant \epsilon$ is contained in an interval of length $\leqslant \epsilon$; we then put

$$q(x) = \text{infimum of the set of all } \epsilon \text{ associated with } x.$$

Does the function q has properties analogous to those of the function p of Problem 3?

5. Let E be a vector space over $\mathbf{R}$, and let $\mathscr{V}$ be the set of convex subsets V of E containing O and such that, for every line D in E containing O, the point O is interior to the interval $D \cap V$.

We shall say that a subset X of E is *open* if for every $x \in X$ there exists a $V \in \mathscr{V}$ such that $x + V \subset X$.

(a) Show that the collection of these "open sets" defines a topology on E which is compatible with the vector space structure of E, and that $\mathscr{V}$ constitutes a neighborhood base of O in this topology.

(b) Given an algebraic basis $B = (a_i)_{i \in I}$ of E, show that for every family $(\alpha_i)_{i \in I}$ of numbers > 0, the convex envelope of the set of elements $\alpha_i a_i$ and $-\alpha_i a_i$ belongs to $\mathscr{V}$, and that these convex envelopes form a neighborhood base of O.

(c)   Show that every linear functional on E is continuous in this topology.

6. Let E be a vector space over **R**; show that if E is infinite-dimensional, the weak topology on E associated with the family of all the linear functionals on E is different from the topology defined in Problem 5.

7. Let E be a vector space over **K**. Given two topologies on E which are compatible with the vector space structure of E, we denote by $\mathscr{V}_1$ and $\mathscr{V}_2$ the collection of neighborhoods of O for each of these topologies. Show that the collection $\mathscr{V}$ of subsets of E of the form $V_1 \cap V_2$, where $V_1 \in \mathscr{V}_1$ and $V_2 \in \mathscr{V}_2$, is the collection of neighborhoods of O for a topology which is compatible with the vector space structure of E.

8. Let E be a topological vector space over **K**, and let f be a linear functional (not identically zero) on E. Show that if the hyperplane $H = f^{-1}(0)$ is closed, then f is continuous. (Show first that there exists an a such that $f(a) = 1$, and use the fact that the complement of $f^{-1}(a)$ is a neighborhood of O.)

TOPOLOGY ASSOCIATED WITH A FAMILY OF SEMINORMS

9. We shall say that a subset X of a vector space E with a $\mathscr{P}$-topology is *bounded* if every seminorm $p \in \mathscr{P}$ is bounded on X. Prove that the class of bounded sets is closed under the following operations:

Closure, convex envelope, image under a continuous linear mapping, finite union, finite vector sum, finite product.

Show that every compact set is bounded, and that for every convergent sequence (x_n), the set of elements x_n is bounded.

10. Let E be a vector space over **R**, and let X be a convex subset of E such that

$$E = \bigcup_{k \in \mathbf{R}_+} kX.$$

For every $x \in E$ we put

$$p(x) = \text{infimum of those } k > 0 \text{ such that } x \in kX.$$

Show that p is positive-homogeneous and convex, and that when X is symmetric, p is a seminorm; when is it a norm? Show that

$$\{x : p(x) < 1\} \subset X \subset \{x : p(x) \leqslant 1\}.$$

11. Let E be a vector space over **R**, F a vector subspace of E, and p a mapping of E into **R** such that for every x, $y \in E$ and every $\lambda \in \mathbf{R}_+$,

$$p(\lambda x) = \lambda p(x), \qquad p(x + y) \leqslant p(x) + p(y).$$

(a) Let f be a linear functional on E such that $f(x) \leqslant p(x)$ for every $x \in F$; show that for every $a \in E$ and every u, $v \in F$ we have

$$f(u) - p(u - a) \leqslant f(a) \leqslant p(v + a) - f(v).$$

(b) More generally, let f be a linear functional defined only on F and such that $f(x) \leqslant p(x)$ for every $x \in F$. For every $a \in E$ we put

$$k_a = \sup_{u \in F}(f(u) - p(u - a)), \qquad K_a = \inf_{v \in F}(p(v + a) - f(v)).$$

Show that k_a and K_a are finite and $k_a \leqslant K_a$.

(c) We maintain the hypotheses of (b), and assume $a \notin F$; let k be any number in $[k_a, K_a]$.
   For every $x \in F$ and every $\lambda \in \mathbf{R}$ we put

$$g(x + \lambda a) = f(x) + \lambda k.$$

Show that g is a linear functional on the vector subspace F_a of E generated by F and a, that g is identical with f on F, and that $g(y) \leqslant p(y)$ for every $y \in F_a$.

12. Let E and p be as in the preceding problem. Let $\mathscr{F}$ be the set of pairs (F, f), where F is a vector subspace of E and f is a linear functional on F such that $f \leqslant p$ on F. We shall write

$$(F_1, f_1) \leqslant (F_2, f_2),$$

and say that (F_2, f_2) is an extension of (F_1, f_1), if $F_1 \subset F_2$ and if f_1 is the restriction of f_2 to F_1.

(a) Show that this relation is an order relation on $\mathscr{F}$, and that $\mathscr{F}$, with this order, is inductive (see 16.9).

(b) Deduce from the preceding problem that every maximal element of $\mathscr{F}$ is of the form (E, f).

13. Let E, p, $\mathscr{F}$ be defined as in Problem 12.

(a) Show that every $(F, f) \in \mathscr{F}$ has an extension (E, g). Show, in particular, that there always exists a linear functional f on E such that $f \leqslant p$ on E.

(b) Show that a necessary and sufficient condition for the extension
(E, g) of (F, f) to be unique is that, with the notation of Problem
11, $k_a = K_a$ for every $a \in E$. (The results of this problem
constitute the Hahn-Banach theorem, whose applications in
Analysis are manifold.)

14. Let E be a vector space over **R**, with a separated $\mathscr{P}$-topology.
Show, using Problem 13, that for every $x \neq O$ in E there exists a continuous linear functional f on E such that $f(x) \neq 0$.

15. Show that the norm of every normed space E over **R** is the upper
envelope of a family of seminorms of the form $|l|$, where $l \in E'$ (use
Problem 13).

Deduce from this that if $\mathscr{P}$ is an infinite family of seminorms on a
vector space E, and if $\bar{\mathscr{P}}$ denotes the family of seminorms on E which
are upper envelopes of subfamilies of $\mathscr{P}$, the topologies on E associated
with $\mathscr{P}$ and $\bar{\mathscr{P}}$ are not in general identical.

Indicate several cases in which these topologies are identical.

16. Let B be the closed unit ball in a normed space E over **R**. Show
that for every $x \in E$ such that $\|x\| = 1$, there exists a continuous linear
functional on E such that $\|f\| = 1$ and $f(x) = 1$ (use Problem 13).

17. Let E and F be vector spaces over the same field **K**, and let f be a
bilinear form on E $\times$ F. We shall say that f puts E and F *in duality* if

(a) for every $x \neq O$ in E, there exists $y \in F$ such that $f(x, y) \neq 0$;

(b) for every $y \neq O$ in F, there exists $x \in E$ such that $f(x, y) \neq 0$.

The weak topology associated with the family of linear functionals
$l_y : x \to f(x, y)$ (where $y \in F$) is called the weak topology on E
associated with f.

Show that this topology is separated, and that if E is infinite-
dimensional, this topology cannot be defined by a norm (show,
to this end, that every neighborhood of O contains a vector
subspace of E with finite codimension).

Show that every linear functional l on E which is continuous
in the weak topology just defined is of the form l_y.

18. Let D be the open disk $\{z : |z| < 3\}$ of **C**, and let K be the compact
set $\{z : |z| \leqslant 1\}$. For every $f \in \mathscr{H}(D)$ (see 3.7) we put

$$p(f) = \sup_{z \in K} |f(z)|.$$

(a) Show that p is a norm on $\mathscr{H}(D)$.

(b) Show that the topology defined by p on $\mathcal{H}(D)$ is not identical with the topology of uniform convergence on every compact set (use the sequence (f_n) of functions $f_n(z) = e^{n(z-2)}$).

19. Let A be a countable subset of $[0, 1]$, and let α be a mapping of A into $(0, \infty)$ such that $\Sigma_{t\in A}\,\alpha(t) < \infty$. For every $x \in \mathcal{C}([0, 1], \mathbf{R})$ we put

$$\|f\| = \sum_{t\in A} \alpha(t)|f(t)|.$$

(a) Show that $\|f\|$ is a seminorm on $\mathcal{C}([0, 1], \mathbf{R})$; when is it a norm? Is it then equivalent to the norm of uniform convergence?

(b) Show that two such seminorms define the same topology on $\mathcal{C}([0, 1], \mathbf{R})$ only if the corresponding sets A and A' are identical and the ratios α/α' and α'/α are bounded.

TOPOLOGY ASSOCIATED WITH A NORM

20. Show that every compact subset of a normed space is bounded.

21. Show that if X and Y are compact subsets of a normed space, the union of the line segments joining a point of X with a point of Y is compact (use the product $X \times Y$).

22. Let E be a normed space, and X, Y two subsets of E. Show that if X is compact and Y closed, then $X + Y$ is closed.

23. Show that in every normed space, the closure of the open unit ball is the closed unit ball, and its boundary is the unit sphere

$$\{x : \|x\| = 1\}.$$

24. Let E and F be normed spaces over $\mathbf{R}$, and let f be a mapping of E into F such that:

(a) $f(x + y) = f(x) + f(y)$ for all $x, y \in E$;

(b) f is bounded on the unit ball of E.

Show that f is linear and continuous.

25. Let X be a closed subset of a complete normed space E. Show that for X to be compact, it is necessary and sufficient that for every $\epsilon > 0$ there exist a covering of X by a finite family of balls of radius ϵ.

26. Let E be a normed space.

(a) Show that if every series (a_n) in E which is absolutely convergent is convergent, then E is complete.

(b) Show that if every series (a_n) in E such that $\| a_n \| \leqslant 2^{-n}$ is convergent, then E is complete.

How can these results be extended to every metric space E?

27. Let E be a vector space with a seminorm p. We shall write $x \sim y$ if $p(x - y) = 0$.

Show that this relation is an equivalence relation on E which is compatible with the vectorial structure of E and with the seminorm, in a sense which is required to make precise, and that the equivalence class containing O is a vector subspace of E. Let $\tilde{E}$ be the quotient space of E by this equivalence relation; show that $\tilde{E}$ can be given a unique normed vector space structure such that the canonical mapping $x \to \tilde{x}$ of E onto $\tilde{E}$ is a linear mapping such that $\| \tilde{x} \| = p(x)$.

We shall say that $\tilde{E}$ is the normed space associated with E.

COMPARISON OF NORMS

28. For every $x \in \mathscr{C}^1([0, 1], \mathbf{R})$ we put

$$\| x \| = \sup(| x(t)| + | x'(t)|).$$

Show that $\| x \|$ is a norm; is it equivalent to the norm

$$(\sup | x(t)| + \sup | x'(t)|)?$$

29. Let E be the vector subspace of $\mathscr{C}^1([0, 1], \mathbf{R})$ consisting of the x such that $x(0) = 0$.

For every $x \in E$ we put

$$\| x \| = \sup | x(t) + x'(t)|.$$

Show that $\| x \|$ is a norm on E, equivalent to the norm

$$(\sup | x(t)| + \sup | x'(t)|).$$

30. Compare, on $\mathscr{C}^1([0, 1], \mathbf{R})$, the norms

$$\sup | x(t)|; \qquad \sup | x(t)| + \int_0^1 | x(t)| \, dt;$$

$$\sup | x(t)| + \sup | x'(t)|; \qquad \sup | x(t)| + \int_0^1 | x'(t)| \, dt.$$

31. Show that in the space l^1 over $\mathbf{K}$, the norms $\sum | x_n |$ and $\sup | x_n |$ are not equivalent.

32. For every $x \in \mathscr{C}^1([0, 1], \mathbf{R})$ we define a positive number $p(x)$ by

$$p^2(x) = x^2(0) + \int_0^1 x'^2(t) \, dt.$$

Show that p is a norm, and that convergence in this norm implies uniform convergence.

NORMS AND CONVEX FUNCTIONS

33. Let E be a normed space, and let S be the unit sphere $\{x : \| x \| = 1\}$ of E. Assume that for all $x, y \in S$ one has

$$\left\| \frac{x + y}{2} \right\| \leqslant 1 - \varphi(\| x - y \|),$$

where φ is an increasing mapping of $[0, \infty)$ into $\mathbf{R}_+$, with $\varphi(u) > 0$ for every $u > 0$.

Show that for every closed convex set $X \subset E$, every point $x \in E$ has a unique projection on X.

34. Let E be a vector space over $\mathbf{R}$. The space $E_c = E \times E$ with the ordinary addition and the multiplication by elements $(\alpha + i\beta)$ of $\mathbf{C}$ defined by

$$(\alpha + i\beta)(u, v) = (\alpha u - \beta v, \beta u + \alpha v),$$

is called the *complexification* of E.

(a) Show that E_c is a vector space over $\mathbf{C}$, and that if E is imbedded in E_c by identifying the element $u \in E$ with the element (u, O) of E_c, then the subset E of E_c generates E_c.

(b) If E is normed, show that one can extend the norm of E, in several ways in general, to a norm on the vector space E_c over $\mathbf{C}$; show that these various norms are equivalent. Show that E and E_c are simultaneously complete or incomplete.

(c) If E is a real prehilbert space, show that its scalar product can be extended in a unique way to a scalar product on E_c, and give an expression for this extension.

35. Let E be a vector space over $\mathbf{C}$; by a *subscalar product* on E we shall mean a mapping q of $E \times E$ into $\mathbf{R}_+$ such that

$$q(x, y) = q(y, x); \tag{1}$$
$$q(\lambda x, y) = | \lambda | q(x, y); \tag{2}$$
$$q(u + v, y) \leqslant q(u, y) + q(v, y); \tag{3}$$
$$q^2(x, y) \leqslant q(x, x) q(y, y). \tag{4}$$

(a) Show that $(q(x, x))^{1/2}$ is a seminorm on E.

(b) Show that every sum, every limit, and every upper envelope of subscalar products is a subscalar product.

(c) Show that if $(x \mid y)$ is a scalar product on E, its absolute value is a subscalar product.

36. Let E and F be vector spaces over **R**; let A be a convex subset of $E \times F$, and let f be a convex function on A. We denote by X the projection of A on E, and for every $x \in X$ we put

$$g(x) = \inf_{(x,y)\in A} f(x, y).$$

Show that when g is finite on X, g is convex.

37. Let E be a normed space over **R**.

(a) Show that the mapping $x \rightarrow \| x \|$ of E into **R** is convex and of Lipschitz class with ratio 1.

(b) Show that the mapping $(x, y) \rightarrow \| x - y \|$ of $E \times E$ into **R** is convex and of Lipschitz class.

> For every nonempty subset A of E, and for every $x \in E$, we now put

$$d_A(x) = \inf_{y\in A} \| x - y \|; \qquad D_A(x) = \sup_{y\in A} \| x - y \|.$$

(c) Show that if A is bounded, D_A is a convex function of Lipschitz class with ratio 1.

(d) We assume henceforth that A is convex; show that d_A is then convex (use Problem 36).

(e) Put $A' = \complement A$, and let f be the function defined by

$$f(x) = d_A(x) \text{ for } x \in A'; \qquad f(x) = -d_{A'}(x) \text{ for } x \in A.$$

Show that f is convex in E.

38. We denote by E the vector space $\mathscr{C}([0, 1], \mathbf{R})$ taken with the norm of uniform convergence.

(a) Show that for all $a, b \in E$ such that $a \leqslant b$, the set of $x \in E$ such that $a \leqslant x \leqslant b$ is a bounded closed convex set in E.

(b) For every $\epsilon > 0$ we denote by X_n the set of $x \in E$ such that

$$x(0) = 1; \qquad 0 \leqslant x(t) \leqslant 1 \quad \text{on} \quad [0, 1/n]; \qquad x(t) = 0 \quad \text{on} \quad [1/n, 1].$$

Show that (X_n) is a decreasing sequence of bounded closed convex sets in E, and that the intersection of the X_n is empty.

39. Let E be as in the preceding problem, and let X be the set of $x \in E$ which are $\geqslant 0$, decreasing and such that

$$1 \leqslant x(0) \leqslant 2 \quad \text{and} \quad \int_0^1 x(t)\, dt = x(0) - 1.$$

(a) Show that X is a bounded closed convex subset of E, and that $d(O, X) = 1$.

(b) Show that there exists no $x \in X$ such that $d(O, x) = 1$.

LINEAR FUNCTIONALS ON NORMED SPACES

40. Let E be the space $\mathscr{C}([0, 1], \mathbf{R})$ taken with the norm of mean convergence.

(a) Show that the linear functional $x \to \int_0^1 \varphi(t)x(t)\, dt$ on E, where $\varphi \in E$, is continuous. Find its norm.

(b) Show, on the other hand, that if $\varphi(t) = t^{-1/2}$, this linear functional is not continuous.

(c) Show that the $x \in E$ such that $\int_0^1 x(t)\, dt = 0$ form a closed hyperplane in E.

(d) Show that the set of monomials t^n is a total set in E.

(e) Show that the quadratic functional $x \to \int_0^1 x^2(t)\, dt$ is not continuous on E.

41. Show that the linear functional $x \to x'(0)$ is not continuous on $\mathscr{C}^1([0, 1], \mathbf{R})$ taken with the norm of uniform convergence.

42. In the space $\mathscr{C}([0, 1], \mathbf{R})$ taken with the norm of uniform convergence, let E be the set of x such that $\int_0^1 x(t)\, dt = 0$.

Show that every $u \in \mathscr{C}([0, 1], \mathbf{R})$ has a unique primitive belonging to E; we denote this primitive by T_u.

Show that T is linear and calculate its norm.

43. Let E be the vector space $\mathscr{C}([0, 1], \mathbf{R})$ taken with the norm of uniform convergence.

Let (t_n) be a sequence of points in $[0, 1]$ which are everywhere dense on $[0, 1]$; for every $x \in E$ we put

$$l(x) = \sum_n (-2)^{-n} x(t_n).$$

(a) Show that l is a continuous linear functional on E.

(b) Show that l does not attain its supremum over the closed unit ball of E at any point of this ball.

44. Let X be a compact space, and let $\mathcal{M}(X)$ be the topological dual of the vector space $\mathscr{C}(X, \mathbf{R})$ taken with the norm of uniform convergence.

(a) Show that every linear functional on $\mathscr{C}(X, \mathbf{R})$ which is positive on the set of functions $x \geqslant 0$ belongs to $\mathcal{M}(X)$.

(b) Let (a_n) be a sequence of points of X, and let (α_n) be a sequence of real numbers such that $\Sigma \mid \alpha_n \mid < \infty$; for every $x \in \mathscr{C}(X, \mathbf{R})$ we put

$$\mu(x) = \sum \alpha_n x(a_n).$$

Show that μ is an element of $\mathcal{M}(X)$, and that its norm is equal to $\Sigma \mid \alpha_n \mid$.

45. We now assume $X = [0, 1]$; let μ and μ_n be the linear functionals defined by

$$\mu(x) = \int_0^1 x(t)\, dt \quad \text{and} \quad \mu_n(x) = 1/n \sum_1^n x(p/n).$$

(a) Calculate the norms of μ, μ_n, and $\mu - \mu_n$.

(b) Show that the sequence (μ_n) does not converge to μ in the sense of the norm on $\mathcal{M}(X)$, but does converge to μ in the $\sigma(E', E)$ topology on $\mathcal{M}(X) = \mathscr{C}(X, \mathbf{R})'$ (see 3.11).

TOPOLOGICAL DUAL AND BIDUAL

46. Let E be a normed space over $\mathbf{R}$, F a vector subspace of E, and f a continuous linear functional on F.

Using the relation $|f(x)| \leqslant \|f\| \|x\|$ and Problem 13, show that there exists a linear functional g on E which is an extension of f, and such that $\|g\| = \|f\|$.

47. Let E be a normed space over $\mathbf{R}$. Deduce from the preceding problem that for every $x \in E$ there exists an $l \in E'$ such that

$$\|l\| = 1 \quad \text{and} \quad l(x) = \|x\|.$$

48. Let E be a normed space over $\mathbf{R}$, E' its topological dual, and E'' the topological dual of E' (called the *bidual* of E).

(a) For every $x \in E$, we denote by φ_x the linear functional $l \to l(x)$ on E'; show that $\varphi_x \in E''$ and that $\| \varphi_x \| \leqslant \| x \|$.

(b) Using the preceding problem, show that $\| \varphi_x \| = \| x \|$, and that the linear mapping φ of E into E'' is an isometry.

(c) Deduce from this that every normed space over **R** can be imbedded in a complete normed space; extend this result to normed spaces over **C**.

(d) Show, by taking for E the space $\mathscr{C}([0, 1], \mathbf{R})$ with the topology of uniform convergence, that even when E is complete, E″ in general contains points which do not belong to E (identified here with $\varphi(\mathrm{E})$).

*49. Let E be a normed space, and let A be a convex subset of E.

(a) Show that if A is everywhere dense on E in the weak topology of E, the same is true in the strong topology (use Problem 13).

(b) Show, on the other hand, that in every infinite-dimensional normed space E, the complement A of the unit ball is everywhere dense on E in the weak topology of E.

COMPACT LINEAR MAPPINGS

50. Let f be a linear mapping of a normed space E into a normed space F; f is said to be *compact* if $\overline{f(\mathrm{X})}$ is compact for every bounded set $\mathrm{X} \subset \mathrm{E}$.

(a) Show that for f to be compact, it is necessary and sufficient that $\overline{f(\mathrm{B})}$ be compact (where B denotes the closed unit ball of E).

(b) Show that every compact linear mapping is continuous, but that the converse is false.

(c) Show that every $f \in \mathscr{L}(\mathrm{E}, \mathrm{F})$ such that $f(\mathrm{E})$ is finite-dimensional is compact.

(d) Show that if E is finite-dimensional, then f is compact.

(e) Show that if f and g are compact, so is $f + g$. Deduce from this that the set $\mathrm{C}(\mathrm{E}, \mathrm{F})$ of compact linear mappings of E into F is a vector subspace of $\mathscr{L}(\mathrm{E}, \mathrm{F})$.

*(f) Show, using Problem 25, that if F is complete, then $\mathrm{C}(\mathrm{E}, \mathrm{F})$ is closed in $\mathscr{L}(\mathrm{E}, \mathrm{F})$.

51. Let E, F, G be normed spaces, $f \in \mathscr{L}(\mathrm{E}, \mathrm{F})$, $g \in \mathscr{L}(\mathrm{F}, \mathrm{G})$. Show that if one of the mappings f, g is compact, then $f \circ g$ is compact.

52. Let E be a normed space over **K**, let $\lambda \in \mathbf{K}$, and let $f \in \mathscr{L}(\mathrm{E})$. We denote by E_λ the set of $x \in \mathrm{E}$ such that $f(x) = \lambda x$.

Show that E_λ is a closed vector subspace of E.

Show that when f is compact, E_λ is finite-dimensional (use Theorem 7.6).

53. Let E be the space $\mathscr{C}([0, 1], \mathbf{C})$ taken with the norm of uniform convergence; given $K \in \mathscr{C}([0, 1]^2, \mathbf{C})$, we denote by T the linear mapping of E into itself defined by

$$Tx(t) = \int_0^1 K(t, u)x(u)\, du.$$

(a) Verify that $Tx \in E$, and then show that T is continuous; calculate its norm, or at least an upper bound for the norm.

(b) Show that when K is a polynomial, $T(E)$ is finite-dimensional. Deduce from this, using the Stone-Weierstrass theorem and Problem 50, that T is compact for every K.

54. Same as the preceding problem, but E taken with the norm of mean convergence (or mean convergence of order $p \geqslant 1$).

55. Let (k_n) be a bounded sequence of scalars, and let T be the mapping of the normed space l^p into itself defined as follows:

For every $x = (x_n)$, $T(x)$ is the point $(k_n x_n)$.

Show that a necessary and sufficient condition for T to be compact is that the sequence (k_n) have limit 0.

56. Let E be the space $\mathscr{C}([0, 1], \mathbf{R})$ taken with the norm of uniform convergence, and let T be the mapping of E into itself defined by

$$Tx(t) = \int_0^t x(u)\, du.$$

(a) Show that T^n $(n > 1)$ can be defined by a relation of the form

$$T^n x(t) = \int_0^1 K_n(t, u)x(u)\, du,$$

where $K_n(t, u)$ is a continuous function of (t, u) on $[0, 1]^2$.

(b) Calculate the norm of T^n in $\mathscr{L}(E)$; show that the family (T^n) is summable in $\mathscr{L}(E)$, and calculate its sum.

(c) Use these results to solve the equation

$$(I - T)x = g,$$

where g is a given element of E, I is the identity mapping in E, and x is the unknown.

57. More generally, let X be a compact space; let E be the space $\mathscr{C}(X, \mathbf{R})$ taken with the norm of uniform convergence, and let T be a linear mapping of E into E.

(a) Show that if $Tx \geqslant 0$ for every $x \geqslant 0$, then T is continuous. From now on we assume in addition that for every integer n we have

$$Tu + T^2u + \cdots + T^nu \leqslant ku,$$

where k is a constant $\geqslant 0$, and u is the unit element of E ($u(t) = 1$ for every $t \in X$).

(b) Show that

$$\lim_{n \to \infty}(T^nu(t)) = 0$$

for every t, and that $T^{p+q}u \leqslant kT^pu$ for all integers p, $q \geqslant 1$. Deduce from this that the sequence (T^nu) converges uniformly to O (use Problem 86, Chapter I).

(c) Show that for every $x \in E$, $\| T^nx \| \leqslant A \| x \| \lambda^n$, where A and λ are positive constants, with $\lambda < 1$.

(d) Deduce from this that the mapping $x \to x - Tx$ is an isomorphism of E onto E, and give an expression for the general solution of the inequality $x \geqslant Tx$.

COMPLETE NORMED SPACES

58. Let E be the subset of $\mathscr{C}([0, 1], \mathbf{R})$ consisting of the continuous functions x of bounded variation such that $x(0) = 0$; and for every $x \in E$, let $p(x)$ denote the total variation of x on $[0, 1]$.

(a) Show that E is a vector space, and that p is a norm on this space.

(b) Show that p is not continuous on E taken with the norm of uniform convergence, but only lower semicontinuous.

(c) Show that E, taken with the norm p, is a complete normed space.

*59. Given a number $p \geqslant 1$, for every $f \in \mathscr{C}(\mathbf{R}, \mathbf{C})$ we denote by $\| f \|$ the positive, finite or infinite number defined by

$$\| f \|^p = \lim_{a \to \infty} \sup (1/2a) \int_{-a}^{a} |f(t)|^p \, dt.$$

We then let B_p denote the subset of $\mathscr{C}(\mathbf{R}, \mathbf{C})$ consisting of the f such that $\| f \| < \infty$.

(a) Show that B_p is a vector subspace of $\mathscr{C}(\mathbf{R}, \mathbf{C})$ and that $\| f \|$ is a seminorm on B_p; show by an example that it is not a norm.

(b) For every $u \in \mathbf{R}$ and every $f \in \mathrm{B}_p$, let f_u denote the function defined by $f_u(x) = f(x - u)$.
Show that $\|f_u\| = \|f\|$.

(c) Show that the set S_p of $f \in \mathrm{B}_p$ such that $\|f\|^p$ is exactly the limit of

$$(1/2a) \int_{-a}^{a} |f(t)|^p \, dt$$

is closed in B_p.

(d) We denote by $\mathscr{B}_p$ the normed space associated with B_p (see Problem 27); $\mathscr{B}_p$ is called the *Besicovitch space* of index p. Show that this normed space is complete.

*60. Let E and F be normed spaces, with E complete, and let A be a subset of $\mathscr{L}(\mathrm{E}, \mathrm{F})$ such that, for every $x \in \mathrm{E}$, the set of points $f(x)$, $f \in \mathrm{A}$, is bounded (in F).

Let φ be the mapping of E into $\mathbf{R}_+$ defined by

$$\varphi(x) = \sup_{f \in \mathrm{A}} \|f(x)\|.$$

(a) Show that φ is lower semicontinuous and convex.

(b) Deduce from the lower semicontinuity of φ and from the completeness of E that there exists a nonempty open set in E on which φ is bounded from above (use Problems 102, 103, 104 of Chapter I).

(c) Deduce from this that A is a bounded subset of $\mathscr{L}(\mathrm{E}, \mathrm{F})$.

61. Let E and F be normed spaces, with E complete, and let (f_n) be a sequence of elements of $\mathscr{L}(\mathrm{E}, \mathrm{F})$ such that, for every $x \in \mathrm{E}$, the sequence $(f_n(x))$ has a limit $f(x)$.
Show, using the preceding problem, that $f \in \mathscr{L}(\mathrm{E}, \mathrm{F})$.

*62. Let E and F be normed spaces, with E complete, and let f be a linear mapping of E into F.

We assume that there exists a subset A of E whose complement is a countable union of nondense subsets of E, and such that the restriction of f to A is continuous (we point out that all the f which can be explicitly defined in Analysis have this property).

(a) Show that there exists a translate $\mathrm{A}' = \mathrm{A} + a$ of A containing O which has the same properties as A; show that there exists an open ball B with center O such that $\| f(x) \| \leqslant 1$ for every $x \in A' \cap B$.

(b) Using Problems 102, 103, and 104 of Chapter I, show that

$$B \subset \tfrac{1}{2}[(A' \cap B) + (A' \cap B)].$$

Deduce from this that f is continuous.

SEPARABLE NORMED SPACES

We recall that a metric space is said to be *separable* if it contains a finite or countable everywhere dense set.

63. (a) Show that for a normed space to be separable, it is necessary and sufficient that it contain a finite or countable total subset.

(b) Deduce from this that each of the spaces $\mathscr{C}^p([0, 1], \mathbf{K})$ is separable.

(c) Same question as (b), for the space $\mathscr{C}([0, 1], \mathbf{K})$ taken with the norm of mean convergence of order p (where $p \geqslant 1$).

(d) Show that a necessary and sufficient condition for l_I^p to be separable is that I be finite or countable.

64. Let E be a vector space with two norms p, q such that $p \leqslant kq$ (where $k > 0$).

Show that if E, taken with the norm q, is separable, then E taken with the norm p is also separable.

*65. Let E be a normed space with a countable algebraic basis $(a_n)_{n \in \mathbf{N}}$ such that $\| a_n \| = 1$ for every n.

(a) Show that for every sequence (α_n) of numbers > 0 such that $\sum \alpha_n < \infty$, the sequence (b_n), where $b_n = \sum_0^n \alpha_i a_i$, is a Cauchy sequence.

(b) For every $n > 0$, we denote by d_n the distance from a_n to the vector space generated by $(a_0, a_1, ..., a_{n-1})$, and we define the sequence (α_n) recursively by the following conditions:

$$\alpha_0 = \alpha_1 = 1; \qquad \alpha_{n+1} = 3^{-1}\alpha_n d_n .$$

Show that the Cauchy sequence (b_n) associated with the sequence (α_n) does not converge in E.

(c) Deduce from this that no infinite-dimensional Banach space has a countable algebraic basis.

66. Let E denote the vector space of bounded sequences $x = (x_n)$ of complex numbers, taken with the norm $\| x \| = \sup_n | x_n |$.

(a) What is the adherence E_0 in E of the vector space of sequences $x = (x_n)$ which have only a finite number of terms $\neq 0$?

(b) What is the adherence in E of the vector space of sequences $x = (x_n)$ such that $\Sigma | x_n | < \infty$?

(c) Show that the set of sequences $x = (x_n)$ such that $\Sigma | x_n | \leqslant 1$ is closed in E.

(d) Show that E is not separable, while on the contrary E_0 is.

(e) Show that the vector subspace of E formed by the sequences $x = (x_n)$ such that $\lim_{n \to \infty} x_n$ exists is complete and separable.

67. (a) Show that for any distinct real numbers λ, μ, the element

$$f(t) = e^{i\lambda t} - e^{i\mu t}$$

of the space B_p defined in Problem 59 has norm $\geqslant 1$.

(b) Deduce from this that the normed space $\mathscr{B}_p$ associated with B_p is not separable (use the family of functions $e^{i\lambda t}$).

DISCONTINUOUS LINEAR MAPPINGS

68. Let E be a vector space over **K**, and let $\mathscr{L}$ be the collection of linearly independent subsets of E, ordered by inclusion.

(a) Show that $\mathscr{L}$ is an inductive set.

(b) Show that every maximal linearly independent subset of E generates E.

(c) Deduce from this that E contains an algebraic basis.

69. Let B be an algebraic basis of a vector space E over **K**, and let f be an arbitrary mapping of B into **K**.

(a) Show that there exists a unique linear functional g on E such that $g(x) = f(x)$ for every $x \in B$.

(b) We now assume that E is an infinite-dimensional normed space; let (a_n) be an infinite sequence of distinct points of B. We denote by f the function on B defined by

$$f(a_n) = n\| a_n \| \quad \text{for every } n;$$
$$f(x) = 0 \quad \text{if } x \text{ is not an } a_n.$$

Show that the linear functional g associated with f is not continuous.

(c) Using the same idea, show that the set of discontinuous linear functionals on an infinite-dimensional normed space has cardinality at least equal to that of the set of continuous linear functionals.

PRODUCTS OF NORMED SPACES AND DIRECT SUMS

70. Let E be a normed space, and let A and B be vector subspaces of E, of which E is the direct algebraic sum (in other words, $A + B = E$ and $A \cap B = \{O\}$).

For every $x \in E$, we denote by x_A and x_B the components of x in A and B.

(a) Show that if the mapping $x \to x_A$ is continuous, the same is true of the mapping $x \to x_B$, and that A and B are then closed in E.

(b) Show that the mapping $(u, v) \to u + v$ of the normed space $A \times B$ into E is then an isomorphism, and that if A and B are complete, so is E.

(c) Show that the continuity of x_A can be expressed by saying that the distance between the unit spheres of A and B is $\neq 0$.

*71. Let E be the space $\mathscr{C}([0, \pi], \mathbf{R})$ taken with the norm of uniform convergence. Let E_1 (E_2) be the adherence of the subspace of E generated by the functions 1 and $\cos n! \, t$ $(x^n/n + \cos n! \, t)$ (where $n \in \mathbf{N}^*$).

(a) Show that $E_1 \cap E_2 = \{O\}$.

(b) Show that $E_1 + E_2$ is distinct from E; deduce from this that an incomplete normed space can be the direct algebraic sum of two complete vector subspaces.

FINITE-DIMENSIONAL NORMED SPACES

72. Let E_p be the vector space of polynomials $P(x)$ with complex coefficients and degree $\leqslant p$.

Let $z_0, z_1, ..., z_p$ be distinct points of $\mathbf{C}$; put

$$\| P \| = | P(z_0)| + \cdots + | P(z_p)|.$$

Show that $\| P \|$ is a norm on E_p, and that the different norms obtained by varying the points z_i are equivalent. Is the mapping $P \to P'$, where $P'(z) = zP(z)$, of E_p into E_{p+1} continuous?

73. Show that if there exists, in a normed space E, a compact set with nonempty interior, then E is finite-dimensional.

*74. Show that in every n-dimensional normed space E over **R**, there exists a basis $(a_1, a_2, ..., a_n)$ of E such that if (x_i) denotes the coordinates of x in this basis, we have

$$\sum |x_i| \leqslant \|x\| \leqslant n \sum |x_i|.$$

(*Hint*: Use the function $\langle$determinant of $(b_1, b_2, ..., b_n)\rangle$ and seek to maximize it, subject to the condition that the b_i have norm 1).

Show, at least for $n = 2$, that the constant n in the inequality above cannot be replaced by a smaller constant.

75. Study the problem, analogous to the preceding one, obtained by replacing $\sum |x_i|$ by $(\sum |x_i|^2)^{1/2}$, and n by another constant.

**76. Prove the property assumed without proof in Problem 84.

SUMMABLE FAMILIES OF REAL OR COMPLEX NUMBERS

77. Let (ω_i) be a family of subintervals of $[0, 1]$, and let a_i denote the length of ω_i.

Show that if $\sum a_i < 1$, the family (ω_i) cannot cover $[0, 1]$. More precisely, show that the union of the ω_i has a complement in $[0, 1]$ which cannot be finite or countable.

(First study carefully the case of a finite family; then pass to the general case by a suitable use of the theorem of Heine-Borel-Lebesgue.)

78. Construct a family $(a_{p,q})$ of real numbers (where $p, q \in \mathbf{N}$) such that

    (a) $a_{p,q} = a_{q,p}$;

    (b) for every p, the family $(a_{p,q})_{q \in \mathbf{N}}$ is summable with sum 0;

    (c) the family $(a_{p,q})$ is not summable.

*79. Let (a_n) be a sequence of complex numbers such that $\sum |a_n|^2 < \infty$; show that the family with general term $a_p a_q/(p + q)$ (where $p, q \geqslant 1$) is summable.

80. Let $x \in \mathbf{C}$, with $|x| < 1$; prove the identities

$$\sum_1^\infty \frac{x^{2n-1}}{1 - x^{2n-1}} = \sum_1^\infty \frac{x^n}{1 - x^{2n}} ; \qquad \sum_1^\infty \frac{nx^n}{1 - x^n} = \sum_1^\infty \frac{x^n}{(1 - x^n)^2}.$$

SUMMABLE FAMILIES IN TOPOLOGICAL GROUPS AND NORMED SPACES

81. (a) Let G be an arbitrary topological group, and let A be a subset of G. Show that $\bar{A}$ is the intersection of the sets $A \cdot V$ (as well as $V \cdot A$), where V runs through the set $\mathscr{V}$ of neighborhoods of the identity e of G) (use the fact that the symmetric neighborhoods of e form a base for $\mathscr{V}$).

(b) Deduce from this that the closed neighborhoods of e form a base for $\mathscr{V}$.

82. Let E be a normed space, I an index set, and p a real number $\geqslant 1$. We denote by $l_I^p(E)$ the subset of $\mathscr{F}(I, E)$ consisting of the families $a = (a_i)_{i \in I}$ of elements of E such that $\sum_i \| a_i \|^p < \infty$.

(a) Show that $l_I^p(E)$ is a vector subspace of $\mathscr{F}(I, E)$ and that $(\sum_i \| a_i \|^p)^{1/p}$ is a norm on this space.

(b) Show that when E is complete, $l_I^p(E)$ is complete, and conversely.

(c) Suppose E is a normed algebra, and define a multiplication in $l_I^p(E)$ as follows:

If $a = (a_i)$ and $b = (b_i)$, the point $c = a \cdot b$ is the point $(a_i b_i)$.

Verify that this multiplication is meaningful, and that it makes $l_I^p(E)$ a normed algebra.

83. Let E be a complete normed space, and let $(a_i(n))_{i \in I}$ be a sequence of families of elements of E such that for every integer n, $\| a_i(n) \| \leqslant \lambda_i$, where the family of positive numbers λ_i is summable.

Show that if for every $i \in I$, $\lim_{n \to \infty} a_i(n) = a_i$, then the family (a_i) is summable and the sums $s_n = \sum_i a_i(n)$ converge to $s = \sum_i a_i$.

Extend this result to the case where the families $(a_i(n))$ are replaced by a family $(a_i(\lambda))$ depending on a parameter $\lambda \in L$, and where for every i, $a_i(\lambda)$ converges to a_i along a filter base $\mathscr{B}$ on L.

*84. We shall use the following property:

There exists a sequence (α_n) of numbers > 0 which converges to 0, and such that for every $n \geqslant 1$ and for every n-dimensional normed space E over **R**, there exist n vectors a_1, a_2, ..., a_n of norm 1 in E such that every partial sum of the a_i has norm $\leqslant n\alpha_n$.

Using this property and Problem 95, show that in every infinite-dimensional normed space E there exists a sequence (b_n) which is summable but not absolutely summable.

*85. We consider the mappings f of **R** into **R** such that for every summable family (a_i) of real numbers, the family $(f(a_i))$ is also summable.

    (a) Show that these f are characterized by the fact that f is of Lipschitz class at the point 0, in a sense which it is required to make precise. (Use Problem 99.)

    (b) Extend this result to the mappings f of one finite-dimensional vector space into another.

    (c) Can it be extended to infinite-dimensional normed spaces?

86. Let $(a_i)_{i\in I}$ be a finite family of elements of a vector space E over **R**. We assume that the sum of every finite subfamily of the family (a_i) belongs to a convex subset C of E containing O.

Show that for every family $(\lambda_i)_{i\in I}$ of elements of $[0, 1]$, the sum of every finite subfamily of the family $(\lambda_i a_i)$ also belongs to C.

One is advised to use one of the following methods:

    (a) Use induction on the number of elements of I.

    (b) First prove the property when $E = \mathbf{R}$ and C is an affine halfline of **R**; then prove it when E is finite-dimensional by using the fact that every closed convex set in E is an intersection of affine halfspaces.

87. Let $(a_i)_{i\in I}$ be a family of elements of a normed space E over **C**, and let $(\lambda_i)_{i\in I}$ be a family of elements of **C** such that $|\lambda_i| \leqslant 1$ for every i.

Show that if the sum of every finite subfamily of $(a_i)_{i\in I}$ is of norm $\leqslant k$, the sum of every finite subfamily of $(\lambda_i a_i)_{i\in I}$ is of norm $\leqslant 4k$ (and even $\leqslant 2k$ if the λ_i are real).

88. Let E be a complete normed space over **K**, and let $(a_i)_{i\in I}$ be a summable family of elements of E.

    (a) Show that for every bounded family $(\lambda_i)_{i\in I}$ of elements of **K**, the family $(\lambda_i a_i)$ is summable.

    (b) Let $(\lambda_i)_{i\in I}$ be a family of mappings of a set X into **K** such that for every $i \in I$ and every $x \in X$, $|\lambda_i(x)| \leqslant K$ (where $K < \infty$). Show that the family $(\lambda_i(x)a_i)_{i\in I}$ is uniformly summable on X; deduce from this that if X is a topological space and if the λ_i are continuous, the mapping $x \to \Sigma_i \lambda_i(x)a_i$ of X into E is continuous.

    *(c) Use this result to prove that the set of sums $\Sigma_i \lambda_i a_i$, where the λ_i are restricted only by the condition $|\lambda_i| \leqslant 1$, is a convex compact set in E. (Use Problem 87 for this problem.)

89. Let (a_n) (where $n \geqslant 1$) be a sequence of elements of a normed space E, and put

$$b_{n,p} = \frac{na_n}{p(p+1)} \qquad \text{(where } 1 \leqslant n \leqslant p\text{)}.$$

Show that the families (a_n) and $(b_{n,p})$ are simultaneously summable (or nonsummable) and that their sums are equal. (Use Problem 86.)

SERIES; COMPARISON OF SERIES AND SUMMABLE FAMILIES

90. Let (a_n) be a sequence of numbers $\geqslant 0$ such that $\Sigma a_n = \infty$. What can one say about the convergence of the series with general term

$$a_n/(1 + a_n); \qquad a_n/(1 + a_n^2); \qquad a_n/(1 + na_n); \qquad a_n/(1 + n^2a_n)?$$

91. Let (a_n) and (b_n) be two positive convergent series; show that the series $(\sqrt{a_nb_n})$ is convergent.

92. Let (a_n) and (b_n) be two sequences of numbers > 0. Show that when $b_{n+1}/b_n \leqslant a_{n+1}/a_n$ for every n, the convergence of the series (a_n) implies that of the series (b_n).

93. Let (a_n) be a positive decreasing sequence; show that if the series (a_n) converges, the sequence (na_n) tends to 0 (consider the sums $\Sigma_n^{2n} a_i$). Is the converse true?

94. Let (a_n) be a sequence of numbers $\geqslant 0$, and put

$$b_n = \frac{a_1 + a_2 + \cdots + a_n}{n}.$$

If the series (a_n^2) converges, what can one say about the series (b_n^2)?

95. Let (α_n) be an increasing sequence of numbers > 0 which converges to $+\infty$. Show that there exists a positive convergent series (a_n) and a divergent series (A_n) such that $A_n \leqslant \alpha_n a_n$.

$$\left(\text{Take} \qquad a_n = \frac{1}{\sqrt{\alpha_n - 1}} - \frac{1}{\sqrt{\alpha_n}} \qquad \text{and} \qquad A_n = \sqrt{\alpha_n} - \sqrt{\alpha_{n-1}} \, . \right)$$

96. Show that for every positive convergent series (a_n) there exists a positive increasing sequence (α_n) with limit $+\infty$ such that the series (α_na_n) is still convergent.

97. Show that for every positive divergent series (a_n) there exists a positive decreasing sequence (α_n) with limit 0 such that the series $(\alpha_n a_n)$ is still divergent.

98. Let f_n be a sequence of increasing mappings of $\mathbf{R}_+$ into $\mathbf{R}_+$. Show that there exists an increasing mapping f of $\mathbf{R}_+$ into $\mathbf{R}_+$ such that, for every n,

$$\lim_{x \to \infty} f(x)/f_n(x) = +\infty.$$

Deduce from this that if the rapidity of convergence of a positive series is measured by the rapidity of growth of the quotient

$$\varphi(p) = 1/(a_{p+1} + a_{p+2} + \cdots),$$

then, for any given sequence of positive convergent series, there exists a positive series which converges faster than each series of this sequence.

99. Let (λ_n) be a sequence of numbers $\geqslant 0$ such that for every positive convergent series (a_n), the series $(\lambda_n a_n)$ is convergent. Prove that the sequence (λ_n) is bounded.

100. Let (a_n) be a decreasing sequence of numbers > 0, and let $k > 1$; for every integer $n \geqslant 1$, we denote by k_n the nearest integer to k^n.

Show that the series (a_n) and $(k_n a_{k_n})$ converge or diverge simultaneously.

Deduce from this a criterion for the convergence of the series $(n^{-\alpha})$ and similar series such as $(n^{-1}(\log n)^{-\alpha})$.

101. Let (z_n) be a sequence of complex numbers, with real part $\geqslant 0$. Show that if the series (z_n) and $(z_n{}^2)$ converge, the series $(z_n{}^2)$ is absolutely convergent.

102. Let f be a mapping of $\mathbf{R}$ into $\mathbf{R}$ with a continuous second derivative and such that $f(0) = 0$, and let (a_n) be a sequence of real numbers.

Show that if the series (a_n) and $(a_n{}^2)$ converge, the same is true of the series $(f(a_n))$.

103. Let (a_n) be a sequence of real numbers with limit 0, and such that the series $(a_n{}^+)$ and $(a_n{}^-)$ are divergent.

Show that for every number $\lambda \in \mathbf{R}$, there exists a permutation π of $\mathbf{N}$ such that the series $(a_{\pi(n)})$ is conditionally convergent and has sum λ.

104. Find and prove a similar result concerning sequences (a_n) of elements of $\mathbf{R}^n$ (start with $n = 2$).

105. Let (a_n) be a sequence of elements of a normed space; show that if the series (na_n) converges, then the series (a_n) converges.

106. Study the convergence of the series with general term

$$(-1)^n/(\sqrt{n} + (-1)^n); \qquad (-1)^n/(2n + (-1)^n n); \qquad (-1)^n/(n + \cos n\pi).$$

*107. Let (λ_n) be a sequence of elements of **K**; prove the equivalence of the following properties:

   (a) The series with general term $|\lambda_n - \lambda_{n+1}|$ is convergent.

   (b) For every convergent series (a_n) of elements of **K**, the series $(\lambda_n a_n)$ is convergent.

*108. Let (a_n) be a sequence of elements of a normed space E. Show that if the series (a_n) is convergent, there exists a decreasing sequence (α_n) of positive numbers with limit 0 and a sequence (b_n) of elements of E such that $a_n = \alpha_n b_n$, and such that the set of sums $(b_1 + b_2 + \cdots + b_n)$ is bounded in E.

(The last two problems concern converses of Abel's rule.)

109. Let E and F be normed spaces, and f a continuous bilinear mapping of E $\times$ F into a complete normed space G. Let (a_n) $((b_n))$ be a sequence of elements of E (F).

   Show that if the series (a_n) converges, and if the series $(\| b_n - b_{n+1} \|)$ converges, then the series $(f(a_n, b_n))$ converges.

110. Let (a_n) be a sequence of elements of a normed space; we put

$$s_n = a_1 + a_2 + \cdots + a_n .$$

Show that if the series (a_n) has sum s, then the sequence $((s_1 + s_2 + \cdots + s_n)/n)$ converges to s.

111. We consider the mappings f of **R** into **R** such that for every real convergent series (a_n), the series $(f(a_n))$ is convergent.

   Show that these f are characterized by the fact that there exists a neighborhood of 0 in **R** on which f is linear.

*112. Extend the preceding result to mappings f of $\mathbf{R}^2$ into **R**, and then to mappings f of one topological vector space E into another F.

SUMMABLE SERIES AND FAMILIES OF FUNCTIONS

113. Let $(a_n z^n)$ be a power series with complex coefficients such that $\Sigma |a_n| < \infty$. Show that this series is uniformly convergent on the closed disk $\{z : |z| \leqslant 1\}$ of **C**. What can be said about its sum?

114. For every $f \in \mathscr{C}(\mathbf{R}, \mathbf{R})$ we put

$$\|f\| = \int_{\mathbf{R}} |f(t)| \, dt;$$

let E be the subset of $\mathscr{C}(\mathbf{R}, \mathbf{R})$ consisting of the f such that $\|f\| < \infty$.

(a) Show that E is a vector space and that $\|f\|$ is a norm on E.

(b) Does the series with general term f_n $(n \geq 1)$, where

$$f_n(t) = (-1)^n e^{-n|t|} \,,$$

converge in E ? Does it converge uniformly on certain intervals of $\mathbf{R}$?

115. Show that the positive series with general term $x^2(1 + x^2)^{-(n+1)}$ is convergent for every $x \in \mathbf{R}$, and that it is uniformly convergent on every compact set not containing 0, but not on $[0, 1]$.

116. Show that for every compact set K in $\mathbf{C}$, the series with general term $(n^2 - z^2)^{-1}$, after the deletion of a finite number of terms, is uniformly convergent on K. What can be deduced concerning its sum ?

117. For each of the series whose general term will be given below, determine the set of $x \in \mathbf{R}$ for which the series converges, then determine the compact sets in $\mathbf{R}$ on which these series converge uniformly. Next, study the same problem for $x \in \mathbf{C}$ (for the logarithm we assume $\log(1 + u)$ defined for $|u| < 1$ by its power series expansion):

$$n^{-3/2} \cos n^2 x; \quad \sin x^n; \quad \sin x/n^2; \quad 2^n \sin x/3^n;$$
$$n^{3/2} \sin x/n^3; \quad 1 - \cos x/n; \quad 1/(n + x)^2; \quad x \cos(2n + 1)x^2;$$
$$x^{(1 + 1/2 + \cdots + 1/n)}; \quad \log(1 + x^n); \quad \log(\cos x/n).$$

What can be said about the sums of these series ?

*118. Let (a_n) be a sequence of complex numbers, and (λ_n) an increasing sequence of real numbers with limit $+\infty$.

Show that if the series with general term $a_n e^{-\lambda_n z}$ (where $z \in \mathbf{C}$) converges at a point z_0, then it converges uniformly on every sector of the form $\{z : |\arg(z - z_0)| \leq k < \pi/2\}$. (First reduce it to the case where $z_0 = 0$, then imitate the proof of Abel's rule.)

119. Let f be a lower semicontinuous mapping of $[0, 1]$ into $\mathbf{R}_+$. Show, using Problem 9, Chapter II, that there exists a sequence (a_n) of continuous mappings of $[0, 1]$ into $\mathbf{R}_+$ such that, for every x, the series $(a_n(x))$ is convergent and has sum $f(x)$.

Show that if $f > 0$, one can require in addition that the a_n be polynomials.

120. Let (a_n) be a sequence of elements of $\mathscr{C}([0, 1], \mathbf{R})$ such that, for every $x \in [0, 1]$, the series with general term $| a_n(x) |$ is convergent.

Show that for every x the series with general term $a_n(x)$ is convergent, and that if $f(x)$ denotes its sum, then f is the difference of two lower semicontinuous functions.

Using the preceding problem, state and prove a converse of this property.

121. Let X be a set, E a complete normed space, (a_n) a sequence of mappings of X into E, and (λ_n) a decreasing sequence of mappings of X into $\mathbf{R}_+$.

(a) By slightly modifying the calculations involved in the proof of Proposition 10.14, show that if one puts

$$k_p(x) = \sup_{q \geqslant p} \| a_p(x) + \cdots + a_q(x) \|,$$

the series with general term $\lambda_n(x)a_n(x)$ is uniformly convergent on X when the sequence $(\lambda_p(x)k_p(x))$ tends to 0 uniformly on X.

(b) Show that this holds, in particular, in the following two cases:
   (1) The set of sums $a_0(x) + \cdots + a_n(x)$ is bounded on E, and the sequence $(\lambda_n(x))$ tends to 0 uniformly on X.
   (2) The series with general term $a_n(x)$ is uniformly convergent on X, and λ_0 is bounded.

122. Show that if a power series with general term $a_n x^n$ (where $a_n \in \mathbf{C}$) is convergent for $x = 1$, it is uniformly convergent on the interval $[0, 1]$.

Deduce from this, for example, using the classical power series expansion for $\log(1 + x)$, that

$$\log 2 = 1 - 1/2 + 1/3 - \cdots + (-1)^{n+1}/n + \cdots$$

123. Show that the sum of the series $((-1)^n/(2n^{1/2} + \cos x))$ (where $n \geqslant 1$) is uniformly convergent on $\mathbf{R}$ and that its sum is continuous.

124. Show that the series with general term

$$x \sin nx/(2n^{1/2} + \cos x) \qquad (\text{where } n \geqslant 1)$$

is uniformly convergent on every compact set in the open interval

$(-2\pi, 2\pi)$. What is the behavior of the sum in the neighborhood of the point 2π?

125. Let (a_n) be a convergent series of elements of a complete normed space E. Study the convergence and uniform convergence of the series with general terms

$$\left(\frac{x^n}{1+x^n}\right) a_n ; \qquad \left(\frac{x^n}{1+x^{2n}}\right) a_n \qquad \text{(where } x \in [0, \infty)\text{)}.$$

126. Study the summability and the uniform summability of the families with general terms

$$x^{p+q}; \qquad x^{pq}; \qquad (-1)^p x^{p(2q+1)} \qquad \text{(where } p, q \in \mathbf{N} \text{ and } x \in \mathbf{C}\text{)}.$$

127. Let X and Y be topological spaces, $a \in X$, $b \in Y$, and let (f_n) be a sequence of mappings of X into Y such that

$$\lim_{n \to \infty} f_n(a) = b.$$

The sequence (f_n) is said to converge uniformly at the point a if, for every neighborhood V of b in Y, there exists a neighborhood U of a in X and an integer n_0 such that $f_n(U) \subset V$ for every $n \geqslant n_0$.

(a) Show that if the sequence (f_n) converges pointwise on X to a mapping f, and if b has a neighborhood base of closed sets, the uniform convergence of the sequence (f_n) at a and the continuity of the f_n at a implies the continuity of f at a.

(b) Suppose that Y is a normed space, and we are given a sequence (g_n) of mappings of X into Y, continuous at a, such that $\sum \|g_n(x)\|$ is everywhere finite, and continuous at a. Show that the series (g_n) converges uniformly at a.

*128. Let (f_i) be a family of continuous mappings of a compact topological space X into a finite-dimensional normed space E. Show the equivalence of the following statements:

(a) The family (f_i) is uniformly summable.

(b) The family $(\|f_i(x)\|)$ is summable for every $x \in X$, and its sum is a continuous function of x. When X is noncompact, show that the implication $a \Rightarrow b$ still holds, but one does not always have $b \Rightarrow a$ (give an example).

MULTIPLIABLE FAMILIES AND INFINITE PRODUCTS OF COMPLEX NUMBERS

129. Using the inequality $1 + x \leqslant e^x$, which is valid for all real x, prove by induction that for every finite family (a_i) of numbers $\geqslant 0$ (respectively, in $[-1, 0]$), one has

$$1 + \sum a_i \leqslant \prod (1 + a_i) \leqslant \exp\left(\sum a_i\right).$$

Deduce from this in a simple way that for every family $(a_i)_{i \in I}$ of numbers $\geqslant 0$ (respectively, in $[-1, 0]$) the multipliability of the family $((1 + a_i))_{i \in I}$ and the summability of the family $(a_i)_{i \in I}$ are equivalent.

130. Let (a_n) be a sequence of numbers $\geqslant 0$ (with $a_0 > 0$); put

$$b_n = a_n/(a_0 + a_1 + \cdots + a_n).$$

Show that the series (a_n) and (b_n) converge and diverge simultaneously, and that when they converge, one has

$$a_0 \bigg/ \sum a_n = \prod_1^\infty (1 - b_n).$$

131. Let (a_n) be a sequence of numbers $\geqslant 0$. Show that the series with general term $a_n/(1 + a_0)(1 + a_1) \cdots (1 + a_n)$ is always convergent and its sum is

$$1 - \left(1 \bigg/ \prod_i (1 + a_i)\right).$$

132. Let $(a_i)_{i \in I}$ be a summable family of elements of **C**, and let $\mathscr{F}$ denote the collection of finite subsets of I. For every $K \in \mathscr{F}$ we put

$$u_K = \prod_{i \in K} a_i \qquad (\text{and} \quad u_K = 1 \quad \text{if} \quad K = \varnothing).$$

Show that the family $(u_K)_{K \in \mathscr{F}}$ is summable and that its sum is equal to

$$\prod_i (1 + a_i).$$

133. Let P denote the set of prime numbers $p \geqslant 2$. Deduce from the preceding problem that for every number $s > 1$, the family of numbers $(1 - p^{-s})^{-1}$ (where $p \in P$) is multipliable and has product

$$\sum_0^\infty n^{-s}.$$

134. Show, by the same method, that for every $x \in \mathbf{C}$ such that $|x| < 1$, the family $((1 + x^{2^n}))_{n \in \mathbf{N}}$ is multipliable and has product $1/(1 - x)$.

135. Let x be an element of $\mathbf{C}$ such that $|x| < 1$; we put

$$Q_1 = \prod_1^\infty (1 + x^{2n}); \qquad Q_2 = \prod_1^\infty (1 + x^{2n-1}); \qquad Q_3 = \prod_1^\infty (1 - x^{2n-1}).$$

Show that $Q_1 Q_2 Q_3 = 1$.

136. Let k be a complex number such that $|k| > 1$. For every $z \in \mathbf{C}$ we put

$$P(z) = \prod_1^\infty (1 + z/k^n).$$

(a) Prove that this product is absolutely convergent and that

$$P(kz) = (1 + z)P(z).$$

(b) For every $z \neq 0$, put

$$S(z) = P(z)P(1/z)(1 + z).$$

Show that $S(kz) = kzS(z)$.

(c) Let $(a_1, a_2, ..., a_n)$ and $(b_1, b_2, ..., b_n)$ be two finite sequences of complex numbers $\neq 0$ such that $a_1 a_2 \cdots a_n = b_1 b_2 \cdots b_n$; put

$$M(z) = \frac{S(a_1 z) \cdots S(a_n z)}{S(b_1 z) \cdots S(b_n z)}.$$

Show that $M(z) = M(kz)$; what does this imply for the function $u \to M(e^u)$?

(d) Show that P is the uniform limit, on every compact set, of polynomials in z. What can one conclude about P? Study S and M similarly.

137. Show that the infinite product $\prod_n (1 + i/n)$ is not convergent, but that the infinite product of the absolute values $|1 + i/n|$ is convergent.

138. Let (u_n) be a sequence of complex numbers such that

$$|u_n| \leqslant kn^{-\alpha} \qquad \text{(where } k > 0 \text{ and } \alpha > 0\text{)}.$$

Show that there exists an integer p, depending only on α, such that the convergence of the infinite product of the numbers $1 + u_n$ is equivalent to the convergence of the series with general term

$$v_n = u_n - u_n^2/2 + \cdots + (-1)^{p+1}u_n^p/p.$$

139. Using the fact that the multiplicative topological group $\mathbf{R}_+^*$ is isomorphic to the additive group $\mathbf{R}$, define a metric on $\mathbf{R}_+^*$ compatible with the topology of $\mathbf{R}_+^*$ and invariant under the "translations" of this group.

Show that $\mathbf{R}_+^*$, taken with such a metric, is complete.

140. We denote by U the multiplicative group of complex numbers z such that $|z| = 1$, taken with the topology induced by that of $\mathbf{C}$.

(a) Using the fact that the topological group $\mathbf{C}^*$ is isomorphic to the product $\mathbf{R}_+^* \times U$, show that there exists a metric on $\mathbf{C}^*$ compatible with its topology, and invariant under the "translations" of $\mathbf{C}^*$.

(b) Show that $\mathbf{C}^*$, taken with such a metric, is complete.

(c) Use this to obtain a new proof of the fact that every family of elements of $\mathbf{C}^*$ satisfying the Cauchy criterion (for multiplication) is multipliable in $\mathbf{C}^*$.

NORMED ALGEBRAS

141. Show that every norm on $\mathbf{C}$ (considered as a vector space over $\mathbf{R}$) which satisfies the relation $\| xy \| = \| x \| \| y \|$ is identical with the classical norm. Would the same conclusion hold if it were assumed only that $\| x^2 \| = \| x \|^2$ for every x?

142. Is the norm

$$\|f\| = \sup |f(x)| + \sup |f'(x)| + \cdots + \sup |f^{(n)}(x)|$$

on the vector space $\mathscr{C}^{(n)}([0, 1], \mathbf{R})$ compatible with its algebraic structure?

143. Let $(a_n X^n)$ and $(b_n U^n)$ be two formal series with complex coefficients, with $b_0 = 0$.

Let $(c_n U^n)$ be the formal series obtained by substituting for X the formal sum $\Sigma b_n U^n$.

Let A be a Banach algebra; we assume that the series $(a_n X^n)$ and $(b_n U^n)$ have radius of convergence equal to α and β, respectively, and we put

$$f(x) = \sum a_n x^n \qquad \text{for every } x \text{ such that} \quad \| x \| < \alpha;$$

$$g(u) = \sum b_n u^n \qquad \text{for every } u \text{ such that} \quad \| u \| < \beta.$$

Show that for every u such that $\| u \| < \beta$ and $\Sigma \, | \, b_n \, | \, \| u \|^n < \alpha$, the series $(c_n u^n)$ is absolutely convergent, and that its sum is $f(g(u))$.

144. Let A be a Banach algebra with a unit e.

(a) Show that for every $u \in A$ such that $\| u \| < 1$, the power series

$$u - u^2/2 + \cdots + (-1)^{n+1} u^n/n + \cdots$$

is convergent and that its sum is continuous on the open ball $B(O, 1)$; we shall denote this sum by $\log(e + u)$.

(b) Show, using the preceding problem, that

$$\exp(\log(e + u)) = e + u \qquad \text{for every} \quad u \in B(O, 1).$$

$$\log(\exp x) = x \qquad \text{for every } x \text{ such that} \quad \| x \| < \tfrac{1}{2}.$$

Deduce from this that the image of the open ball $B(O, \tfrac{1}{2})$ under the mapping $x \to \exp x$ is an open neighborhood of e, and that the restriction of this mapping to $B(O, \tfrac{1}{2})$ is a homeomorphism.

ELEMENTARY PROPERTIES OF PREHILBERT SPACES

145. Let f be an arbitrary bilinear functional on a vector space E over **C**. Show that there exist $x \neq O$ in E such that $f(x, x) = 0$.

146. Let E be a normed space over **K**; show that if, for every vector subspace F of dimension 2 in E, the norm of F is associated with a scalar product on F, then the norm of E is also associated with a scalar product on E.

147. Let E be a normed space over **K** such that, for all $x, y \in E$,

$$\| x + y \|^2 + \| x - y \|^2 = 2\| x \|^2 + 2\| y \|^2.$$

Show that the norm of E is associated with a scalar product.

148. By a quadratic form on a vector space E over **R** is meant a mapping f of E into **R** such that for all $x, y \in E$ and all $\lambda, \mu \in$ **R**,

$$f(\lambda x + \mu y) = a\lambda^2 + 2b\lambda\mu + c\mu^2,$$

where a, b, and c depend on x and y only.

Show that $b(x, y)$ is a bilinear functional on E, and that $b(x, x) = f(x)$.

Deduce from this that if a norm p on E is such that p^2 is a quadratic form, then $b(x, y)$ is a scalar product on E, and p is the norm associated with it.

149. Show that every vector space E over **K** can be provided with a scalar product (use an algebraic basis of E).

150. By a *sesquilinear* form on a vector space E (over **K**) is meant any mapping $(x, y) \to f(x, y)$ of $E \times E$ into **K** which is linear in x and conjugate-linear in y.

Let f be a continuous sesquilinear form on a normed space E. We denote by $b(f)$ (respectively, $q(f)$) the infimum of the positive numbers k such that

$$|f(x, y)| \leqslant k \| x \| \| y \| \qquad \text{(respectively, } |f(x, x)| \leqslant k \| x \|^2\text{)}.$$

(a) Show that $q \leqslant b \leqslant 4q$.

(b) Show that when $f(x, x)$ is real for every x, or when the norm of E is associated with a scalar product, one can replace 4 by 2; and show that when both conditions are satisfied, then $q = b$.

151. Let E be a prehilbert space over **C**, and let f be a sesquilinear form on E.

Show that the image of $E \dot{-} O$ under the mapping $x \to f(x, x)/\| x \|^2$ is a convex subset of **C**. From this, using Problem 149, deduce that for every sesquilinear form f on a vector space E, the image of $E \dot{-} O$ under the mapping $x \to f(x, x)$ is convex.

152. Let E and F be prehilbert spaces over **K**, and let f be a mapping of E into F such that $f(O) = O$, and such that for every $x, y \in E$

$$\| f(x) - f(y) \| = \| x - y \| \qquad \text{(in other words, } f \text{ is an isometry).}$$

Show that f is linear.

153. Show that the norm of the space $l_1^2(E)$ defined in Problem 82 can be defined by a scalar product only when E is itself a prehilbert space.

154. Let $(E_i)_{i \in I}$ be a family of prehilbert spaces over the same field **K**, whose scalar products and norms will be denoted by $(x \mid y)_i$ and $\| x \|_i$, respectively. We denote by F the vector space of families $x = (x_i)_{i \in I}$ such that $x_i \in E_i$, and for every $x \in F$ we put

$$f(x) = \sum_i (x_i \mid x_i)_i.$$

(a) Show that the set E of x such that $f(x) < \infty$ is a vector subspace of F.

(b) Show that for all x, $y \in E$, the family of numbers $(x_i \mid y_i)_i$ is summable and that its sum, which we shall denote by $(x \mid y)$, is a scalar product on E.

(c) Show that the prehilbert space E (which is called the *direct sum* of the E_i) is complete when each of the E_i is complete (and conversely).

155. Let f be a continuous mapping of **R** into **C** such that

$$\int_{\mathbf{R}} |f(t)|^2 \, dt < \infty.$$

Show that

$$\left| \int_{\mathbf{R}} f(t)f(t-a) \, dt \right| \leqslant \int_{\mathbf{R}} |f(t)|^2 \, dt$$

for every $a \in \mathbf{R}$.

156. Let (a_n) be a sequence of elements of **C** such that $\sum |a_n|^2 < \infty$. Show that

$$\left| \sum a_n a_{n+1} \right| \leqslant \sum |a_n|^2.$$

157. We denote by P the subset of the Hilbert space l^2 over **R** consisting of the points $x = (x_n)$ such that $|x_n| \leqslant 1/n$.

Show that P is a compact subset of l^2 (one can use the criterion for the compactness of metric spaces and Proposition 9.23).

158. Let D be a domain of $\mathbf{R}^n$, with finite total volume, and let E be the set of real harmonic functions f in D such that the intergal of f^2 over D is finite.

(a) Show that E is a vector space, and that

$$(f \mid g) = \int_{D} f(x)g(x) \, dx$$

is a scalar product on E. We denote the corresponding norm by $\| f \|$.

(b) Show that for every $f \in D$,

$$\int_{D} |f(x)| \, dx \leqslant k\| f \|,$$

where k denotes a constant to be determined.

(c) Using an elementary mean value property of harmonic functions, show that if $\lim_{n \to \infty} \| f_n \| = 0$, the sequence (f_n) converges uniformly to O on every compact set.

(d) Deduce from this that the prehilbert space E is complete.

159. Let F and G be vector subspaces of a real prehilbert space E. Show that if there exists a number $k \geqslant 0$ such that

$$|(x \mid y)| = k \, \| x \| \, \| y \|$$

for every $x \in F$ and $y \in G$, then either F and G have dimension 1, or $k = 0$, that is, F and G are orthogonal.

160. Let E be a prehilbert space over **K**, and let F and G be vector subspaces of E which do not coincide with {O}. By the *angle* between F and G is meant the angle α defined by

$$0 \leqslant \alpha \leqslant \pi; \quad \cos \alpha = \sup \frac{|(u \mid v)|}{\| u \| \, \| v \|} \quad \text{where} \quad u \in F, \quad v \in G.$$

Now let φ denote the mapping $(u, v) \to u + v$ of the normed space $F \times G$ onto the subspace $F + G$ of E.

Show that a necessary and sufficient condition for φ to be a homeomorphism is that $\alpha \neq 0$.

161. Let X and Y be two normed spaces isomorphic to l^2, and let φ be the mapping of X into Y defined as follows:

If $x = (x_n)$, then $\varphi(x)$ is the point $(n^{-1}x_n)$.

Show that the graph Γ of φ in $X \times Y$ is a vector subspace of $X \times Y$ isomorphic to X.

Show that if we denote by X' the subspace $X \times O$ of $X \times Y$, then $X' + \Gamma$ is everywhere dense on $X \times Y$ but is not identical with it.

162. Let E be a prehilbert space over **R**, and let $E \times E$ be provided with the structure of the direct sum of E with E (Problem 154). Let f be a linear bijective mapping of E to E which is norm preserving.

For every $k \in \mathbf{R}$, we denote by $\Gamma(k, f)$ the graph in $E \times E$ of the mapping $x \to kf(x)$ of E into E. Show that the angle α of every vector of $\Gamma(k, f)$ with $\Gamma(k', f)$ is a constant defined by the relation

$$\cos \alpha = \frac{|1 + kk'|}{(1 + k^2)^{1/2}(1 + k'^2)^{1/2}}.$$

ORTHOGONAL PROJECTION. STUDY OF THE DUAL

163. Let X be a complete convex subset of a prehilbert space E over **R**. Using Theorem 15.1, show that X is an intersection of closed affine halfspaces of E (defined as sets of the form $\{x : f(x) \leqslant k\}$, where $f \in E'$ and $k \in$ **R**).

Show that when X is a cone, X is an intersection of closed halfspaces of the form $\{x : f(x) \leqslant 0\}$, where $f \in E'$.

164. Let (X_n) be a decreasing sequence of complete convex subsets of a prehilbert space E. For every $x \in E$ we denote by $d_n(x)$ the distance from x to X_n, and put

$$d(x) = \lim_{n \to \infty} d_n(x).$$

Show that if $d(x) < \infty$ for at least one x, the same is true for every x; we assume this to be the case from this point on. We then denote by $A(x, \epsilon, n)$ the intersection of X_n and the closed ball with center x and radius $(d(x) + \epsilon)$.

  (a) Show that when ϵ tends to 0 and n tends to $+\infty$, the diameter of $A(x, \epsilon, n)$ tends to 0.

  (b) Deduce from this that the intersection X of the X_n is non-empty, and that $d(x) = d(x, X)$.

165. Let Y be a bounded complete convex subset of a prehilbert space E, and let f be a numerical lower semicontinuous convex function on Y. Show, using the preceding problem, that f is bounded from below on Y, and that the set of points x of Y where f attains its infimum is a nonempty complete convex set.

Give an application of this property to the continuous linear functionals on E, and compare with the example of Problem 43.

166. Let A and B be complete convex subsets of a prehilbert space E, at least one of which is bounded. Show that there exists $a \in A$ and $b \in B$ such that

$$d(a, b) = d(A, B).$$

167. Extend the result of the preceding problem to the case where A and B are unbounded, but where $d(x, y)$ tends to infinity as $\| x \|$ and $\| y \|$ tend to infinity with $x \in A$ and $y \in B$. Show by an example in **R**² that if this condition is not satisfied, the assertion can be false.

168. Let (C_n) be an increasing sequence of complete convex subsets of a prehilbert space E, such that $C = \overline{U C_n}$ is also complete.

For every $x \in E$, we denote by $P_n(x)$ $(P(x))$ the projection of x on C_n (C); show that

$$P(x) = \lim_{n \to \infty} P_n(x).$$

169. Let E be a prehilbert space over **R**, C a complete convex subset of E, and f a continuous linear functional on E.

Show that there exists a unique point of C at which $\| x \|^2 + f(x)$ attains its infimum.

170. Let E be a prehilbert space and E' its topological dual. For every $a \in E$, we denote by φ_a the linear functional $x \to (x \mid a)$ on E. Show that the image $\varphi(E)$ of E in E' under the conjugate-linear mapping φ is an everywhere dense vector subspace of E'.

Deduce from this that every prehilbert space E is isomorphic to an everywhere dense vector subspace of a Hilbert space.

171. Let V_1 and V_2 be affine varieties of a prehilbert space E, and let $x_1 \in V_1$, $x_2 \in V_2$.

Show the equivalence of the following properties:

(a) $d(x_1, x_2) = d(V_1, V_2)$.

(b) $x_1 - x_2$ is orthogonal to V_1 and V_2.

172. Let E be a real Hilbert space, and let P be a closed convex cone in E. We denote by P^* the set of $x \in E$ such that $(x \mid y) \leqslant 0$ for every $y \in P$. Show that P^* is also a closed convex cone and that $(P^*)^* = P$ (use Problem 163).

173. Let E be a real Hilbert space, and let P and Q be closed convex cones in E such that $P^* = Q$ (from which also $Q^* = P$ by the preceding problem).

Show the equivalence of the following properties:

(a) $z = x + y$, $x \in P$, $y \in Q$; $(x \mid y) = 0$.

(b) $x = $ projection of z on P; $y = $ projection of z on Q.

174. Let E be a prehilbert space, and F a vector subspace of E such that $F = F^{00}$.

Show by an example that it is not always true that every point of E has a projection on F.

175. Let P be a mapping of a prehilbert space E into itself which satisfies the relations

$$(P(x) \mid y) = (x \mid P(y)); \qquad P(P(x)) = P(x) \qquad \text{for all } x, y \in E.$$

Show that P is linear and continuous; show next that if we put

$$F = \{x : P(x) = x\},$$

then $F = F^{00}$ and P is identical with the operator of projection of E on F.

176. Let E be a prehilbert space. Show that if P is a linear mapping of E into E such that $P^2 = P$ and $\| P \| \leqslant 1$, then P is a projection operator.

177. (a) Show that if P_1, P_2, ..., P_n are projection operators (on a prehilbert space E), to say that $P_1 + \cdots + P_n$ is a projection operator is equivalent to saying that $P_i P_j = O$ for every $i \neq j$.

(b) Now assume E complete. Show that if (P_n) is an infinite sequence of projection operators such that $P_i P_j = O$ for $i \neq j$, then the family (P_n) is summable in $\mathscr{L}(E)$ and its sum is a projection operator.

178. Let E be a Hilbert space, and let A be an element of $\mathscr{L}(E)$.

(a) Show that for every $y \in E$, the mapping $x \to (Ax \mid y)$ is a linear functional on E; deduce from this that there exists a unique element $A_y{}^*$ of E such that $(Ax \mid y) = (x \mid A_y{}^*)$ for every $x \in E$.

(b) Show that the mapping $y \to A_y{}^*$ of E into E is linear, and that the norm of A^* is equal to that of A. The operator A^* is called the *adjoint* of the operator A; A is called *selfadjoint* if $A = A^*$, in other words, if

$$(Ax \mid y) = (x \mid Ay)$$

for all $x, y \in E$.

(c) More generally, let E be a prehilbert space, and let A, $B \in \mathscr{L}(E)$; we shall say that B is the *adjoint* of A if $(Ax \mid y) = (x \mid By)$ for all $x, y \in E$.

Show that every $A \in \mathscr{L}(E)$ has at most one adjoint, and that if B is the adjoint of A, then A is the adjoint of B.

179. Prove the following elementary properties:

(a) $(AB)^* = B^*A^*$.

(b) If A and B are selfadjoint, the selfadjointness of AB is equivalent to the relation $AB = BA$.

(c) If A is selfadjoint, then B^*AB is selfadjoint for any B.

(d) If $A = A^*$, then $((Ax \mid x) = 0$ for every $x)$ is equivalent to $A = O$.

(e) To say that $A = A^*$ is equivalent to saying that $(Ax \mid x)$ is real for every x.

180. Let $(k_i)_{i \in I}$ be a bounded family of elements of **C**, and let A be the mapping of the complex space l_I^2 into itself defined as follows:
If $x = (x_i)_{i \in I}$, Ax is the element $(k_i x_i)_{i \in I}$.
What is the norm of A? What is its adjoint? When is A selfadjoint?

181. We denote by E the space $\mathscr{C}([0, 1], \mathbf{C})$ taken with the scalar product

$$(x \mid y) = \int_0^1 x(t)\bar{y}(t) \, dt;$$

let $k \in E$ and let $K \in \mathscr{C}([0, 1]^2, \mathbf{C})$. We define the elements A and B of $\mathscr{L}(E)$ by the relations

$$Ax(t) = \int_0^1 K(t, u)x(u) \, du; \qquad Bx(t) = k(t)x(t).$$

(a) Show that A and B have adjoints, although E is not complete; under what conditions are A and B selfadjoint?

(b) For every $x \in E$, put

$$Cx(t) = \int_0^1 k(t)u^{-1/4}x(u) \, du, \qquad \text{where} \quad k \in E.$$

Show that $C \in \mathscr{L}(E)$ and calculate its norm, and show that C does not have an adjoint which operates in E.

182. Let E be a prehilbert space, and let A be an element of $\mathscr{L}(E)$ which has an adjoint A^*; we say that A is *positive* if $A = A^*$ and if $(Ax \mid x) \geqslant 0$ for every $x \in E$. We say that A is *positive definite* if in addition $(Ax \mid x) \neq 0$ for every $x \neq O$.
Characterize those of the operators studied in the preceding problem which are positive or positive definite.

183. Let E be a prehilbert space, and let $A \in \mathscr{L}(E)$. Prove the equivalence of the following three properties:

(a) $A^*A = I$ (where I is the identity).

(b) $(Ax \mid Ay) = (x \mid y)$ for all x, $y \in E$.

(c) $\| Ax \| = \| x \|$ for every $x \in E$.

When A has these properties, A is called a *unitary* operator (or orthogonal operator, when **K** is the field **R**), or more simply an isometry.

184. Let E be a prehilbert space, and let $A \in \mathscr{L}(E)$; we shall say that A is a *symmetry* if $(I + A)/2$ is a projection operator.

Using the preceding problem and Problem 175, show that the symmetries are simply the operators which are both unitary and selfadjoint.

185. Let (x_n) be a sequence of points of a prehilbert space E; show that the strong convergence of (x_n) to O is equivalent to the convergence, uniformly on the set of a such that $\| a \| \leqslant 1$, of the sequence $((x_n \mid a))$ to 0. Extend this property to filter bases.

*186. Let (x_n) be a sequence of points of a Hilbert space E such that, for every $a \in E$, the sequence $((x_n \mid a))$ has a limit. Show that the x_n converge weakly to a point $x \in E$, that the sequence $(\| x_n \|)$ is bounded, and that

$$\| x \| \leqslant \liminf_{n \to \infty} \| x_n \|.$$

(One can use Problems 60 and 61.)

*187. Let (x_n) be a sequence of points of a Hilbert space E. Show that if this sequence converges weakly to a point x, there exists a subsequence (x_{α_n}) such that the sequence (b_n), where

$$b_n = 1/n \sum_1^n x_{\alpha_p},$$

converges strongly to x.

188. Show that in an infinite-dimensional prehilbert space E, the point O does not have a countable neighborhood base for the weak topology. Deduce from this that the weak topology of E cannot be defined by a metric.

189. Let E be a prehilbert space, (x_n) a *bounded* sequence of points of E, and X a total subset of E.

Show that for the sequence (x_n) to converge weakly to a point x, it is necessary and sufficient that for every $a \in X$ the sequence $((x_n \mid a))$ converge to $(x \mid a)$. Show, on the other hand, that one can find an unbounded sequence (x_n) in l^2 (which therefore cannot be weakly convergent) and a total subset X of l^2 (for example, the canonical orthonormal basis of l^2) such that for every $a \in X$, the sequence $((x_n \mid a))$ converges to 0.

190. Let E be the space $\mathscr{C}([0, 1], \mathbf{K})$ taken with the scalar product

$$(x \mid y) = \int_0^1 x(t)\bar{y}(t)\, dt.$$

Put

$$x_n(t) = \sin \pi nt;$$

show, using the total subset X of E consisting of the functions $\sin \pi pt$ and $\cos \pi pt$, and the preceding problem, that the sequence (x_n) converges weakly to O.

More generally, let (y_n) be a sequence of functions with continuous derivatives $y_n{}'$ on $[0, 1]$ and such that

$$\lim_{n \to \infty}(\sup_t \mid y_n(t)\mid) = 0;$$

show that the sequence $(y_n{}')$ converges weakly to O in E.

ORTHOGONAL SYSTEMS

191. Let E be a prehilbert space; for every finite sequence $(x_1, x_2, ..., x_n)$ of points of E, the *Gramian* of the x_i is defined as the scalar $G(x_1, x_2, ..., x_n)$ equal to the determinant of the scalar products $(x_i \mid x_j)$.

(a) Show that $G(x_1, ..., x_n) \geqslant 0$ and that the relation $G(x_1, ..., x_n) > 0$ is equivalent to the linear independence of the x_i (make use of an orthonormal basis in the vector space generated by the x_i).

(b) Show that if the x_i are linearly independent, the square of the distance from any point $x \in E$ to the vector space L generated by the x_i is equal to $G(x, x_1, ..., x_n)/G(x_1, ..., x_n)$. (Use the projection of x on L.)

192. Show that every infinite-dimensional Hilbert space E is isomorphic to a vector subspace of E which is distinct from E.

193. Let E be a prehilbert space with an infinite orthonormal basis B. Show that $\bar{\bar{X}} \geqslant \bar{\bar{B}}$ for every everywhere dense subset X of E, and show that there exists an X for which $\bar{\bar{X}} = \bar{\bar{B}}$ (see 16.16).

194. Let E be an arbitrary topological vector space, and let $(a_i)_{i \in I}$ be a family of elements of E. We shall say that this family is *topologically free* if for every $i \in I$, a_i does not belong to the adherence of the vector subspace of E generated by the a_j with index $j \neq i$.

(a) Show that in a prehilbert space, every orthogonal family is topologically free.

(b) Show that every topologically free family is linearly independent, and show by an example that the converse is false.

195. Let E be a topological vector space, and let B be an algebraic basis of E which is topologically free.

Show that the vector subspace of E generated by an arbitrary subset of B is closed.

(a) Deduce from this, using Problem 65, that if E is a Banach space, E is necessarily finite dimensional.

(b) Give an example where B is infinite and E is normed (necessarily incomplete).

196. Let E be a topological vector space. We shall say that a subset A of E is *topologically very free* if it does not contain O, and if for every partition of A into nonempty subsets A_1 and A_2, the vector subspaces generated by A_1 and A_2 have adherences whose intersection is $\{O\}$.

(a) Verify that every orthogonal system in a prehilbert space is topologically very free.

(b) Verify that the canonical "basis" of every l_{I}^p space also has this property.

*(c) Show by an example that even in a prehilbert space, a family can be topologically free without being very free.

197. Let E be the space $\mathscr{C}([0, 1], \mathbf{R})$ taken with the scalar product

$$(x \mid y) = \int_0^1 x(t)y(t)\, dt.$$

Let K be a nonempty and nondense compact set in $[0, 1]$, and let A_K denote the vector subspace of E formed by the functions which vanish at every point of K.

(a) Show that every $x \in E$ such that $x \perp A_K$ equals O.

(b) Show that if the measure of K is zero (in the sense that for every $\epsilon > 0$ there exists a covering of K by a finite family of intervals, the sum of whose lengths is $< \epsilon$), then $\overline{A_K} = E$. Show that otherwise $\overline{A_K} \neq E$.

(c) Deduce from this that there exists a maximal orthogonal system in E which is not total.

198. Let E be the vector subspace of the real space l^2 generated by the vectors of the canonical basis of l^2 with odd indices and by the vectors

$$x_k = (1/1^k, ..., 1/n^k, ...) \qquad \text{(where } k \in \mathbf{N}^*\text{).}$$

Show that the orthogonal system in E consisting of the vectors of the canonical basis of l^2 with odd indices is maximal.

199. Let E be an incomplete prehilbert space. Using Problem 170, show that there exists a closed hyperplane H in E such that there exists no $x \neq O$ in E orthogonal to H.

200. Let $\mathscr{B}_2$ be the Besicovitch space of order 2 defined in Problem 59. For every $x, y \in \mathscr{B}_2$ we put

$$[x, y] = \lim_{a \to \infty} \sup(1/2a) \int_{-a}^{+a} | x(t)y(t)| \, dt.$$

(a) Show that $[x, y] < \infty$, and more precisely that $[x, y] \leqslant \| x \| \| y \|$.

Show that $[x, y]$ is a subscalar product in the sense of Problem 35.

(b) Let A be a vector subspace of S_2 (see Problem 59). Show that for every $x, y \in A$,

$$(1/2a) \int_{-a}^{a} x(t)\bar{y}(t) \, dt$$

has a finite limit as $a \to \infty$, which we shall denote by $(x \mid y)$. Deduce from this that the canonical image of A in $\mathscr{B}_2$ is a prehilbert space.

(c) Let P denote the vector space of linear combinations of functions $e^{i\lambda t}$ (where $\lambda \in \mathbf{R}$).

Show that $P \subset S_2$ and that the family of functions $e^{i\lambda t}$ is an orthonormal system in the prehilbert space P. Deduce from this that the canonical image of P in $\mathscr{B}_2$ has closure $\mathscr{P}$ which is a Hilbert space whose geometric dimension is the cardinality of the continuum.

(d) Show that every element $x \in \mathscr{P}$ is the sum, in $\mathscr{P}$, of a sequence of functions $a_n e^{i\lambda_n t}$ (where the λ_n are distinct) such that $\Sigma | a_n |^2 < \infty$, and that, conversely, every such sequence is summable in $\mathscr{P}$.

(e) Study successively the sequences obtained by setting $a_n = n^{-2}$, λ_n arbitrary, and then $a_n = n^{-1}$, $\lambda_n = n^{-1}$.

How can the difficulty encountered in the second example be explained?

ORTHOGONAL POLYNOMIALS

201. Let E be the subset of $\mathscr{C}([0, 1], \mathbf{R})$ consisting of the functions x such that

$$\int_0^1 x^2(t) \, dt/t < \infty.$$

(a) Show that E is a vector subspace of $\mathscr{C}([0, 1], \mathbf{R})$ and that every function x which has a finite derivative at 0 and satisfies $x(0) = 0$ belongs to E.

(b) For every $x, y \in E$, we put

$$(x \mid y) = \int_0^1 x(t)y(t) \, dt/t.$$

Verify that this integral is meaningful and that it is a scalar product on E.

(c) The Gram-Schmidt orthogonalization procedure applied to the sequence (t^n) (where $n \geqslant 1$) yields polynomials P_1, ..., P_n, ... Calculate P_1, P_2, and P_3 explicitly.

(d) Show that the set of functions in the prehilbert space E which are zero on an interval of the form $[0, a]$ (where $a \neq 0$) is everywhere dense on E. Deduce from this that the orthogonal family (P_n) is total in E.

202. Same as Problem 201, with the weight t^{-1} replaced by $t^{-\alpha}$ (where $\alpha \in \mathbf{R}_+$).

203. Let p be a function $\geqslant 0$ and continuous on the open interval $I = (-1, 1)$, such that:

(a) The set of points $t \in I$ at which $p(t) \neq 0$ is everywhere dense on I.

(b) There exists a polynomial A, not identically zero, such that

$$\int_I A^2(t)p(t) \, dt < \infty.$$

Now let E be the vector subspace of $\mathscr{C}([0, 1], \mathbf{R})$ consisting of the functions x such that

$$\| x \|^2 = \int_{\mathrm{I}} x^2(t)p(t)\, dt < \infty.$$

Show, by a method analogous to that of Problem 201, that the set of polynomials of the form AP (where P is a polynomial) is total in the space E taken with the Hilbert norm $\| x \|$.

204. We put

$$Q_n(t) = \frac{1}{2^n n!} \frac{d^n}{dt^n} (t^2 - 1)^n.$$

(a) Show, using integration by parts, that the sequence of polynomials Q_n is an orthogonal system on $[-1, 1]$ for the scalar product

$$(x \mid y) = \int_{-1}^{1} x(t)\bar{y}(t)\, dt,$$

and that

$$(Q_n \mid Q_n) = \frac{2}{2n + 1}.$$

(b) Verify that $Q_n(1) = 1$ and deduce from this that Q_n is related to the Legendre polynomial P_n defined in the text by

$$Q_n(t) = P_n(t)/P_n(1),$$

and calculate $P_n(1)$.

(c) Show that the Q_n satisfy the recursion relation

$$nQ_n = (2n - 1)Q_{n-1} - (n - 1)Q_{n-2}$$

and that every Q_n satisfies the differential equation

$$\frac{d}{dt}\left((1 - t^2)\frac{dQ_n}{dt}\right) + n(n + 1)Q_n = 0.$$

205. Let E be the prehilbert space E_p (see 17.3) obtained for $p(t) = e^{-t}$ on the interval $[0, \infty)$.

(a) We put

$$L_n(t) = \frac{1}{n!} e^t \frac{d^n}{dt^n} (e^{-t} t^n).$$

Verify that L_n is a polynomial of degree n, that the L_n form an orthogonal system in E, and calculate $(L_n \mid L_n)$.

(b) Verify that $L_n(0) = 1$, and deduce from this that L_n is related to the Laguerre polynomial P_n defined in the text by

$$L_n(t) = P_n(t)/P_n(0),$$

and calculate $P_n(0)$.

(c) Show that for every $\alpha \geqslant 0$, the function $e^{-\alpha t}$ belongs to E, and calculate its Fourier coefficients $\gamma_{n,\alpha}$ with respect to the orthogonal system (L_n).

(d) Show that the family $(\gamma_{n,\alpha} L_n)$ has sum $e^{-\alpha t}$ in E.

(e) Show, by means of a suitable change of variables and the Stone-Weierstrass theorem, that the functions $e^{-nt} (n \in \mathbf{N})$ form a total system in E.

(f) Deduce from questions (e) and (d) that the polynomials L_n constitute an orthogonal basis of E.

206. (a) Verify that the nth derivative of $\exp(-t^2)$ is of the form $(-1)^n H_n(t) \exp(-t^2)$, where H_n is a polynomial of degree n.

(b) Show that the polynomials H_n are orthogonal in the space E_p associated with the weight $p(t) = \exp(-t^2)$ on $[0, \infty)$. Deduce from this that they are proportional to the polynomials which were called the Hermite polynomials in the text.

(c) Verify the recursion relation

$$H_n = 2tH_{n-1} - 2(n-1)H_{n-2} ; \qquad H_0 = 1; \qquad H_1(t) = 2t.$$

(d) Show that H_n satisfies the differential equation

$$H_n'' - 2tH_n' + 2nH_n = 0,$$

and that

$$H_n' = 2nH_{n-1} .$$

DEFINITIONS AND AXIOMS

We are concerned only with vector spaces over $\mathbf{K}$ (where $\mathbf{K} = \mathbf{R}$ or $\mathbf{C}$).

Axioms of topological vector spaces. A topological vector space E is a set with a vector space structure and a topology such that:

TVS 1: The topology of E is compatible with the additive group structure of E;

TVS 2: The mapping $(\lambda, x) \to \lambda x$ of $\mathbf{K} \times E$ into E is continuous.

TOTAL SET. A subset X of a TVS E is said to be *total* if the set of linear combinations of elements of X is everywhere dense on E.

SEMINORM. A *seminorm* on a vector space E is a mapping p of E into $\mathbf{R}_+$ such that, for all x, $y \in E$ and every $\lambda \in \mathbf{K}$,

(1) $p(\lambda x) = |\lambda| p(x);$

(2) $p(x + y) \leqslant p(x) + p(y).$

One says that p is a *norm* if $p(x) \neq 0$ for every $x \neq O$.

The open *p-ball* with center a and radius $\rho > 0$ in E is the set $\{x : p(x - a) < \rho\}$.

$\mathscr{P}$-TOPOLOGY ON A VECTOR SPACE E. Let $\mathscr{P} = (p_i)$ be a family of seminorms on E. Every finite intersection of open p_i-balls with center a is called an *open $\mathscr{P}$-ball* with center a in E.

The *$\mathscr{P}$-topology* on E is the topology whose open sets are arbitrary unions of open $\mathscr{P}$-balls.

NORMED SPACE. A *normed space* is a vector space together with a norm p.

It is taken with the topology associated with the metric $d(x, y) = p(x - y)$.

When it is complete relative to this metric, it is called a *Banach space*.

SUMMABLE FAMILIES IN A SEPARATED COMMUTATIVE TOPOLOGICAL GROUP G. A family $(a_i)_{i \in I}$ of elements of G is said to be *summable*, with sum A (where $A \in G$), if for every neighborhood V of A there exists a finite subset J_0 of I such that, for every finite subset J of I containing J_0, one has

$$\sum_{i \in J} a_i \in V.$$

ABSOLUTELY SUMMABLE FAMILIES IN A NORMED SPACE E. A family (a_i) of elements of E is said to be *absolutely summable* if the family of their norms $\| a_i \|$ is summable in $\mathbf{R}$.

MULTIPLIABLE FAMILIES IN $\mathbf{C}$. A family $(a_i)_{i \in I}$ of elements of $\mathbf{C}$ is said to be multipliable in $\mathbf{C}$, with product p, if for every $\epsilon > 0$ there exists a finite subset J_0 of I such that, for every finite subset J of I containing J_0, one has

$$\left| p - \prod_{i \in J} a_i \right| \leqslant \epsilon.$$

NORMED ALGEBRA. A *normed algebra* is an algebra over **K** together with a norm such that $\| xy \| \leqslant \| x \| \| y \|$.

When in addition it is complete in this norm, it is called a *Banach algebra*.

HERMITEAN FORMS. A *hermitean form* on a vector space E over **K** is a mapping φ of E × E into **K** such that:

(1) For every y, $\varphi(x, y)$ is linear in x.

(2) For every x, $y \in$ E, $\varphi(y, x) = \overline{\varphi(x, y)}$.

It is said to be *positive* if $\varphi(x, x) \geqslant 0$ for every x, and *positive definite* if in addition $\varphi(x, x) \neq 0$ for every $x \neq O$; in this last case one can show that $\varphi(x, x)^{1/2}$ is a norm on E.

PREHILBERT SPACE. A *prehilbert space* is a vector space together with a positive-definite hermitean form (generally denoted by $(x \mid y)$) and the norm associated with this form.

When E is complete in this norm, it is called a *Hilbert space*.

ORTHOGONAL BASIS. An *orthogonal basis* of a prehilbert space E is a family (a_i) of nonzero elements of E such that:

(1) This family is total in E.

(2) The a_i are pairwise orthogonal (that is, $(a_i \mid a_j) = 0$ if $i \neq j$).

When in addition $\| a_i \| = 1$ for every i, (a_i) is called an *orthonormal basis*.

NOTATION

$B(a, \rho)$	2.5	l_I^p	8.8
$\mathscr{B}(X, \mathbf{K})$	3.1	$\mathscr{L}(E)$, $\mathscr{L}(E, F)$	1.7, 4.6
$\mathscr{C}(X, \mathbf{K})$	3.1	$\mathscr{L}(E_1, ..., E_n ; F)$	6.2
$\mathscr{C}^r([0, 1]^n, \mathbf{K})$	3.2	$p(x)$	2.1
$\mathscr{C}^\infty([0, 1]^n, \mathbf{K})$	3.3	$P_X(x)$	15.1
$\mathscr{D}_K^r(\mathbf{R}^n, \mathbf{K})$	3.4	$(x \mid y)$, xy	14.5
$\mathscr{D}^r(\mathbf{R}^n, \mathbf{K})$	3.9	$X \perp Y$	14.11
$\mathscr{E}^r(A, \mathbf{K})$	3.8	X^0, X^{00}	14.15
$\mathscr{E}^\infty(A, \mathbf{K})$	3.8	$\sum_{i \in I} a_i$	9.1
E', E*	1.8		
$\mathscr{F}(X, \mathbf{K})$	3.10	$\prod_{i \in I} a_i$	12.1
K	1.1	$\| x \|$	2.1
l^p	3.5	$\| f \|$	4.6

BIBLIOGRAPHY

BOURBAKI, N., *Topologie Générale, Groupes Topologiques; Nombres Réels*, Chapters 3 and 4. Actual. Sci. Ind., No. 906, Hermann, Paris.

BOURBAKI, N., *Espaces Vectoriels Topologiques*, Chapters 1 and 2. Actual. Sci. Ind., No. 1189. Hermann, Paris.

BOURBAKI, N., *Algèbre, Formes Sesquilinéaires et Formes Quadratiques*, Chapter 9. Actual. Sci. Ind., No. 1272. Hermann, Paris.

DIEUDONNÉ, J., *Foundations of Modern Analysis*. Academic Press, New York, 1960.

GRAVES, L., *The Theory of Functions of Real Variables*. McGraw-Hill, New York, 1956.

HALMOS, P., *Finite Dimensional Vector Spaces*. Van Nostrand, Princeton, New Jersey, 1958.

HALMOS, P., *Introduction to Hilbert Space*. Chelsea, New York, 1961.

MACSHANE, E. J., and BOTTS, P. A., *Real Analysis*. Van Nostrand, Princeton, New Jersey, 1959.

OSTROWSKI, A., *Vorlesungen über Differential- und Integralrechnung*. Basel, 1951.

More advanced books (research level)

DUNFORD, N., and SCHWARTZ, J. T., *Linear Operators*, Part I, 1958; Part II, 1964. Wiley (Interscience), New York.

EDWARDS, R. E., *Functional Analysis*. Holt, Rinehart and Winston, New York, 1965.

FRIEDRICHS, K., *Functional Analysis and Applications*. New York Univ. Press, New York, 1949.

HILLE, E., and PHILLIPS, R. S., *Functional Analysis and Semi-Groups* (Amer. Math. Soc. Colloq. Publ.,Vol. 31). Providence, Rhode Island, 1957.

LOOMIS, L. H., *An Introduction to Abstract Harmonic Analysis*. Van Nostrand, Princeton, New Jersey, 1958.

RIESZ, F., and NAGY, B. von Sz., *Leçons d'Analyse Fonctionelle*. Budapest, 1952. (English translation: Ungar, New York, 1955.)

STONE, M. H., *Linear Transformations in Hilbert Space* (Amer. Math. Soc. Colloq. Publ., Vol. 8). Providence, Rhode Island, 1932, 1951.

YOSIDA, K., *Functional Analysis*. Academic Press, New York, 1965.

Subject Index

Roman numbers refer to chapters; Arabic numbers to sections within the chapter; *prob.* to problems appearing at the end of the chapter.

A

Abel's rule, III-10.15
Adherence, I-6.1
Algebra, Banach, III-13.1
  normed, III-13.1
Angle between two vectors, III-14.17
Ascoli, I-23.2
Associativity, of families, III-9.11
  of series, III-10.5

B

Ball (open, closed), I-15.5, III-2.5
basis, algebraic, III-prob. 68
  orthogonal, orthonormal, III-16.5
Bidual, III-prob. 48
Bolzano-Weierstrass, I-3.3
Boundary, I-6.5
Bounded (set), III-prob. 9

C

Cauchy criterion, for families, III-9.4
  for products, III-12.2
  for series, III-10.2
  uniform, III-11.2
Cauchy sequence, I-2.2, 20.1
  filter base, I-20.7
Cauchy-Schwartz inequality, III-14.4
Closed set, I-1.2, 5.2
Closure, I-6.2
Commutativity, for families, III-9.10
  for series, III-10.6
Compact, I-11.1
Compact linear mapping, III-prob. 50
Compactification, I-12.5

Complexification, III-prob. 34
Connected, I-13.1
  arcwise, I-13.13
Connected component, I-13.10
Continuum, I-13.7
Convergence, absolute, normwise,
  III-11.5, 11.7
  in mean of order p, III-3.6
  pointwise, I-22.1
  uniform, I-22.3, III-11.7
    at a point, III-prob. 127
Convolution product, III-13.7
Coordinates, III-16.2

D

Dense, I-6.7
Diameter, I-15.6
Dilation, III-1.3
Dimension, geometric, III-16.16
Dini, I-22.9
Direct sum, III-prob. 154
Discontinuity of the first kind, II-13.1
Distribution of order r, III-3.13
Domain, I-13.8
Dual, of a Hilbert space, III-15.8
  topological, III-1.8, 4.8
Duality, III-prob. 17

E

Ecart, I-15.2
Equicontinuous, I-23.1
Equivalent metrics, I-17.6
Exponential on a normed algebra, III-13.21
Extended line, I-5.1

F

Family, absolutely summable, III-8.12, 9.17
    multipliable, III-9.1, 12.1
    normwise multipliable, III-12.11
    normwise summable, III-11.5
    summable, in a group, III-9.1
    topologically free, III-prob. 194, 195
    uniformly bounded (from above, from below), II-3.2
    uniformly summable, III-11.1
Form, Hermitean, III-14.2
    positive Hermitean, III-14.3
    sequilinear, III-prob. 150
Fourier coefficient, III-16.6
Functional, conjugate-linear, III-14.1
    continuous linear, III-1.8
Function, bounded from above, from below, II-2.2
    continuous, I-7.1
    convex (strictly convex, concave), II-16.1, 16.3, 16.4, 19.1
    numerical, II-1
    positive-homogeneous, II-19.5
    regulated, II-13.3
    step, II-13.3
    supremum (infimum) of, II-2.1

G

Geodesic, II-11.7
Gramian, III-prob. 191
Gram-Schmidt orthogonalization procedure, III-16.11

H

Hahn-Banach theorem, prob. 11, 12, 13
Heine-Borel-Lebesgue, I-3.2
Homeomorphism, I-7.6
Hyperplane, median, III-14.16

I

Inductive, III-16.9
Inequalities of Hölder and Minkowski, II-20.6, 20.7

Interior, I-6.4
Interval, I-4.1
Intrinsic parametrization of a curve, II-11.6
Invertible element, III-13.24
Isometry, I-15.4
Isomorphism, of Hilbert spaces, III-16.16
    of normed spaces, III-5.1
    of prehilbert spaces, III-14.10, 16.13

L

Length, I-24.6
Limit, I-8.1, 8.6
Limit superior (inferior), II-4.1
Lipschitz class, I-17.3
Locally compact, I-12.1
    connected, I-13.11

M

Mean relative to a monotone function, II-20.1
Metric, I-15.1
Metrizable, I-16.6
Modulus of continuity, I-17.2
Multilinear mapping, III-6.1

N

Neighborhood, I-1.3, 5.3
Neighborhood base, I-5.4
Norm, III-2.1
Norms, equivalent, III-4.4

O

Open set, I-1.1, 5.1
    elementary, I-10.1
Operator, adjoint, selfadjoint, III-prob. 178
    positive, positive definite, III-prob. 182
    unitary, III-prob. 183
Orthogonal (vectors, sets), III-14.11
    systems, III-16.1
        maximal, III-16.7
Orthogonal polynomials, III-17.3, 17.4
Orthonormal systems, III-16.1
Oscillation, I-15.6
Oscillation of a function, at a point, II-4.4
    on a set, II-2.1

P

p-ball, III-2.5
$\mathscr{P}$-ball, III-2.7
$\mathscr{P}$-topology, III-2.8
Period, I-14.2
Point, accumulation, I-1.3
  adherent, I-8.4
  isolated, I-1.4
Polynomials, Legendre, etc., III-17.4, prob. 203, 204, 205
Product, of spaces (product space), I-10.1
  of normed spaces, III-6
  of summable families, III-9.22, 13.15
  infinite, absolutely convergent, III-12.7
  infinite, commutatively convergent, III-12.7
  scalar, III-14.5
    associated real, III-14.6
  subscalar, III-prob. 35
Projection on a set, III-15
Pythagorean theorem, III-14.12

R

Radius of convergence, III-13.16
Radon measure, III-3.12
Rectifiable, I-24.5
Relatively compact, I-12.6

S

Seminorm, III-2.1
Series, absolutely convergent, III-10.8
  alternating, III-10.16
  commutatively convergent, III-10.6
  conditionally convergent, III-10.13
  double, triple, III-8.7
  Fourier, III-17
  in a group, III-10.1
  power, III-13.16
Space, Banach, III-4.1
  Besicovitch, III-prob. 59
  complete, I-20.5

  finite dimensional, III-7.6
  Hilbert, III-14.5
  locally convex, III-2.18
  metric, I-15.1
  normed, III-4.1
  prehilbert, III-14.5
  separable, III-prob. 63
  separated, I-8.2
  topological, I-5.1
Sphere, I-15.5
Stability of isomorphisms, III-5.7
Subspace, I-9.1
Successive approximations, I-21.1
Supporting line, II-17.5
Symmetry, III-prob. 184
Theorems of finite increase, II-15.1, 15.5

T

Topological group, I-14.1
Topology, of pointwise convergence, III-3.10
  of uniform compact convergence, III-3.7
  on a Hilbert space, III-15.10
  strong, III-15.10
  weak, III-2.11, 3.11
Total set, III-1.10
Total variation, I-24.2

U

Unit sphere, III-prob. 33
Upper (lower) envelope of a family of functions, II-3.1
Upper (lower) semicontinuity, II-7.1

V

Value, adherent, I-8.8

W

Well-linked, I-19.1